OFFICIAL BLUE BOOK OF UNITED STATES COINS™

 THE OFFICIAL BLUE BOOK®

HANDBOOK OF

UNITED STATES COINS

R.S. YEOMAN

EDITOR

KENNETH BRESSETT

67th Edition
2010
Illustrated Catalog and Prices Dealers
Pay for Coins—1616 to Date

Containing Mint records and wholesale prices for U.S. coins from 1616 to the present time, including colonials, regular issues, commemoratives, territorials, gold, Proof sets, and Mint sets. Information on collecting coins—how coins are produced—mints and mintmarks—grading of coins—location of mintmarks—preserving coins—starting a collection—history of mints—and interesting descriptions of all U.S. copper, nickel, silver, and gold coins. Illustrated.

Handbook of United States Coins™
THE OFFICIAL BLUE BOOK OF UNITED STATES COINS™

THE OFFICIAL BLUE BOOK and OFFICIAL BLUE BOOK OF UNITED
STATES COINS are trademarks of Whitman Publishing, LLC.

WCG™ • OCG™

www.whitman**books**.com

Printed in the United States of America.

The WCG™ pricing grid used throughout this publication is patent pending.

OCG™ Collecting Guide

Whitman Publishing, LLC, does not deal in coins; the values shown here are
not offers to sell or buy but are included only as general information.
Descriptions of coins are based on the most accurate data available, but
could contain beliefs that may change with further research or discoveries.
Correspondence regarding this book may be sent to the publisher at the
address above.

For a complete listing of numismatic reference
books, supplies, and storage products, visit us at
www.whitman**books**.com

CONTENTS

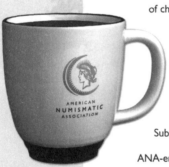

CONTRIBUTORS TO THE SIXTY-SEVENTH EDITION

Special Consultant: Philip Bressett

Whitman Publishing extends its thanks to these members of the coin-buying community who have contributed pricing for this year's *Handbook of United States Coins*. Their data were compiled and then reviewed by editor Kenneth Bressett and consultant Phil Bressett. This process ensures input from a broad range of dealers and auctioneers from across the country—experts who buy, sell, and trade coins every day and know the market inside and out.

Mark Albarian	Chuck Furjanic	Bradley S. Karoleff	William P. Paul
Jeff Ambio	Jeff Garrett	Robert Lecce	Maurice Rosen
Lee J. Bellisario	Dennis M. Gillio	Julian M. Leidman	Gerald R. Scherer Jr.
J.H. Cline	Ira M. Goldberg	Stuart Levine	Cherie Schoeps
Elizabeth W. Coggan	Lawrence Goldberg	Denis W. Loring	Richard Schwary
Alan Cohen	Kenneth M. Goldman	David McCarthy	Richard Snow
Gary Cohen	J.R. Grellman	Chris McCawley	David M. Sundman
James H. Cohen	Ash Harrison	Robert T. McIntire	Steve Tanenbaum
Adam Crum	Gene L. Henry	Lee S. Minshull	Ben Todd
Silvano DiGenova	John W. Highfill	Scott P. Mitchell	David Wnuck
Sheridan Downey	Jesse Iskowitz	Michael C. Moline	Mark S. Yaffe
Steven Ellsworth	Steve Ivy	Mike Orlando	
Mike Fuljenz	Donald H. Kagin	Robert M. Paul	

Special credit is due to the following for service in past editions of the Handbook:

Gary Adkins	Marc Crane	Richard A. Lecce	Robert Rhue
David Akers	John Dannreuther	David Leventhal	Tom Rinaldo
John Albanese	Tom DeLorey	Kevin Lipton	Greg Rohan
Mark Albarian	Silvano DiGenova	Andy Lustig	Leonard R. Saunders
Buddy Alleva	Kenneth Duncan	Dwight N. Manley	Mary Sauvain
Richard S. Appel	Steven Ellsworth	Chris McCawley	Gerald Scherer Jr.
Michael Aron	John Feigenbaum	Harry Miller	Cherie Schoeps
Richard M. August	Dennis Gillio	Robert Mish	James A. Simek
Richard A. Bagg	Ronald Gillio	Paul Montgomery	Craig Smith
Mitchell A. Battino	Ron Guth	Charles Moore	William J. Spencer
Lee J. Bellisario	James Halperin	Richard Nachbar	Lawrence R. Stack
Jack Beymer	John Hamrick	Chris Napolitano	Anthony J. Swiatek
Mark R. Borckardt	Karl D. Hirtzinger	Paul Nugget	Anthony Terranova
Q. David Bowers	James J. Jelinski	John M. Pack	Jerry Treglia
H. Robert Campbell	A.M. Kagin	William S. Panitch	Frank Van Valen
Alan R. Cohen	Mike Kliman	Joel Rettew Jr.	Fred Weinberg
Steve Contursi	John J. Kraljevich Jr.	Joel Rettew Sr.	Douglas Winter

Special photo credits are due to the following:

Douglas F. Bird, Steve Contursi, Bill Fivaz, Ira & Larry Goldberg Coins & Collectibles, heritagecoins.com, Tom Mulvaney, the Museum of the American Numismatic Association, Noyes–Lusk DVD Photo Project, Numismatic Guaranty Corporation of America (NGC), Brent Pogue, Sarasota Rare Coin Gallery, the Smithsonian Institution, Rick Snow, Spectrum, Stack's Rare Coins of New York, Superior Galleries, Anthony Swiatek, and the United States Mint.

Since 1942, annually revised editions of the *Official Blue Book of United States Coins*™ have aided thousands of people who have coins to sell or are actively engaged in collecting United States coins. The popular coin-folder method of collecting by date has created ever-changing premium values, based on the supply and demand of each date and mint. Through its panel of contributors, the Blue Book has, over the years, reported these changing values. It also serves as a source of general numismatic information to all levels of interest in the hobby.

The values shown are representative prices paid by dealers for various United States coins. These are averages of prices assembled from many widely separated sources. On some issues slight differences in price among dealers may result from proximity to the various mints or heavily populated centers. Other factors, such as local supply and demand or dealers' stock conditions, may also cause deviations from the prices listed. While many coins bring no premium in circulated grades, they usually bring premium prices in Mint State and Proof. Extremely rare and valuable coins are usually sold at public auction, and prices vary according to current demand.

THIS BOOK LISTS PRICES MANY COIN DEALERS WILL PAY.

Premium prices are the average amount dealers will pay for coins (according to condition) if required for their stock. This book is not a retail price list.

IF YOU HAVE COINS TO SELL

Whitman Publishing, LLC, is not in the rare coin business; however, chances are that the dealer from whom you purchased this book is engaged in the buying and selling of rare coins—contact him first. In the event that you purchased this book from a source other than a numismatic establishment, consult your local telephone directory for the names of coin dealers (they will be found sometimes under the heading of "Stamp and Coin Dealers"). If you live in a city or town that does not have any coin dealers, obtain a copy of one of the trade publications (such as *Coin World* or *Numismatic News*) or check the Internet in order to obtain the names and addresses of many of the country's leading dealers. Information or sample copies may be obtained by writing to the individual publisher.

Current average *retail* valuations of all U.S. coins are listed in Whitman's *A Guide Book of United States Coins*™ by R.S. Yeoman, edited by Kenneth Bressett, Whitman Publishing, LLC, Atlanta, GA ($29.95 Large Print Edition; $19.95 spiralbound hardcover; $16.95 hardcover; $14.95 coilbound).

HOW TO READ THE CHARTS

A dash in a price column indicates that coins in that grade exist even though there are no current sales or auction records from them. (The dash does *not* necessarily mean that such coins are excessively rare.) Italicized prices indicate unsettled or speculative values. A number of listings of rare coins do not have prices or dashes in certain grades. This indicates that they are not available or not believed to exist in those grades.

Mintages of Proof coins are listed in parentheses.

Italicized mintages are estimates.

Numismatics or coin collecting is one of the world's oldest hobbies, dating back several centuries. Coin collecting in America did not develop to any extent until about 1840, as our pioneer forefathers were too busy carving a country out of wilderness to afford the luxury of a hobby. The discontinuance of the large-sized cent in 1857 caused many people to attempt to accumulate a complete set of the pieces while they were still in circulation. One of the first groups of collectors to band together for the study of numismatics was the American Numismatic Society, founded in 1858 and still a dynamic part of the hobby. Lack of an economical method to house a collection held the number of devotees of coin collecting to a few thousand until Whitman Publishing and other manufacturers placed low-priced coin boards and folders on the market in the 1930s. Since that time, the number of Americans collecting coins has increased many-fold.

THE PRODUCTION OF COINS

To collect coins intelligently it is necessary to have some knowledge of the manner in which they are produced. Coins are made in factories called "mints." The Mint of the United States was established at Philadelphia by a resolution of Congress dated April 2, 1792. The act also provided for the coinage of gold eagles ($10), half eagles, and quarter eagles; silver dollars, half dollars, quarter dollars, dimes (originally spelled "disme"), and half dismes or half dimes; and copper cents and half cents. The first coins struck were one-cent and half-cent pieces, in March of 1793 on a hand-operated press. Most numismatic authorities consider the half disme of 1792 the first United States coinage, quoting the words of George Washington as their authority. Washington, in his annual address, November 6, 1792, said, "There has been a small beginning in the coining of the half dimes, the want of small coins in circulation calling the first attention to them." Though the half disme is considered America's first coinage, it was not the first coinage produced by the Mint; these coins were produced off premises in July of 1792 before the mint was completed. In the new Philadelphia Mint are a number of implements from the original mint, and some coins discovered when the old building was wrecked. These coins included half dismes, and the placard identifying them states that Washington furnished the silver and gave the coined pieces to his friends as souvenirs.

Prior to the adoption of the Constitution, the Continental Congress arranged for the issuance of copper coins under private contract. These are known as the *Fugio cents* from their design, which shows a sundial and the Latin word "fugio"—"I Fly" or, in connection with the sundial, "Time Flies." The ever-appropriate motto "Mind Your Business" is also on the coin.

In the manufacture of a given coin, the first step is the cutting of the die. Prior to the latter part of the 19th century, dies for United States coins were "cut by hand." Briefly, this method is as follows: the design having been determined, a drawing the exact size of the coin is made. A tracing is made from this drawing. A piece of steel is smoothed and coated with transfer wax, and the tracing impressed into the wax. The engraver then tools out the steel where the relief or raised effect is required. If the design is such that it can all be produced by cutting away steel, the die is hardened and ready for use. Some dies are not brought to a finished state, as some part of the design can perhaps be done better in relief. In that case, when all that can be accomplished to advantage in the die is completed, it is hardened, a soft-steel impression is taken from it, and the unfinished parts are then completed. This piece of steel is in turn hardened and, by a press, driven into another piece of soft steel, thus making a die which, when hardened, is ready for the making of coins.

This hand method of cutting dies accounts for the many die varieties of early United States coins. Where the amount of coinage of a given year was large enough to wear out many dies, each new die placed in the coining press created another die variety of that year. The dies being cut by hand, no two were exactly alike in every detail, even though some of the major elements such as the head or wreath, were sunk into the die by individual master punches. Of the cents dated 1794, more than sixty different die varieties have been discovered.

Thousands of dies are now used by the mints of the United States each year, but they are all made from one master die, which is produced in the following manner:

After the design is settled upon, the plaster of paris or wax model is prepared several times the actual size of the coin. When this model is finished an electrotype (an exact duplicate in metal) is made and prepared for the reducing lathe. The reducing lathe is a machine that works on the principle of the pantograph, only in this case the one point traces or follows the form of the model while another much smaller point in the form of a drill cuts away the steel and produces a reduced-size die of the model. The die is finished and details are sharpened or worked over by an engraver with chisel and graver. The master die is used to make duplicates in soft steel which are then hardened and ready for the coining press. To harden dies, they are placed in cast-iron boxes packed with carbon to exclude the air, and when heated to a bright red are cooled suddenly with water.

In the coinage operations the first step is to prepare the metal. Among the alloys that have been used are the following: silver coins, 90% silver and 10% copper; five-cent pieces, 75% copper and 25% nickel; one-cent pieces, 95% copper and 5% zinc. (The 1943 cent consists of steel coated with zinc; and the five-cent piece of 1942–1945 contains 35% silver, 56% copper, and 9% manganese.) Under the Coinage Act of 1965, the composition of dimes, quarters, and half dollars was changed to eliminate or reduce the silver content of these coins. The copper-nickel "clad" dimes, quarters, half dollars, and dollars are composed of an outer layer of copper-nickel (75% copper and 25% nickel) bonded to an inner core of pure copper. The silver clad half dollar and dollar have an outer layer of 80% silver bonded to an inner core of 21% silver, with a total content of 40% silver. Current cents are made from a core of 99.2% zinc, 0.8% copper, with a plating of pure copper. Dollars are composed of a pure copper core with outer layers of manganese-brass.

Alloys are melted in crucibles and poured into molds to form ingots. The ingots are in the form of thin bars and vary in size according to the denomination of the coin. The width is sufficient to allow three or more coins to be cut from the strips.

The ingots are next put through rolling mills to reduce the thickness to required limits. The strips are then fed into cutting presses which cut circular blanks of the approximate size of the finished coin. The blanks are run through annealing furnaces to soften them; next they move through tumbling barrels, rotating cylinders containing cleaning solutions which clean and burnish the metal; and finally into centrifugal drying machines.

The blanks are next fed into a milling machine which produces the raised or upset rim. The blank, now called a *planchet,* is now ready for the coining press.

The planchet is held firmly by a collar, as it is struck under heavy pressure varying from 40 tons for the one-cent pieces and dimes to 170 tons for silver dollars. Upper and lower dies impress the design on both sides of the coin. The pressure is sufficient to produce a raised surface level with that of the milled rim. The collar holding the blank for silver or clad coins is grooved. The pressure forces the metal into the grooves of the collar, producing the "reeding" on the edge of the finished coin.

HOW A PROOF COIN IS MADE

Selected dies are inspected for perfection and are highly polished and cleaned. They are again wiped clean or polished after every 15 to 25 impressions and are replaced frequently to avoid imperfections from wear. Coinage blanks are polished and cleaned to assure high quality in striking. They are then hand fed into the coinage press one at a time, each blank receiving two blows from the dies to bring up sharp, high-relief details. The coinage operation is done at slow speed. Finished Proofs are individually inspected and are handled by gloves or tongs. They also receive a final inspection by packers before being sonically sealed in special plastic cases.

Certain coins, including Lincoln cents, Buffalo nickels, quarter eagles, half eagles, eagles, and double eagles, between the years 1908 and 1916, were made with Matte Proof (nickel and silver) and Sand Blast and Satin Proof (gold) finishes. These later Proofs have a dull frosted surface which was either applied to the dies, or produced by special treatment after striking.

MINTS AND MINTMARKS

In addition to the Philadelphia Mint, the U.S. government has from time to time established branch mints in various parts of the country. At present a branch mint operates in Denver and another in San Francisco. Starting in 1968, Proof sets and some of the regular coins were produced at the San Francisco Mint and Assay Office. The Denver Mint has operated since 1906. A mint was operated at New Orleans from 1838 to 1861 and again from 1879 to 1909. Mints were also in service at Carson City, Nevada, from 1870 to 1893; at Charlotte, North Carolina, from 1838 to 1861; at Dahlonega, Georgia, from 1838 to 1861; and at San Francisco since 1854. The U.S. government also operated a mint in the Philippines in the early 1900s.

Coins struck at Philadelphia before 1979 (except 1942 to 1945 five-cent pieces) do not bear a mintmark. Historically the mintmark was used only for branch mints. Recent exceptions include the Lincoln cent and the Kennedy half dollar, which both use the P for Philadelphia. All coins struck after 1967 have the mintmark on the obverse. The letters signifying the various mints are as follows:

C—Charlotte, North Carolina (gold coins only; 1838–1861)
CC—Carson City, Nevada (1870–1893)
D—Dahlonega, Georgia (gold coins only; 1838–1861)
D—Denver, Colorado (1906 to date)
O—New Orleans, Louisiana (1838–1861; 1879–1909)
P—Philadelphia, Pennsylvania (1793 to date; P not used in early years)
S—San Francisco, California (1854 to date)
W—West Point, New York (1984 to date)

The mintmark is of utmost importance to collectors because, historically, coinage of the branch mints has often been much smaller than quantities struck at Philadelphia. Many early coins of the branch mints are very scarce.

DISTINGUISHING MARKS

The illustrations and explanations in this section will help the collector identify certain well-known varieties.

Half Cents of 1795–1796 Showing Location of Pole to Cap

The end of the pole lies parallel with the lines of the bust, which is pointed. On some coins, the pole is missing due either to engraver error (while cutting the die) or to an error in "relapping" (when the die is ground to remove wear, clash marks, etc.).

Pole to Cap   No Pole to Cap

Stemless Wreath Variety of Half Cents and Large Cents

For this variety, the difference is on the reverse side. Illustrations below show both Stemless and Stems to Wreath types for comparison—stemless wreath found on the 1804, 1805, and 1806 half cents; and on the 1797, 1802, and 1803 large cents.

Stemless Wreath   Stems to Wreath

1864 Bronze Indian Head Cent With "L" on Ribbon

A small "L," the initial of the designer James B. Longacre, was added to the Indian design late in 1864 and was continued through 1909. For coins in less than Fine condition, this small letter will often be worn away. The point of the bust is rounded on the 1864 variety without "L"; the bust is pointed on the

variety with "L." The initial must be visible, however, for the 1864 variety to bring the higher premium. If the coin is turned slightly so that the portrait faces the observer, the highlighted details will usually appear to better advantage.

Designer Initials, Overstrikes, Die-Doublings, and Date Varieties

During 1909, initials appeared on the reverse of the Lincoln cent.
Starting in 1918, they appear below the shoulder.

Prior to 1990, mintmarks for all mints were usually applied directly to working dies at Philadelphia in a hand-punching operation. Occasionally, a die was accidentally marked with one letter on top of another.

Dies are produced by impressing the raised coin design of a hub into the end of a cylinder of steel. In early years the Mint made use of old dies by repunching the dates on their dies with new numbers. That practice was stopped prior to 1909. Since that time, all overdated coins have been the result of errors that occur when two different-dated hubs have been used in die preparation, and one is impressed over the other by accident.

1938-D, D Over S   **1918-S, 8 Over 7**   **1942, 2 Over 1**
Buffalo Nickel   *A variety of the kind on this*   **Mercury Dime**
                        quarter dollar is rarely found in
                        coinage of the 20th century.

**Large Date Cent
(1960)**

**Small Date Cent
(1960)**

**1955, Doubled-Die Obverse
Lincoln Cent**

**Large Date Cent
(1982)**

**Small Date Cent
(1982)**

CONDITIONS OF COINS

Essential Elements of the Official ANA Grading System

Proof—A specially made coin distinguished by sharpness of detail and usually with a brilliant, mirrorlike surface. *Proof* refers to the method of manufacture and is not a condition, but normally the term implies perfect condition unless otherwise noted.

    Gem Proof (PF-65)—Brilliant surfaces with no noticeable blemishes or flaws. A few scattered, barely noticeable marks or hairlines.

    Choice Proof (PF-63)—Reflective surfaces with only a few blemishes in secondary focal places. No major flaws.

    Proof (PF-60)—Surface may have several contact marks, hairlines, or light rubs. Luster may be dull and eye appeal lacking.

Mint State—The terms *Mint State (MS)* and *Uncirculated (Unc.)* are used interchangeably to describe coins showing no trace of wear. Such coins may vary to some degree because of blemishes, toning, or slight imperfections, as described in the following subdivisions:

    Perfect Uncirculated (MS-70)—Perfect new condition, showing no trace of wear. The finest quality possible, with no evidence of scratches, handling, or contact with other coins. Very few regular-issue coins are ever found in this condition.

    Gem Uncirculated (MS-65)—An above average Uncirculated coin that may be brilliant or lightly toned and that has very few contact marks on the surface or rim. MS-67 through MS-62 indicate slightly higher or lower grades of preservation.

    Choice Uncirculated (MS-63)—Has some distracting contact marks or blemishes in prime focal areas. Luster may be impaired.

    Uncirculated (MS-60)—Has no trace of wear but may show a number of contact marks, and surface may be spotted or lack some luster.

Choice About Uncirculated (AU-55)—Evidence of friction on high points of design. Most of the mint luster remains.

About Uncirculated (AU-50)—Traces of light wear on many of the high points. At least half of the mint luster is still present.

Choice Extremely Fine (EF-45)—Light overall wear on highest points. All design details are very sharp. Some of the mint luster is evident.

Extremely Fine (EF-40)—Light wear on design throughout, but all features sharp and well defined. Traces of luster may show.

Choice Very Fine (VF-30)—Light, even wear on the surface and highest parts of the design. All lettering and major features are sharp.

Very Fine (VF-20)—Moderate wear on high points of design. All major details are clear.

Fine (F-12)—Moderate to considerable even wear. Entire design is bold with overall pleasing appearance.
Very Good (VG-8)—Well worn with main features clear and bold, although rather flat.
Good (G-4)—Heavily worn, with design visible but faint in areas. Many details are flat.
About Good (AG-3)—Very heavily worn with portions of lettering, date, and legend worn smooth. The date may be barely readable.

Important: Damaged coins, such as those that are bent, corroded, scratched, holed, nicked, stained, or mutilated, are worth less than those without defects. Flawless Uncirculated coins are generally worth more than values quoted in this book. Slightly worn coins ("sliders") that have been cleaned and conditioned ("whizzed") to simulate Uncirculated luster are worth considerably less than perfect pieces.

Unlike damage inflicted after striking, manufacturing defects do not always lessen values. Examples include colonial coins with planchet flaws and weakly struck designs; early silver and gold with weight-adjustment "file marks" (parallel cuts made prior to striking); and coins with "lint marks" (surface marks due to the presence of dust or other foreign matter during striking).

Brief guides to grading are placed before each major coin type. Grading standards are not scientific and often vary among collectors, dealers, and certification services. For more on grading, consult the *Official ANA Grading Standards for United States Coins.*

PRESERVING AND CLEANING COINS

Most numismatists will tell you to "never clean a coin" and it is good advice! Cleaning coins almost always reduces their value. Collectors prefer coins in their original condition.

Some effort should be made to protect Uncirculated and Proof coins so they won't need cleaning. Tarnish on a coin is purely a chemical process caused by oxygen in the air acting on the metal, or by chemicals with which the coin comes in contact. One of the most common chemicals causing tarnish is sulphur; most paper, with the exception of specially manufactured "sulphur-free" kinds, contains sulphur due to the sulphuric acid that is used in paper manufacture; therefore do not wrap coins in ordinary paper. Also keep Uncirculated and Proof coins away from rubber bands (a rubber band placed on a silver coin for a few days will produce a black stripe on the coin where the band touched). The utmost in protection is obtained by storing the coin in an airtight box, away from moisture and humidity, and by using holders made of inert materials.

Many coins become marred by careless handling. Always hold the coin by the edge. The accompanying illustration shows the right and wrong way to handle numismatic specimens. It is a breach of numismatic etiquette to handle another collector's coin except by the edge, even if it is not an Uncirculated or Proof piece.

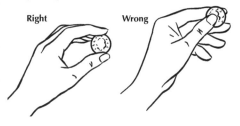

Right   Wrong

STARTING A COLLECTION

One may start a collection of United States coins with very little expense by systematically assembling the various dates and mintmarks of all the types and denominations that are now in general circulation, using Whitman's many different coin folders and albums.

With the exception of the price paid for the coin folder, collecting coins received in everyday business transactions entails no expense whatsoever; a Jefferson nickel taken out of circulation, for example, can always be spent for five cents if the occasion arises. Filling an album or two out of circulation is probably the best method of determining whether coin collecting appeals to you. Not everyone can be a successful coin collector. It requires patience, intelligence of a high order, and a certain desire to know the meaning behind a lot of things that at first glance appear meaningless. You may not be cut out to be a collector but you'll never know until you look further into the subject, and if by the time an album or two of coins are collected you have no burning desire to acquire many more different coins, you will probably never be a collector. However, chances are that you will be, because if you have read this far in this book, it shows that you are interested in the subject.

Perfection is the goal of every endeavor and coin collecting is no exception. After an album has been filled with circulated specimens, the next step will be to replace them with coins in Uncirculated condition, or perhaps to start collecting an obsolete series; in either case, it will be necessary to purchase some coins from dealers or other collectors. The most logical way to keep abreast of the market, or obtain the addresses of the country's leading dealers, is to subscribe to one or more of the trade publications. These magazines carry advertisements of various dealers listing coins for sale. Moreover, through these sources the beginner may obtain price lists and catalogs from the dealers.

There are several good reference books available at reasonable prices which will be helpful to the collector who wishes to know more about U.S. coins and paper money. R.S. Yeoman's *A Guide Book of United States Coins™* (the "Red Book") lists retail values of all regular U.S. coins and also lists all coins of the U.S. colonial period and private and territorial gold coins, plus tokens, pattern coins, errors, and other numismatic collectibles.

Most coin, book, and hobby dealers can supply the following titles:

The Official Red Book®: A Guide Book of United States Coins™—R.S. Yeoman, edited by Kenneth Bressett

A Guide Book of Morgan Silver Dollars: A Complete History and Price Guide—Q. David Bowers

The Expert's Guide to Collecting and Investing in Rare Coins—Q. David Bowers

Coin Collecting: A Beginner's Guide to the World of Coins—Kenneth Bressett

History of the United States Mint and Its Coinage—David W. Lange

T*he Official ANA Grading Standards for United States Coins*—Kenneth Bressett, et al.

A Guide Book of United States Type Coins—Q. David Bowers

Join a Coin Club

Beginners should join a "coin club" if they live in a city which has one. Associating with more experienced collectors will be of great benefit. Practically all larger cities have one or more clubs and they are being rapidly organized in smaller towns. Trade publications carry information about coin clubs and events such as coin shows and conventions.

The American Numismatic Association is a national organization that collectors can join. The ANA web site (www.money.org) has a list of member coin clubs throughout the United States. Contact the ANA by mail at 818 North Cascade Avenue, Colorado Springs, CO 80903, or by phone at 719-632-2646.

Early American coins are rare in conditions better than those listed and are consequently valued much higher.

BRITISH NEW WORLD ISSUES

Sommer Islands (Bermuda)

This coinage, issued around 1616, was the first struck for England's colonies in the New World. The coins were known as "Hogge Money" or "Hoggies."

The pieces were made of copper lightly silvered, in four denominations: shilling, six-pence, threepence, and twopence, indicated by Roman numerals. The hog is the main device and appears on the obverse side of each. SOMMER ISLANDS is inscribed within beaded circles. The reverse shows a full-rigged galleon with the flag of St. George on each of four masts.

Shilling

	G	VG	F	VF	EF
Twopence	$3,000	$4,500	$6,500	$15,000	$30,000
Threepence		65,000			
Sixpence	2,750	4,000	6,500	15,000	30,000
Shilling	3,600	5,200	15,000	30,000	45,000

Massachusetts

"New England" Coinage (1652)

In 1652 the General Court of Massachusetts ordered the first metallic currency to be struck in the British Americas, the New England silver threepence, sixpence, and shilling. These coins were made from silver bullion procured principally from the West Indies. Joseph Jenks made the punches for the first coins at his Iron Works in Saugus, Massachusetts, close to Boston where the mint was located. John Hull was appointed mintmaster; his assistant was Robert Sanderson.

NE Shilling (1652)

	G	VG	F	VF
NE Threepence *(unique)*				—
NE Sixpence *(8 known)*	$20,000	$40,000	$50,000	$125,000
NE Shilling	25,000	45,000	70,000	150,000

Willow Tree Coinage (1653–1660)

The simplicity of the design on the N.E. coins invited counterfeiting and clipping of the edges. Therefore, they were soon replaced by the Willow Tree, Oak Tree, and Pine Tree series. The Willow Tree coins were struck from 1653 to 1660, the Oak Trees 1660 to 1667, and the Pine Trees 1667 to 1682. All of them (with the exception of the Oak Tree twopence) bore the date 1652. Many varieties of all of these coins exist. Values shown are for the most common types.

Sixpence

	Fair	G	VG	F	VF
1652 Willow Tree Threepence *(3 known)*		—	—	—	—
1652 Willow Tree Sixpence *(14 known)*	$6,500	$16,000	$25,000	$50,000	$110,000
1652 Willow Tree Shilling	8,000	18,000	30,000	70,000	130,000

Oak Tree Coinage (1660–1667)

Twopence   Threepence

	G	VG	F	VF	EF	AU
1662 Oak Tree Twopence	$375	$500	$1,500	$2,750	$3,750	$7,000
1652 Oak Tree Threepence	380	650	1,700	3,250	4,900	8,500
1652 Oak Tree Sixpence	400	700	1,800	4,000	7,000	13,000
1652 Oak Tree Shilling	450	750	1,850	4,000	7,000	8,500

Pine Tree Coinage (1667–1682)

The first Pine Tree coins were minted on the same size planchets as the Oak Tree pieces. Subsequent issues of the shilling were narrower and thicker, to conform to the size of English coins.

Shilling, Large Planchet (1667–1674)   Shilling, Small Planchet (1675–1682)

See next page for chart.   **17**

	G	VG	F	VF	EF	AU
1652 Pine Tree Threepence	$350	$550	$1,000	$2,200	$3,300	$5,250
1652 Pine Tree Sixpence	400	600	1,200	2,700	3,400	6,000
1652 Pine Tree Shilling, Large Planchet	450	750	1,600	3,200	5,000	8,000
1652 Pine Tree Shilling, Small Planchet	400	650	1,350	3,000	3,700	6,000

Maryland
Lord Baltimore Coinage

In 1659, Cecil Calvert, Lord Baltimore and Lord Proprietor of Maryland, had coinage struck in England for use in Maryland. There were four denominations: shilling, sixpence, fourpence (groat) in silver, and copper penny (denarium). The silver coins have the bust of Lord Baltimore on the obverse, and the Baltimore family arms with the denomination in Roman numerals on the reverse.

Fourpence (groat)   Lord Baltimore Shilling

	G	VG	F	VF	EF	AU
Penny copper (9 known)	—	—	—	—	—	—
Fourpence	$800	$1,700	$3,500	$7,500	$12,000	$19,000
Sixpence	700	1,300	2,500	5,000	7,000	10,000
Shilling.................................	1,000	1,700	3,500	7,000	10,000	15,000

New Jersey
St. Patrick or Mark Newby Coinage

Mark Newby, who came to America from Dublin, Ireland, in November 1681, brought copper pieces believed by numismatists to have been struck in England circa 1663 to 1672. These are called St. Patrick coppers. The coin received wide circulation in the New Jersey Province, having been authorized to pass as legal tender by the General Assembly in May 1682. The smaller piece, known as a farthing, was never specifically authorized for circulation in the colonies.

St. Patrick Farthing

	G	VG	F	VF	EF	AU
St. Patrick "Farthing"	$90	$150	$400	$1,400	$2,750	$5,000
St. Patrick "Halfpenny"	170	390	800	1,850	5,000	

COINAGE AUTHORIZED BY BRITISH ROYAL PATENT
American Plantations Tokens

These tokens struck in nearly pure tin were the first royally authorized coinage for the British colonies in America. They were made under a franchise granted in 1688 to Richard Holt. Restrikes were made circa 1828 from original dies.

	G	F	EF	AU	Unc.
(1688) James II Plantation Token Farthing					
1/24 Part Real	$125	$300	$750	$1,000	$2,000
1/24 Part Real, Restrike	60	170	375	550	950

Coinage of William Wood
Rosa Americana Coins

William Wood, an Englishman, obtained a patent from King George I to make tokens for Ireland and the American colonies. The Rosa Americana pieces were issued in three denominations—halfpenny, penny, and twopence—and were intended for use in America.

Penny

	VG	F	VF	EF	AU	Unc.
(No date) Twopence, Motto in Ribbon	$90	$170	$375	$700	$1,500	$3,000
1722 Halfpenny, DEI GRATIA REX UTILE DULCI	55	125	210	450	825	1,800
1722 Penny	55	125	210	450	825	1,800
1722 Twopence	80	160	300	550	1,000	2,200

Halfpenny

	VG	F	VF	EF	AU	Unc.
1723 Halfpenny	$40	$100	$175	$450	$900	$1,850

Entry continued on next page.

Twopence

	VG	F	VF	EF	AU	Unc.
1723 Penny	$40	$110	$200	$400	$650	$1,500
1723 Twopence *(illustrated)*	90	130	300	500	900	1,800

Wood's Hibernia Coinage

The type intended for Ireland had a seated figure with a harp on the reverse side and the word HIBERNIA. Denominations struck were the halfpenny and the farthing with dates 1722, 1723, and 1724. Although these have no association with the Americas, because of the connection with William Wood many American collectors desire to obtain them.

1722, Hibernia Halfpenny

First Type

Second Type

	VG	F	VF	EF	AU	Unc.
1722 Farthing, second type	$125	$220	$400	$750	$1,200	$3,000
1722 Halfpenny (first or second type)	40	55	110	250	400	650

1723, Hibernia Farthing

1724, Hibernia Halfpenny

	VG	F	VF	EF	AU	Unc.
1723 Farthing	$20	$35	$80	$150	$250	$500
1723 Halfpenny	20	30	75	150	225	500
1724 Farthing	40	90	250	400	650	1,300
1724 Halfpenny	32	75	170	325	500	1,000

Virginia Halfpennies

In 1773, coinage of a copper halfpenny was authorized for Virginia by the British Crown. The style is similar to the regular English coinage. These pieces did not arrive in Virginia until 1775, but after then they did circulate on a limited basis. Most examples know today are Uncirculated, by virtue of a hoard of several thousand pieces that came to light in the 19th century and was distributed in numismatic channels.

	VG	F	VF	EF	AU	Unc.
1773 Halfpenny	$30	$50	$125	$225	$350	$600

EARLY AMERICAN AND RELATED TOKENS

Elephant Tokens

London Elephant Tokens

The London Elephant tokens were struck circa 1672 to 1694. Although they were undated, two examples are known to have been struck over 1672 British halfpennies. Most are struck in copper, but one is made of brass. The legend on this piece, GOD PRESERVE LONDON, is probably just a general plea for divine aid and not a specific reference to the outbreak of plague in 1665 or the great fire of 1666.

These pieces were not struck for the colonies, and probably did not circulate widely in America, although a few may have been carried there by colonists. They are associated with the 1694 Carolina and New England Elephant tokens, through a shared obverse die.

	VG	F	VF	EF	AU	Unc.
(1694) Halfpenny, GOD PRESERVE LONDON, Thick or Thin Planchet	$160	$300	$550	$900	$1,600	$2,200

Carolina Elephant Tokens

Although no law is known authorizing coinage for Carolina, very interesting pieces known as Elephant Tokens were made with the date 1694. These copper tokens were of halfpenny denomination. The reverse reads GOD PRESERVE CAROLINA AND THE LORDS PROPRIETERS. 1694.

The Carolina pieces were probably struck in England and perhaps intended as advertising to heighten interest in the Carolina Plantation.

	VG	F	VF	EF
1694 CAROLINA	$2,500	$4,000	$7,000	$12,000

New England Elephant Tokens

Like the Carolina Tokens, the New England Elephant Tokens were believed to have been struck in England as promotional pieces to increase interest in the American colonies.

	VG	F	VF	EF
1694 NEW ENGLAND	$18,000	$25,000	$50,000	$70,000

New Yorke in America Token

Little is known about the origin of this token. The design of a heraldic eagle on a regulated staff with oak leaf finials is identical to the crest found on the arms of William Lovelace, governor of New York, 1663 to 1673. It seems likely that this piece is a token farthing struck by Lovelace for use in New York.

	VG	F
(Undated) Brass or Copper	$3,500	$11,000
(Undated) Pewter	—	—

Gloucester Tokens

This token appears to have been a private coinage by a merchant of Gloucester (county), Virginia. The only specimens known are struck in brass. The exact origin and use of these pieces are unknown.

	F
1714 Shilling, brass *(2 known)*	$65,000

Higley or Granby Coppers

The Higley coppers were private issues. All the tokens were made of pure copper. There were seven obverse and four reverse dies. The first issue, in 1737, bore the legend THE VALUE OF THREEPENCE. After a time the quantity exceeded the local demand, and a protest arose against the value of the piece. The inscription was changed to VALUE ME AS YOU PLEASE.

	G	VG	F	VF
1737 THE VALVE OF THREE PENCE, CONNECTICVT, 3 Hammers	$5,000	$9,000	$16,000	$45,000
1737 THE VALVE OF THREE PENCE, I AM GOOD COPPER, 3 Hammers	5,500	9,500	16,000	45,000
1737 VALUE ME AS YOU PLEASE, I AM GOOD COPPER, 3 Hammers	5,500	9,500	16,000	45,000
(1737) VALUE ME AS YOU PLEASE, J CUT MY WAY THROUGH, Broad Axe	5,500	9,500	16,000	45,000
1739 VALUE ME AS YOU PLEASE, J CUT MY WAY THROUGH, Broad Axe	6,500	11,000	20,000	75,000

Hibernia–Voce Populi Coins

These coins, struck in the year 1760, were made in Dublin. Although these have no connection with America, they have been listed in numismatic publications in the United States for a long time and are collected by tradition.

Farthing (1760)   Halfpenny (1760)

	G	VG	F	VF	EF	AU	Unc.
1760 Farthing	$130	$180	$300	$950	$1,350	$2,100	$4,000
1760 Halfpenny	40	75	115	200	380	800	1,500

Pitt Tokens

William Pitt is the subject of these pieces, probably intended as commemorative medalets. He was a friend to the interests of America. The halfpenny served as currency during a shortage of regular coinage.

	VG	F	VF	EF	AU	Unc.
1766 Farthing		$4,000	$12,000			
1766 Halfpenny	$200	400	850	$1,500	$2,400	$4,750

Rhode Island Ship Medals

Although this medal has a Dutch inscription, the spelling and design indicate an English or Anglo-American origin. It is believed that this token was struck in England circa 1779–1780 as propaganda to persuade the Dutch to sign the Treaty of Armed Neutrality. Specimens are known in brass, copper, tin, and pewter. As with many colonial issues, modern copies exist.

1778–1779, Rhode Island Ship Medal

Values shown are for brass or copper pieces. Those struck in pewter are rare and valued higher.

	VF	EF	AU	Unc.
Rhode Island Ship Medal	$550	$1,000	$1,800	$3,000

John Chalmers Issues

John Chalmers, a silversmith, struck a series of silver tokens at Annapolis in 1783. Certain of the dies were by Thomas Sparro, who also engraved bank note plates. As most examples show wear today, these pieces seem to have served well in commerce.

	VG	F	VF	EF	AU
1783 Threepence	$900	$1,800	$3,000	$6,250	$10,000

	VG	F	VF	EF	AU
1783 Sixpence	$1,300	$3,000	$6,000	$11,000	$17,000
1783 Shilling	700	1,300	2,200	5,000	9,500

FRENCH NEW WORLD ISSUES

None of the coins of the French regime is strictly American. They were all general issues for the French colonies of the New World. The copper of 1717 to 1722 was authorized by edicts of 1716 and 1721 for use in New France, Louisiana, and the French West Indies.

Copper Sou or Nine Deniers

	VG	F	VF
1721-B (Rouen)	$80	$250	$650
1721-H (La Rochelle)	45	100	275
1722-H	45	100	275

French Colonies in General

Coined for use in the French colonies, these circulated only unofficially in Louisiana, along with other foreign coins and tokens. Most were counterstamped RF (République Française) for use in the West Indies. The mintmark A signifies the Paris Mint.

	VG	VF	EF	AU
1767 French Colonies, Sou	$45	$200	$400	$1,000
1767 French Colonies, Sou, Counterstamped RF	40	100	225	450

SPECULATIVE ISSUES, TOKENS, AND PATTERNS

Nova Constellatio Coppers

The Nova Constellatio pieces were struck supposedly by order of Gouverneur Morris. Evidence indicates that they were all struck in Birmingham, England, and imported for American circulation as a private business venture.

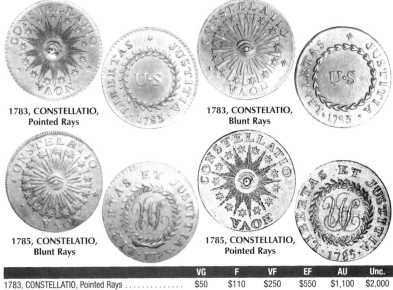

1783, CONSTELLATIO,
Pointed Rays

1783, CONSTELATIO,
Blunt Rays

1785, CONSTELATIO,
Blunt Rays

1785, CONSTELATIO,
Pointed Rays

	VG	F	VF	EF	AU	Unc.
1783, CONSTELLATIO, Pointed Rays	$50	$110	$250	$550	$1,100	$2,000
1783, CONSTELLATIO, Blunt Rays	55	125	275	700	2,200	2,750
1785, CONSTELLATIO, Blunt Rays	60	125	300	750	1,850	3,400
1785, CONSTELLATIO, Pointed Rays	50	120	270	600	1,000	2,000

Immune Columbia Pieces

Nearly all of these are very rare. Many if not most seem to be unofficial, including pieces produced at the private Machin's Mills mint in Newburgh, New York.

1785, Copper,
Star Reverse

1785, George III
Obverse

	G	VG	F	VF	EF	AU
1785 Copper, Star Reverse			$8,000	$14,000	$17,000	
1785, George III Obverse	$2,500	$4,000	6,000	8,000		

1787, IMMUNIS COLUMBIA, Eagle Reverse

	G	VG	F	VF	EF	AU
1785, VERMON AUCTORI Obverse, IMMUNE COLUMBIA	$3,200	$5,500	$7,500	$18,000		
1787, IMMUNIS COLUMBIA, Eagle Reverse	150	375	800	2,000	$3,750	$6,500

Confederatio Coppers

Some Confederatio coppers may have been patterns, but others seem to have been made in limited numbers for general circulation. This will explain why the die with the CONFEDERATIO legend was combined with other designs such as a bust of George Washington, Libertas et Justitia of 1785, Immunis Columbia of 1786, the New York "Excelsiors," Inimica Tyrannis Americana, and others. In all there were 13 dies struck in 14 combinations. There are two types of the Confederatio reverse. In one instance the stars are contained in a small circle; in the other, larger stars are in a larger circle.

| **Typical Obverse** | **Small Circle Reverse** | **Large Circle Reverse** |

	VF
1785, Stars in Small Circle, various obverses	$29,000
1785, Stars in Large Circle, various obverses	26,000

Speculative Patterns

| **1786, IMMUNIS COLUMBIA** | **Eagle Reverse** | **Shield Reverse** |

	VF
1786, IMMUNIS COLUMBIA, Eagle Reverse	$30,000
1786, IMMUNIS COLUMBIA, Shield Reverse	25,000

Chart continued on next page.

	VF
(No date) (1786) Washington Obverse, Shield Reverse	—
1786, Eagle Obverse, Shield Reverse	$30,000
1786, Washington Obverse, Eagle Reverse *(2 known)*	—

COINAGE OF THE STATES
New Hampshire

New Hampshire was the first of the states to consider the subject of coinage following the Declaration of Independence.

William Moulton was empowered to make a limited quantity of coins of pure copper, authorized by the State House of Representatives in 1776.

	VG
1776 New Hampshire Copper	$20,000

Massachusetts

The coinage of Massachusetts copper cents and half cents in 1787 and 1788 was under the direction of Joshua Witherle. These were the first coins bearing the denomination "cent" as established by Congress. Many varieties exist, the most valuable being that with arrows in the eagle's right talon (on the left side of the coin).

1787 Half Cent   1787 Cent

1788 Half Cent   1788 Cent

	G	F	VF	EF	AU	Unc.
1787 Half Cent	$45	$120	$300	$650	$1,000	$1,800
1787 Cent, Arrows in Right Talon	4,200	10,000	25,000			
1787 Cent, Arrows in Left Talon *(illustrated)*	45	120	325	700	1,700	3,000

	G	F	VF	EF	AU	Unc.
1788 Half Cent	$50	$125	$300	$675	$1,500	$2,000
1788 Cent	40	110	275	650	1,500	2,200

Connecticut

Authority for establishing a mint near New Haven was granted by the state to Samuel Bishop, Joseph Hopkins, James Hillhouse, and John Goodrich in 1785. Today, well over 300 different die varieties are known of Connecticut coppers dated from 1785 to 1788. These pieces circulated widely and effectively; most are seen with significant evidence of circulation.

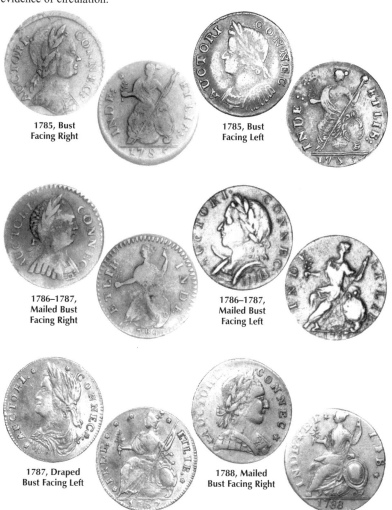

1785, Bust Facing Right

1785, Bust Facing Left

1786–1787, Mailed Bust Facing Right

1786–1787, Mailed Bust Facing Left

1787, Draped Bust Facing Left

1788, Mailed Bust Facing Right

Entry continued on next page.

1788, Mailed Bust Facing Left

1788, Draped Bust Facing Left

	G	VG	F	VF	EF
1785, Bust Facing Right	$35	$45	$95	$300	$800
1785, Bust Facing Left	100	175	300	850	1,500
1786, Mailed Bust Facing Right	40	50	100	275	950
1786 Mailed Bust Facing Left	35	45	100	200	500
1787, Mailed Bust Facing Right	42	65	175	475	800
1787, Mailed Bust Facing Left	25	35	75	200	475
1787, Draped Bust Facing Left	25	35	75	225	500
1788, Mailed Bust Facing Right	25	50	100	300	700
1788, Mailed Bust Facing Left	25	32	80	210	550
1788, Draped Bust Facing Left	25	35	100	250	600

New York and Related Issues
Brasher Doubloons

Perhaps the most famous pieces coined before the establishment of the U.S. Mint at Philadelphia were those produced by a well-known goldsmith and jeweler, Ephraim Brasher of New York.

Brasher produced a gold piece weighing about 408 grains, approximately equal in value to a Spanish doubloon (about $15.00).

The punch-mark EB appears in either of two positions as illustrated. This mark is found on some foreign gold coins as well, and probably was so used by Brasher as evidence of his testing of their value. Many modern forgeries exist.

	EF
1787 New York gold doubloon, EB on Breast	—
1787 New York gold doubloon, EB on Wing	—

Copper Coinage

No coinage was authorized for New York following the Revolutionary War, although several propositions were considered. The only coinage laws passed were those regulating coins already in use.

	G	VG	F	VF
1786, NON VI VIRTUTE VICI	$2,750	$4,250	$8,000	$17,000

	G	VG	F	VF	EF
1787 EXCELSIOR Copper, Eagle on Globe Facing Right	$1,000	$2,000	$4,000	$10,000	$18,000
1787 EXCELSIOR Copper, Eagle on Globe Facing Left	1,000	2,000	3,500	9,000	17,000

1787, George Clinton and New York Arms

1787, Indian and New York Arms

1787, Indian and Eagle on Globe

	G	VG	F	VF	EF
1787, George Clinton and New York Arms	$4,500	$8,000	$14,000	$25,000	—
1787, Indian and New York Arms	3,500	5,500	10,000	19,000	$40,000
1787, Indian and Eagle on Globe	6,000	9,000	16,000	30,000	70,000

Nova Eborac Coinage for New York

**1787, NOVA EBORAC Reverse,
Seated Figure Facing Right**

**1787, NOVA EBORAC Reverse,
Seated Figure Facing Left**

	Fair	G	F	VF	EF	AU
1787, NOVA EBORAC, Seated Figure Facing Right . . .	$30	$60	$175	$600	$1,500	$2,500
1787, NOVA EBORAC, Seated Figure Facing Left	30	50	150	500	900	1,700

New Jersey

On June 1, 1786, the New Jersey Colonial legislature granted to Thomas Goadsby, Albion Cox, and Walter Mould authority to coin some three million coppers no later than June 1788, on condition that they delivered to the treasurer of the state "one-tenth part of the full sum they shall strike and coin," in quarterly installments. These coppers were to pass current at 15 to the shilling. Produced in significant quantities, these coins are often seen in the market today and are widely collectible, although certain varieties can be rare and especially valuable.

Narrow Shield

Wide Shield

	G	F	VF	EF	AU
1786, Narrow Shield	$25	$100	$300	$700	$1,300
1786, Wide Shield	30	125	350	900	1,500

Small Planchet

	G	F	VF	EF	AU
1787, Small Planchet	$30	$100	$300	$650	$1,200
1787, Large Planchet	35	110	375	750	1,600

Fox Before Legend

	G	F	VF	EF	AU
1788, Horse's Head Facing Right	$30	$100	$300	$725	$1,500
1788, Similar, Fox in Legend	75	275	900	1,800	4,500
1788, Horse's Head Facing Left	200	800	2,100	6,000	—

Vermont

Reuben Harmon Jr. was granted permission to coin copper pieces beginning July 1, 1785. The franchise was extended for eight years in 1786. However, in 1787 production was shifted to Machin's Mills, Newburgh, New York, in which Harmon had a proprietary interest. Although the Vermont coins were legally issued there, most other products of Machin's Mills were counterfeits, some dies for which were combined with Vermont pieces, creating several illogical pieces below, including the 1785 Immune Columbia and the 1788 Georgivs III Rex.

1785, IMMUNE COLUMBIA   **1785–1786, Plow Type**   **1786, Baby Head**

	G	VG	F	VF	EF
1785, IMMUNE COLUMBIA	$3,200	$5,500	$7,500	$18,000	—
1785, Plow Type, VERMONTS	175	350	700	1,600	$4,500
1786, Plow Type, VERMONTENSIUM	135	260	500	1,100	2,250
1786, Baby Head	175	350	800	2,400	5,000

33

	1786–1787, Bust Left	1787, BRITANNIA	1787, Bust Right

	G	VG	F	VF	EF
1786, Bust Left	$85	$200	$450	$1,500	$2,600
1787, Bust Left	2,500	5,500	15,000	23,000	—
1787, BRITANNIA	50	85	160	350	950
1787, Bust Right *(several varieties)*	70	135	245	600	1,500

	1788, Bust Right		1788, GEORGIVS III REX

	G	VG	F	VF	EF
1788, Bust Right *(several varieties)*	$60	$110	$225	$500	$1,000
1788, GEORGIVS III REX	325	600	1,400	2,800	7,500

Note: This piece should not be confused with the common British halfpence with similar design and reverse legend BRITANNIA.

PRIVATE TOKENS AFTER CONFEDERATION
North American Tokens

This piece was struck in Dublin, Ireland. The obverse shows the seated figure of Hibernia facing left. Although dated 1781, it is believed to have been struck early in the next century.

	VG	F	VF	EF
1781, Copper or brass	$30	$75	$170	$425

Bar Coppers

The Bar "Copper" is undated and of uncertain origin. It has 13 parallel and uncon-
nected bars on one side. On the other side is the large Roman letter USA monogram.
The design was supposedly copied from a Continental button.

	VG	F	VF	EF	AU
(Undated) (Circa 1785) Bar Copper	$925	$1,750	$3,250	$4,700	$7,000

Auctori Plebis Tokens

This token is sometimes included with the coins of Connecticut as it greatly resem-
bles issues of that state. It was struck in England by an unknown maker, possibly for
use in America.

	G	VG	F	VF	EF	AU	Unc.
1787, AUCTORI PLEBIS	$40	$90	$150	$390	$750	$1,500	$4,000

Mott Store Cards

This item has long been considered an early token because of its date (1789). Most
scholars believe it was most likely produced circa 1809 as a commemorative of the
founding of the Mott Company, and probably served as a business card.

	VG	F	VF	EF	AU	Unc.
1789, Mott Token	$60	$125	$250	$400	$600	$1,000

Standish Barry Threepence

Standish Barry, a Baltimore silversmith, circulated a silver threepence in 1790. The tokens were believed to have been an advertising venture at a time when small change was scarce.

	VG	F	VF
1790 Threepence	$5,000	$11,000	$25,000

Kentucky Tokens

These tokens were struck in England about 1792 to 1794. Each star in the triangle represents a state, identified by its initial letter. These pieces are usually called Kentucky Cents because the letter K (for Kentucky) happens to be at the top. In the 19th century these were often called "triangle tokens," from the arrangement of the stars. Values are for the normal issue with plain edge; lettered edge varieties exist and are scarcer.

	VG	VF	EF	AU	Unc.
(1792–1794) Copper, Plain Edge	$50	$120	$225	$375	$650

Franklin Press Tokens

This piece is an English tradesman's token but, being associated with Benjamin Franklin, has accordingly been included in American collections.

	VG	VF	EF	AU	Unc.
1794, Franklin Press Token	$60	$150	$250	$450	$800

Talbot, Allum & Lee Cents

Talbot, Allum & Lee, engaged in the India trade and located in New York, placed a large quantity of English-made coppers in circulation during 1794 and 1795. ONE CENT appears on the 1794 issue.

1794 Cent,
With NEW YORK

1795 Cent

	G	VG	VF	EF	AU	Unc.
1794 Cent, With NEW YORK	$25	$40	$150	$270	$450	$900
1794 Cent, Without NEW YORK	200	300	1,500	3,000	5,000	
1795 Cent	25	40	125	240	350	700

WASHINGTON PORTRAIT PIECES

An interesting series of coins and tokens dated from 1783 to 1795 bear the portrait of George Washington. The likenesses in most instances were faithfully reproduced and were designed to honor Washington. Many of these pieces were of English origin and made later than the dates indicate.

1783,
Military Bust

1783,
Draped Bust

	F	VF	EF	AU	Unc.
1783, Military Bust	$40	$100	$235	$600	$1,500
1783, Draped Bust	45	110	250	475	1,300

1783, UNITY STATES

	VG	F	VF	EF	AU	Unc.
1783, UNITY STATES	$30	$60	$150	$300	$500	$1,350

Undated Double-Head Cent

	VG	F	VF	EF	AU	Unc.
(Undated) Double-Head Cent	$30	$50	$150	$275	$575	$1,700

Obverse	**Large Eagle Reverse**	**Small Eagle Reverse**

	F	EF	AU	Unc.
1791 Cent, Large Eagle (Date on Obverse)	$225	$450	$750	$1,500
1791 Cent, Small Eagle (Date on Reverse)	250	500	900	1,800

	F	EF	AU
1791 Liverpool Halfpenny, Lettered Edge	$750	$2,300	$4,000

1792, Eagle With Stars, copper	—
1792, Eagle With Stars, silver	—
1792, Eagle With Stars, gold *(unique)*	—

**(1792) Undated Cent,
WASHINGTON BORN VIRGINIA**

**1792 Cent,
WASHINGTON PRESIDENT**

	VG	F	VF
(1792) Undated Cent, WASHINGTON BORN VIRGINIA, copper	$1,200	$2,250	$3,750
1792 Cent, WASHINGTON PRESIDENT, Plain Edge	1,500	3,750	6,000

1792 Getz Pattern

1793 Ship Halfpenny

1795 Halfpenny, Grate Token

	VG	F	VF	EF	AU	Unc.
1792, Getz Pattern, copper	$4,000	$7,000	$14,000	—		
1793 Ship Halfpenny, Lettered Edge	35	110	250	$450	$800	$1,900
1795, Grate Token, Lettered Edge	50	125	250	450	900	1,400
1795, Grate Token, Reeded Edge	30	75	110	250	350	600

	F	VF	EF	AU	Unc.
1795, LIBERTY AND SECURITY Halfpenny, Plain Edge	$75	$200	$400	$800	$1,500
1795, LIBERTY AND SECURITY Halfpenny, Lettered Edge	65	160	325	650	1,700
(1795) Undated, LIBERTY AND SECURITY Penny	165	300	450	850	1,900

	G	F	VF	EF
(1795) NORTH WALES Halfpenny	$60	$150	$385	$850

	F	VF	EF	AU	Unc.
SUCCESS Medal; Large; Plain or Reeded Edge	$135	$275	$500	$900	$1,900
SUCCESS Medal; Small; Plain or Reeded Edge	150	325	600	950	2,000

CONTINENTAL CURRENCY

The Continental Currency pieces probably had some assigned value at their time of issue. The exact nature of their monetary role is uncertain; they might have been patterns, or they might have seen circulation. At any rate, this was the first dollar-sized coin proposed for the United States. They were probably struck in Philadelphia. As with many early pieces, modern replicas exist.

	G	F	VF	EF	AU	Unc.
1776, CURENCY, Pewter *(2 varieties)*	$4,000	$7,000	$11,000	$17,000	$26,000	$42,000
1776, CURENCY, Silver *(2 known)*		150,000				
1776, CURRENCY, Pewter	4,000	7,000	13,000	18,500	30,000	43,000
1776, CURRENCY, EG FECIT, Pewter	4,000	7,000	13,000	18,500	30,000	45,000

FUGIO COPPERS

The first coins issued by authority of the United States were the "Fugio" coppers. The legends have been credited to Benjamin Franklin by many, and the coins, as a consequence, have been referred to as *Franklin cents*.

1787, With Pointed Rays

1787, With Club Rays

	VG	F	VF	EF	AU	Unc.
Pointed Rays, STATES UNITED at Side of Circle *(illustrated)*	$150	$250	$400	$800	$1,000	$2,000
Pointed Rays, UNITED STATES at Side of Circle	150	250	400	800	1,000	2,200
Club Rays, Rounded Ends	250	400	1,000	2,200	4,500	—

The half cent was authorized to be coined April 2, 1792. Originally the weight was to have been 132 grains, but this was changed to 104 grains by the Act of January 14, 1793, before coinage commenced. The weight was again changed to 84 grains January 26, 1796, by presidential proclamation in conformity with the Act of March 3, 1795. Coinage was discontinued by the Act of February 21, 1857. All were coined at the Philadelphia Mint.

LIBERTY CAP (1793–1797)

AG-3 About Good: Clear enough to identify.
G-4 Good: Outline of bust of Liberty clear, no details. Date readable. Reverse lettering incomplete.
VG-8 Very Good: Some hair details. Reverse lettering complete.
F-12 Fine: Most of hair detail visible. Leaves worn, but all visible.
VF-20 Very Fine: Hair near ear and forehead worn, other areas distinct. Some details in leaves visible.
EF-40 Extremely Fine: Light wear on highest parts of head and wreath.
AU-50 About Uncirculated: Only a trace of wear on Liberty's face.

Head Facing Left (1793)

	Mintage	AG-3	G-4	VG-8	F-12	VF-20	EF-40	AU-50
1793	35,334	$900	$1,600	$2,700	$4,000	$7,200	$12,500	$18,000

Head Facing Right (1794–1797)

Pole to Cap	Punctuated Date	No Pole to Cap

	Mintage	AG-3	G-4	VG-8	F-12	VF-20	EF-40	AU-50
1794	81,600	$120	$265	$350	$600	$1,200	$2,750	$5,000
1795, All kinds	139,690							
1795, Lettered Edge, With Pole		80	200	310	525	1,200	2,600	4,200
1795, Lettered Edge, Punctuated Date		80	200	310	525	1,200	2,600	4,200
1795, Plain Edge, Punctuated Date		75	160	260	410	1,000	2,400	3,500
1795, Plain Edge, No Pole		75	160	260	410	1,000	2,400	3,500
1796, With Pole	1,390	3,500	6,750	9,800	14,000	23,000	30,000	
1796, No Pole	*	7,000	15,000	19,000	30,000	45,000	75,000	

* Included in number above.

1797, 1 Above 1, Plain Edge   **1797, Plain Edge**

	Mintage	AG-3	G-4	VG-8	F-12	VF-20	EF-40	AU-50
1797, All kinds	127,840							
1797, 1 Above 1, Plain Edge		$70	$210	$300	$450	$900	$2,000	$3,200
1797, Plain Edge		90	220	300	600	1,000	2,100	3,500
1797, Lettered Edge		200	700	1,100	2,750	6,500	14,000	32,000
1797, Gripped Edge		3,500	13,000	27,000				

DRAPED BUST (1800–1808)

AG-3 About Good: Clear enough to identify.
G-4 Good: Outline of bust of Liberty clear, few details, date readable. Reverse lettering worn and incomplete.
VG-8 Very Good: Some drapery visible. Date and legends complete.
F-12 Fine: Shoulder drapery and hair over brow worn smooth.
VF-20 Very Fine: Only slight wear in previously mentioned areas. Slight wear on reverse.
EF-40 Extremely Fine: Light wear on highest parts of head and wreath.
AU-50 About Uncirculated: Wear slight on hair above forehead.

1st Reverse   **2nd Reverse**

	Mintage	AG-3	G-4	VG-8	F-12	VF-20	EF-40	AU-50
1800	202,908	$17	$35	$45	$60	$150	$300	$500
1802, 2 Over 0	20,266	130	360	800	1,850	5,000	13,500	
1803	92,000	17	35	50	70	160	450	700

Plain 4   **Crosslet 4**   **Stemless Wreath**   **Stems to Wreath**

	Mintage	AG-3	G-4	VG-8	F-12	VF-20	EF-40	AU-50
1804, All kinds	1,055,312							
1804, Plain 4, Stems to Wreath		$18	$40	$60	$95	$175	$470	$1,000
1804, Plain 4, Stemless Wreath		17	35	45	70	95	160	300
1804, Crosslet 4, Stemless Wreath		17	35	45	70	95	160	300
1804, Crosslet 4, Stems to Wreath		17	35	45	70	95	160	300

Entry continued on next page.

1804, "Spiked Chin"   **Small 5**   **Large 5**

	Mintage	AG-3	G-4	VG-8	F-12	VF-20	EF-40	AU-50
1804, "Spiked Chin" ....*		$18	$40	$50	$75	$110	$200	$350
1805, All kinds 814,464								
1805, Medium 5, Stemless Wreath		17	35	45	70	100	160	300
1805, Small 5, Stems to Wreath		110	375	700	1,500	3,000	5,000	
1805, Large 5, Stems to Wreath		17	35	45	70	100	160	300

* Included in "1804, All kinds" mintage (previous page).

Small 6   **Large 6**   **1808, 8 Over 7**   **Normal Date**

	Mintage	AG-3	G-4	VG-8	F-12	VF-20	EF-40	AU-50
1806, All kinds 356,000								
1806, Small 6, Stems to Wreath		$40	$110	$185	$325	$700	$1,400	$3,750
1806, Small 6, Stemless Wreath		17	35	45	55	75	145	290
1806, Large 6, Stems to Wreath		17	35	45	55	75	145	290
1807 476,000		17	35	45	60	100	225	500
1808, 8 Over 7 ....*		30	70	125	300	700	1,750	5,000
1808, Normal Date 400,000		17	35	45	60	100	225	500

* Included in number below.

CLASSIC HEAD (1809–1836)

G-4 Good: LIBERTY only partly visible on hair band. Lettering, date, stars, worn but visible.
VG-8 Very Good: LIBERTY entirely visible on hair band. Lower curls worn.
F-12 Fine: Only partial wear on LIBERTY, and hair at top worn in spots.
VF-20 Very Fine: Lettering clear-cut. Hair only slightly worn.
EF-40 Extremely Fine: Light wear on highest points of hair and leaves.
AU-50 About Uncirculated: Sharp hair detail with only a trace of wear on higher points.
MS-60 Uncirculated: Typical brown to red surface. No trace of wear.
MS-63 Choice Uncirculated: Well-defined color, brown to red. No traces of wear.

1828, 13 Stars   **1828, 12 Stars**

Brilliant or red Uncirculated coins are worth more than prices shown. Spotted, cleaned, or discolored pieces are worth less.

	Mintage	AG-3	G-4	VG-8	F-12	VF-20	EF-40	AU-50	MS-60	MS-63
1809 1,154,572		$14	$25	$30	$35	$55	$90	$150	$325	$425
1810 215,000		14	25	35	60	110	250	450	900	1,500
1811 63,140		45	100	200	350	900	2,700	3,200	4,000	6,000

HALF CENTS

	Mintage	G-4	VG-8	F-12	VF-20	EF-40	AU-50	MS-60	MS-63	PF-63
1825 63,000		$25	$30	$35	$50	$90	$150	$450	$750	
1826 234,000		25	30	35	50	85	125	275	450	
1828, 13 Stars 606,000		23	30	35	45	55	120	190	275	
1828, 12 Stars . . . .*		24	35	40	50	125	150	650	900	
1829 487,000		23	30	35	45	65	95	175	325	
1831 2,200										—
1832 51,000		23	28	32	40	55	95	175	250	$2,500
1833 103,000		23	28	32	40	55	95	175	250	2,500
1834 141,000		23	28	32	40	55	95	175	250	2,500
1835 398,000		23	28	32	40	55	95	175	250	2,500
1836										8,000

* Included in number above.

BRAIDED HAIR (1840–1857)

VG-8 Very Good: Beads in hair uniformly distinct. Hair lines visible in spots.
F-12 Fine: Hair lines above ear worn. Beads sharp.
VF-20 Very Fine: Lowest curl worn; hair otherwise distinct.
EF-40 Extremely Fine: Light wear on highest points of hair and on leaves.
AU-50 About Uncirculated: Very slight trace of wear on hair above Liberty's ear.
MS-60 Uncirculated: No trace of wear. Clear luster.
MS-63 Choice Uncirculated: No trace of wear.
PF-63 Choice Proof: Nearly perfect.

Brilliant or red Uncirculated coins are worth more than prices shown. Spotted, cleaned, or discolored pieces are worth less.

	PF-63		PF-63
1840, Original	$2,700	1845, Original	$3,500
1840, Restrike	2,250	1845, Restrike	3,250
1841,Original	2,600	1846, Original	3,250
1841, Restrike	2,500	1846, Restrike	2,600
1842, Original	2,750	1847, Original	2,600
1842, Restrike	2,500	1847, Restrike	2,600
1843, Original	2,500	1848, Original	2,600
1843, Restrike	2,500	1848, Restrike	2,600
1844, Original	3,500	1849, Original, Small Date	2,900
1844, Restrike	2,600	1849, Restrike, Small Date	2,900

Small Date   Large Date

	Mintage	G-4	VG-8	F-12	VF-20	EF-40	AU-50	MS-60	MS-63	PF-63
1849, Large Date 39,864		$17	$23	$30	$40	$75	$100	$225	$275	—
1850 39,812		17	23	30	40	75	100	225	350	$4,000
1851 147,672		15	20	28	35	50	80	135	250	3,000
1852										3,500
1853 129,694		15	20	28	35	50	80	135	250	
1854 55,358		15	20	28	35	50	80	135	250	3,000
1855 56,500		15	20	28	35	50	80	135	250	3,000
1856 40,430		17	22	30	40	60	85	150	275	3,000
1857 35,180		18	25	45	70	85	130	195	320	3,000

Cents and half cents were the first coins struck under the authority of the United States government. Coinage began in 1793 with laws stating that the cent should weigh exactly twice as much as the half cent. Large cents were coined every year from 1793 to 1857 with the exception of 1815, when a lack of copper prevented production. All were coined at the Philadelphia Mint. Varieties listed are those most significant to collectors. Numerous other die varieties may be found, as each of the early dies was individually made.

FLOWING HAIR (1793)

AG-3 About Good: Date and devices clear enough to identify.
G-4 Good: Lettering worn but readable. No detail on bust.
VG-8 Very Good: Date and lettering distinct, some details of head visible.
F-12 Fine: About half of hair and other details visible.
VF-20 Very Fine: Ear visible, most details visible.
EF-40 Extremely Fine: Wear evident on highest points of hair and back of temple.

Chain Reverse (1793)

| Obverse | AMERI. Reverse | AMERICA Reverse |

	Mintage	AG-3	G-4	VG-8	F-12	VF-20	EF-40
1793, Chain, All kinds	36,103						
1793, AMERI. in Legend		$1,400	$4,000	$7,500	$14,000	$25,000	$42,000
1793, AMERICA		1,300	3,500	6,750	9,500	19,000	34,000

Wreath Reverse (1793)

| Obverse | Wreath Reverse | Strawberry Leaf Variety |

	Mintage	AG-3	G-4	VG-8	F-12	VF-20	EF-40
1793, Wreath, All kinds	63,353						
1793, Vine and Bars Edge		$325	$1,150	$1,700	$2,750	$3,900	$7,000
1793, Lettered Edge		400	1,350	1,800	3,000	4,200	8,000
1793, Strawberry Leaf . . . . (4 known)		—	—	—			

LIBERTY CAP (1793–1796)

1793, Vine and Bars Edge
Chain and Wreath types only.

Lettered Edge (1793–1795)
ONE HUNDRED FOR A DOLLAR

Beaded Border (1793)

Head of 1793 (1793–1794)
Head in high, rounded relief.

Head of 1794 (1794)
*Well-defined hair;
hook on lowest curl.*

Head of 1795 (1794–1796)
*Head in low relief;
no hook on lowest curl.*

	Mintage	AG-3	G-4	VG-8	F-12	VF-20	EF-40
1793, Liberty Cap	11,056	$900	$1,900	$3,750	$6,750	$16,000	$35,000
1794, All kinds	918,521						
1794, "Head of 1793"		225	700	1,400	1,750	4,250	9,500
1794, "Head of 1794"		50	125	200	400	750	1,600
1794, "Head of 1795"		50	125	200	400	700	1,600
1795, Lettered Edge	37,000	50	130	200	400	900	2,400
1795, Plain Edge	501,500	35	115	225	350	700	1,500
1796, Liberty Cap	109,825	75	180	275	600	1,000	2,300

DRAPED BUST (1796–1807)

AG-3 About Good: Clear enough to identify.
G-4 Good: Lettering worn, but clear; date clear. Bust lacking in detail.
VG-8 Very Good: Drapery on Liberty partly visible. Less wear in date and lettering.
F-12 Fine: Hair over brow smooth; some detail showing in other parts of hair.
VF-20 Very Fine: Hair lines slightly worn. Hair over brow better defined.
EF-40 Extremely Fine: Hair above forehead and left of eye outlined and detailed. Only slight wear on olive leaves.

LIHERTY Error

	Mintage	AG-3	G-4	VG-8	F-12	VF-20	EF-40
1796, Draped Bust	363,375	$40	$70	$150	$300	$650	$1,800
1796, LIHERTY Error	*	80	135	325	550	1,600	4,000

* Included in number above.

Gripped Edge		With Stems		Stemless	

	Mintage	AG-3	G-4	VG-8	F-12	VF-20	EF-40
1797, All kinds 897,510							
1797, Gripped Edge, 1796 Reverse		$25	$65	$125	$225	$400	$1,500
1797, Plain Edge, 1796 Reverse		25	65	125	230	425	1,600
1797, 1797 Reverse, With Stems		20	50	100	150	235	800
1797, 1797 Reverse, Stemless		25	65	125	250	600	2,300

1798, 8 Over 7	1799, 9 Over 8	1800 Over 1798	1800, 80 Over 79	

	Mintage	AG-3	G-4	VG-8	F-12	VF-20	EF-40
1798, All kinds 1,841,745							
1798, 8 Over 7		$25	$65	$135	$225	$800	$2,500
1798		13	35	47	110	220	850
1799, 9 Over 8 ....*		700	1,400	2,500	6,000	16,000	
1799, Normal Date ....*		650	1,300	2,200	5,500	14,000	
1800, All kinds 2,822,175							
1800 Over 1798		12	28	50	110	350	1,300
1800, 80 Over 79		12	28	50	100	225	925
1800, Normal Date		12	28	50	100	225	925

* Included in 1798 mintage.

Fraction 1/000	Corrected Fraction	1801 Reverse, 3 Errors

	Mintage	AG-3	G-4	VG-8	F-12	VF-20	EF-40
1801, All kinds 1,362,837							
1801, Normal Reverse		$11	$22	$30	$75	$200	$500
1801, 3 Errors: 1/000, One Stem, and IINITED		25	65	120	325	750	3,000
1801, Fraction 1/000		11	27	40	120	225	750
1801, 1/100 Over 1/000		12	27	42	125	275	900
1802, All kinds 3,435,100							
1802, Normal Reverse		11	24	40	90	175	500
1802, Fraction 1/000		12	30	50	120	250	850
1802, Stemless Wreath		11	24	40	90	175	500

1803, Small Date, Blunt 1	1803, Large Date, Pointed 1	Small Fraction	Large Fraction

LARGE CENTS

	Mintage	AG-3	G-4	VG-8	F-12	VF-20	EF-40
1803, All kinds .3,131,691							
1803, Small Date, Small Fraction	$11	$24	$40	$80	$175	$500
1803, Small Date, Large Fraction	11	24	40	80	175	500
1803, Large Date, Small Fraction	1,000	2,300	4,000	8,000	12,500	
1803, Large Date, Large Fraction	17	33	80	150	400	1,300
1803, 1/100 Over 1/000	11	27	50	100	225	675
1803, Stemless Wreath	11	27	50	100	225	675

Broken Dies

All genuine 1804 cents have crosslet 4 in date and a large fraction.
The 0 in date is in line with O in OF on reverse.

	Mintage	AG-3	G-4	VG-8	F-12	VF-20	EF-40
1804 **(a)** 96,500	$350	$750	$1,200	$1,900	$2,850	$6,500
1805 941,116	11	24	40	80	175	500
1806 348,000	11	27	50	95	225	850

a. Values shown are for coins with normal or broken dies.

Small 1807, 7 Over 6
(Blunt 1)

Large 1807, 7 Over 6
(Pointed 1)

	Mintage	AG-3	G-4	VG-8	F-12	VF-20	EF-40
1807, All kinds 829,221							
1807, Small 7 Over 6, Blunt 1	$410	$1,200	$2,200	$4,500	$8,000	$16,500
1807, Large 7 Over 6	11	24	35	70	175	550
1807, Small Fraction	11	24	35	70	225	600
1807, Large Fraction	11	24	35	70	200	500

CLASSIC HEAD (1808–1814)

AG-3 About Good: Details clear enough to identify.

G-4 Good: Legends, stars, and date worn, but plain.

VG-8 Very Good: LIBERTY all readable. Liberty's ear visible. Details worn but plain.

F-12 Fine: Hair on forehead and before ear nearly smooth. Ear and hair under ear sharp.

VF-20 Very Fine: Some detail in all hair lines. Slight wear on leaves on reverse.

EF-40 Extremely Fine: All hair lines sharp. Very slight wear on high points.

See next page for chart.

	Mintage	AG-3	G-4	VG-8	F-12	VF-20	EF-40
1808	1,007,000	$13	$24	$60	$150	$275	$900
1809	222,867	22	50	110	225	650	1,750

1810, 10 Over 09	1810, Normal Date	1811, Last 1 Over 0	1811, Normal Date

	Mintage	AG-3	G-4	VG-8	F-12	VF-20	EF-40
1810, All kinds	1,458,500						
1810, 10 Over 09		$11	$24	$45	$120	$300	$750
1810, Normal Date		11	24	35	120	260	700
1811, All kinds	218,025						
1811, Last 1 Over 0		16	33	60	210	800	2,500
1811, Normal Date		15	35	70	150	400	850
1812	1,075,500	11	22	35	110	250	650
1813	418,000	13	24	50	125	285	650
1814	357,830	11	22	35	110	250	600

LIBERTY HEAD (1816–1857)

G-4 Good: Details on Liberty's head partly visible. Even wear in date and legends.
VG-8 Very Good: LIBERTY, date, stars, and legends clear. Part of hair cord visible.
F-12 Fine: All hair lines visible. Hair cords uniformly visible.
VF-20 Very Fine: Hair cords only slightly worn. Hair lines only partly worn, all well defined.
EF-40 Extremely Fine: Both hair cords stand out sharply. All hair lines sharp.
AU-50 About Uncirculated: Only traces of wear on hair and highest points on leaves and bow.
MS-60 Uncirculated: Typical brown surface. No trace of wear.
MS-63 Choice Uncirculated: Some distracting contact marks or blemishes in prime focal areas.
Impaired luster possible.

Matron Head (1816–1836)

1817, 13 Stars		1817, 15 Stars

Brilliant or red Uncirculated coins are worth more than prices shown. Spotted, cleaned, or discolored pieces are worth less.

	Mintage	G-4	VG-8	F-12	VF-20	EF-40	AU-50	MS-60	MS-63
1816	2,820,982	$8	$11	$16	$32	$70	$125	$250	$375
1817, 13 Stars	3,948,400	8	10	14	27	50	100	200	350
1817, 15 Stars	*	11	13	16	55	225	350	1,000	—
1818	3,167,000	8	10	14	27	50	90	270	350

* Included in number above.

1819, 9 Over 8

1820, 20 Over 19

	Mintage	G-4	VG-8	F-12	VF-20	EF-40	AU-50	MS-60	MS-63
1819	2,671,000	$9	$11	$15	$27	$55	$125	$185	$350
1819, 9 Over 8	*	10	13	18	36	150	175	300	475
1820	4,407,550	8	10	13	30	60	100	200	350
1820, 20 Over 19	*	10	13	18	45	150	200	500	650
1821	389,000	16	27	60	185	500	1,000	3,500	—
1822	2,072,339	9	12	22	50	100	275	450	750

* Included in number above.

1823, 3 Over 2

1824, 4 Over 2

1826, 6 Over 5

	Mintage	G-4	VG-8	F-12	VF-20	EF-40	AU-50	MS-60	MS-63
1823, 3 Over 2	*	$27	$50	$150	$300	$1,000	$1,800	$3,200	—
1823, Normal Date	*	30	55	175	375	1,350	2,300	3,600	—
1824, 4 Over 2	*	10	18	40	150	550	1,100	2,400	$3,500
1824, Normal Date	1,262,000	8	10	16	75	210	350	950	1,600
1825	1,461,100	8	10	16	45	150	250	800	1,100
1826, 6 Over 5	1,517,425	12	17	37	110	425	600	1,200	2,300
1826, Normal Date	**	8	10	12	45	110	190	400	650
1827	2,357,732	8	10	12	40	80	150	300	600

* Included in number below. ** Included in number above.

Date Size, Through 1828

Date Size, 1828 and Later

	Mintage	G-4	VG-8	F-12	VF-20	EF-40	AU-50	MS-60	MS-63
1828, Large Narrow Date	2,260,624	$8	$10	$14	$40	$70	$150	$400	$650
1828, Small Wide Date	*	8	10	16	50	100	200	500	1,000
1829	1,414,500	8	10	13	40	70	110	250	500
1830	1,711,500	8	10	13	30	60	100	200	400
1831	3,359,260	7	9	12	22	50	100	200	350
1832	2,362,000	7	9	12	22	50	80	175	325
1833	2,739,000	7	9	12	22	50	80	175	325
1834	1,855,100	7	9	12	22	70	100	200	350
1835	3,878,400	7	9	12	22	65	90	200	350
1836	2,111,000	7	9	12	22	55	85	160	300

* Included in number above.

Matron Head Modified (1837–1839)

G-4 Good: Considerably worn. LIBERTY readable.
VG-8 Very Good: Hairlines smooth but visible; outline of ear clearly defined.
F-12 Fine: Hairlines at top of head and behind ear worn but visible. Braid over brow plain; ear clear.
VF-20 Very Fine: All details sharper than for F-12. Only slight wear on hair over brow.
EF-40 Extremely Fine: Hair above ear detailed, but slightly worn.
AU-50 About Uncirculated: Trace of wear on high points of hair above ear and eye and on highest points on leaves and bow.
MS-60 Uncirculated: Typical brown surface. No trace of wear.
MS-63 Choice Uncirculated: Some distracting contact marks or blemishes in prime focal areas. Impaired luster possible.

1839 Over 1836

Brilliant or red Uncirculated coins are worth more than prices shown. Cleaned or discolored pieces are worth less.

	Mintage	G-4	VG-8	F-12	VF-20	EF-40	AU-50	MS-60	MS-63
1837	5,558,300	$7	$9	$12	$22	$65	$90	$160	$240
1838	6,370,200	7	9	12	22	30	85	150	210
1839	3,128,661	7	9	12	22	40	80	150	210
1839, 1839 Over 1836, Plain Cords	*	110	275	550	1,200	3,250	6,000	—	—
1840	2,462,700	7	9	12	18	40	75	150	275
1841	1,597,367	7	9	12	18	40	75	150	275
1842	2,383,390	7	9	12	18	40	75	150	250

* Included in number above.

Small Letters

"Head of 1840"
Petite Head (1839–1843)

"Head of 1844"
Mature Head (1843–1857)

Large Letters

	Mintage	G-4	VG-8	F-12	VF-20	EF-40	AU-50	MS-60	MS-63
1843, Petite, Small Letters	2,425,342	$7	$9	$12	$20	$30	$60	$145	$185
1843, Petite, Large Letters	*	9	11	20	35	70	125	325	600
1843, Mature, Large Letters	*	8	10	16	25	50	90	160	400
1844, Normal Date	2,398,752	7	9	12	20	32	65	120	175
1844, 44 Over 81	*	10	13	20	40	110	225	550	1,200
1845	3,894,804	7	9	12	20	30	70	125	175
1846	4,120,800	7	9	12	20	30	70	125	175
1847	6,183,669	7	9	12	20	30	70	125	175
1847, 7 Over "Small 7"	*	8	11	17	30	65	150	500	950

* Included in number above.

	Mintage	G-4	VG-8	F-12	VF-20	EF-40	AU-50	MS-60	MS-63
1848	6,415,799	$7	$9	$12	$18	$30	$70	$110	$150
1849	4,178,500	7	9	12	18	30	70	125	190
1850	4,426,844	7	9	12	18	30	70	100	150

1844, 44 Over 81   **1851, 51 Over 81**   **1847, 7 Over "Small" 7**

Brilliant or red Uncirculated coins are worth more than prices shown. Spotted, cleaned, or discolored pieces are worth less.

	Mintage	G-4	VG-8	F-12	VF-20	EF-40	AU-50	MS-60	MS-63
1851, Normal Date	9,889,707	$7	$9	$12	$18	$30	$70	$100	$150
1851, 51 Over 81	*	9	11	18	28	70	110	250	425
1852	5,063,094	7	9	12	18	30	70	100	150
1853	6,641,131	7	9	12	18	30	70	100	150
1854	4,236,156	7	9	12	18	30	70	100	150

* Included in number above.

1855, Upright 5's   **1855, Slanting 5's**   **1855, Knob on Ear**

	Mintage	G-4	VG-8	F-12	VF-20	EF-40	AU-50	MS-60	MS-63
1855, All kinds	1,574,829								
1855, Upright 5's		$7	$9	$12	$18	$30	$70	$100	$150
1855, Slanting 5's		7	9	12	18	30	70	125	175
1855, Slanting 5's, Knob on Ear		7	10	14	22	40	90	160	250
1856, Upright 5	2,690,463	7	9	12	18	30	70	100	150
1856, Slanting 5	*	7	9	12	18	30	70	100	150

* Included in number above.

1857, Large Date   **1857, Small Date**

	Mintage	G-4	VG-8	F-12	VF-20	EF-40	AU-50	MS-60	MS-63
1857, Large Date	333,546	$16	$25	$30	$35	$50	$110	$175	$300
1857, Small Date	*	17	27	35	40	55	120	200	325

* Included in number above.

FLYING EAGLE (1856–1858)

The Act of February 21, 1857, provided for the coinage of the small cent. The 1856 Flying Eagle cent was not an authorized Mint issue, as the law governing the new-size coin was enacted after the date of issue. It is believed that nearly 1,000 original strikings and 1,500 or more restrikes were made of the 1856. They are properly referred to as *patterns*.

G-4 Good: All details worn, but readable.

VG-8 Very Good: Details in eagle's feathers and eye evident, but worn.

F-12 Fine: Eagle-head details and feather tips sharp.

VF-20 Very Fine: Considerable detail visible in feathers in right wing and tail.

EF-40 Extremely Fine: Slight wear, all details sharp.

AU-50 About Uncirculated: Slight wear on eagle's left wing and breast.

MS-60 Uncirculated: No trace of wear. Light blemishes.

MS-63 Choice Uncirculated: Some distracting contact marks or blemishes in prime focal areas. Some impairment of luster possible.

PF-63 Choice Proof: Nearly perfect.

| | 1858, 8 Over 7 | | | 1856–1858, Large Letters | | | 1858, Small Letters | |

Brilliant Uncirculated and Proof coins are worth more than prices shown. Spotted, cleaned, or discolored pieces are worth less.

	Mintage	G-4	VG-8	F-12	VF-20	EF-40	AU-50	MS-60	MS-63	PF-63
1856	2,000	$4,200	$4,800	$5,200	$6,750	$8,000	$9,000	$11,000	$13,500	$13,500
1857	17,450,000	13	16	20	28	80	100	200	350	
. . . .	(485)									4,000
1858, Large Letters . . .	24,600,000	13	16	20	28	80	100	200	350	
. . . .	(100)									4,000
1858, 8 Over 7	*		50	110	210	420	725	1,900	5,000	
1858, Small Letters	*	13	16	20	28	80	100	200	350	
. . . .	(200)									4,000

* Included in mintage for 1858, Large Letters.

INDIAN HEAD (1859–1909)

The small cent was redesigned in 1859, and a representation of Miss Liberty wearing an Indian war bonnet was adopted as the obverse device. The 1859 reverse was also changed to represent a laurel wreath. In 1860 the reverse was modified to display an oak wreath with a small shield at the top. From 1859 to 1863, cents were struck in copper-nickel. In 1864 the composition was changed to bronze, although copper-nickel cents were also struck during that year.

G-4 Good: No LIBERTY visible.
VG-8 Very Good: At least some letters of LIBERTY readable on head band.
F-12 Fine: LIBERTY mostly visible.
VF-20 Very Fine: Slight but even wear on LIBERTY.
EF-40 Extremely Fine: LIBERTY sharp. All other details sharp. Only slight wear on ribbon end.
AU-50 About Uncirculated: Very slight trace of wear above the ear and the lowest curl of hair.
MS-60 Uncirculated: No trace of wear. Light blemishes.
MS-63 Choice Uncirculated: Some distracting contact marks or blemishes in prime focal areas. Impaired luster possible.
PF-63 Choice Proof: Nearly perfect.

Without Shield at Top of Wreath (1859 Only)

With Shield on Reverse (1860–1909)

Variety 1 – Copper-Nickel, Laurel Wreath Reverse (1859)

Brilliant or red Uncirculated coins are worth more than prices shown. Spotted, cleaned, or discolored pieces are worth less.

	Mintage	G-4	VG-8	F-12	VF-20	EF-40	AU-50	MS-60	MS-63	PF-63
1859 . . . .*(800)* . .36,400,000		$7	$8	$10	$27	$55	$100	$135	$265	$850

Variety 2 – Copper-Nickel, Oak Wreath With Shield (1860–1864)

	Mintage	G-4	VG-8	F-12	VF-20	EF-40	AU-50	MS-60	MS-63	PF-63
1860 . . . . . .*(1,000)* . .20,566,000		$6.00	$7	$8	$10	$32	$65	$100	$150	$550
1861 . . . . . .*(1,000)* . .10,100,000		11.00	13	18	32	65	85	140	190	600
1862 . . . .*(550)* . .28,075,000		5.50	6	7	9	22	40	65	100	475
1863 . . . .*(460)* . .49,840,000		5.50	6	7	9	22	40	65	100	475
1864 . . . .*(370)* . .13,740,000		8.00	10	14	25	38	65	100	140	500

Variety 3 – Bronze (1864–1909)

1864, Indian Head Cent With "L"

	Mintage	G-4	VG-8	F-12	VF-20	EF-40	AU-50	MS-60	MS-63	PF-63
1864, All kinds 39,233,714										
1864, No L *(150)*		$4	$6	$9	$22	$32	$42	$55	$85	$500
1864, With L *(20)*		27	45	70	100	170	190	225	375	—
1865 . . . .*(500)* . .35,429,286		4	5	9	12	20	35	50	85	350
1866 . . . .*(725)* . .9,826,500		22	25	35	65	100	150	175	275	350
1867 . . . .*(625)* . .9,821,000		22	25	35	65	100	150	175	275	350
1868 . . . .*(600)* . .10,266,500		22	25	35	65	100	150	175	275	350
1869 . . . .*(600)* . .6,420,000		35	40	90	150	225	275	300	450	350
1870 . . . . .*(1,000)* . .5,275,000		28	35	85	135	200	275	300	350	350
1871 . . . .*(960)* . .3,929,500		35	45	125	185	225	300	365	500	375
1872 . . . .*(950)* . .4,042,000		40	60	160	225	300	400	450	650	425
1873 . . . . .*(1,100)* . .11,676,500		11	14	24	38	80	100	120	220	275
1874 . . . .*(700)* . .14,187,500		9	11	15	30	55	85	110	165	250
1875 . . . .*(700)* . .13,528,000		10	14	20	35	50	75	110	165	250
1876 . . . . .*(1,150)* . .7,944,000		15	18	20	60	100	145	185	275	250
1877 . . . .*(900)* . .852,500		500	700	850	1,250	1,600	1,900	2,200	2,800	2,800

Brilliant or red Uncirculated coins are worth more than prices shown. Spotted, cleaned, or discolored pieces are worth less.

	Mintage	G-4	VG-8	F-12	VF-20	EF-40	AU-50	MS-60	MS-63	PF-63
1878	(2,350) . . 5,797,500	$14.00	$18.00	$25.00	$65.00	$100	$145	$165	$250	$220
1879	(3,200) . . 16,228,000	4.00	6.00	8.00	18.00	40	45	50	80	175
1880	(3,955) . . 38,961,000	1.75	2.00	3.00	6.00	15	25	40	70	140
1881	(3,575) . . 39,208,000	1.75	2.00	3.00	5.00	10	16	26	37	140
1882	(3,100) . . 38,578,000	1.75	2.00	3.00	5.00	10	16	26	37	140
1883	(6,609) . . 45,591,500	1.75	2.00	3.00	5.00	10	16	26	37	140
1884	(3,942) . . 23,257,800	2.25	2.50	3.50	6.00	14	20	30	60	140
1885	(3,790) . . 11,761,594	3.00	4.00	6.00	14.00	35	45	60	95	140
1886	(4,290) . . 17,650,000	1.75	3.00	8.00	24.00	65	85	100	125	150
1887	(2,960) . . 45,223,523	1.25	1.50	1.75	2.25	8	14	25	35	140
1888	(4,582) . . 37,489,832	0.85	1.10	1.80	2.75	8	14	25	40	140
1889	(3,336) . . 48,866,025	0.85	1.10	1.80	2.75	6	12	22	35	140
1890	(2,740) . . 57,180,114	0.85	1.10	1.80	2.75	6	12	22	35	140
1891	(2,350) . . 47,070,000	0.85	1.10	1.80	2.75	6	12	22	35	140
1892	(2,745) . . 37,647,087	0.85	1.10	1.80	2.75	6	12	22	35	140
1893	(2,195) . . 46,640,000	0.85	1.10	1.80	2.75	6	12	22	35	140
1894	(2,632) . . 16,749,500	2.00	3.00	4.75	8.50	25	30	40	50	150
1895	(2,062) . . 38,341,574	0.85	1.10	1.30	2.00	6	11	22	28	140
1896	(1,862) . . 39,055,431	0.85	1.10	1.30	2.00	6	11	22	28	140
1897	(1,938) . . 50,464,392	0.85	1.10	1.30	2.00	6	11	22	28	140
1898	(1,795) . . 49,821,284	0.85	1.10	1.30	2.00	6	11	22	28	140
1899	(2,031) . . 53,598,000	0.85	1.10	1.30	2.00	6	11	22	28	140
1900	(2,262) . . 66,831,502	0.80	1.00	1.10	1.50	5	10	18	25	120
1901	(1,985) . . 79,609,158	0.80	1.00	1.10	1.50	5	10	18	25	120
1902	(2,018) . . 87,374,704	0.80	1.00	1.10	1.50	5	10	18	25	120
1903	(1,790) . . 85,092,703	0.80	1.00	1.10	1.50	5	10	18	25	120
1904	(1,817) . . 61,326,198	0.80	1.00	1.10	1.50	5	10	18	25	120
1905	(2,152) . . 80,717,011	0.80	1.00	1.10	1.50	5	10	18	25	120
1906	(1,725) . . 96,020,530	0.80	1.00	1.10	1.50	5	10	18	25	120
1907	(1,475) . 108,137,143	0.80	1.00	1.10	1.50	5	10	18	25	120

**Location of Mintmark S on Reverse
of Indian Cent (1908 and 1909 Only)**

	Mintage	G-4	VG-8	F-12	VF-20	EF-40	AU-50	MS-60	MS-63	PF-63
1908	(1,620) . . 32,326,367	$0.80	$1.10	$1.25	$1.50	$5	$10	$18	$25	$120
1908S	 1,115,000	32.00	42.00	48.00	55.00	80	100	150	250	
1909	(2,175) . . 14,368,470	6.00	7.00	8.00	10.00	12	16	25	32	120
1909S	 309,000	250.00	275.00	300.00	325.00	375	400	485	675	

LINCOLN, WHEAT EARS REVERSE (1909–1958)

Victor D. Brenner designed this cent which was issued to commemorate the 100th anniversary of Abraham Lincoln's birth. The designer's initials V.D.B. appear on the reverse of a limited quantity of cents of 1909. Later in the year they were removed from the dies but restored in 1918 as very small incuse letters beneath the shoulder. The Lincoln type was the first cent to have the motto IN GOD WE TRUST.

G-4 Good: Date worn but apparent. Lines in wheat heads missing. Full rims.
VG-8 Very Good: Half of lines visible in upper wheat heads.
F-12 Fine: Wheat lines worn but visible.
VF-20 Very Fine: Lincoln's cheekbone and jawbone worn but separated. No worn spots on wheat heads.
EF-40 Extremely Fine: Slight wear. All details sharp.
AU-50 About Uncirculated: Slight wear on cheek and jaw and on wheat stalks.
MS-60 Uncirculated: No trace of wear. Light blemishes. Brown or red-brown color.
MS-63 Choice Uncirculated: No trace of wear. Slight blemishes. Red-brown color.
MS-65 Gem Uncirculated: No trace of wear. Barely noticeable blemishes. Nearly full red color.
PF-63 Choice Proof: Reflective surfaces with only a few blemishes in secondary focal places. No major flaws.

Location of mintmark S or D on obverse of Lincoln cent.

Designer's Initials V.D.B. (1909 Only)

No V.D.B. on Reverse (1909–1958)

Brilliant Uncirculated coins are worth more than prices shown. Spotted, cleaned, or discolored pieces are worth less.

	Mintage	G-4	VG-8	F-12	VF-20	EF-40	AU-50	MS-60	MS-63	MATTE PF-63
1909, V.D.B.										
. . . . .(1,194) . . .27,995,000		$6.00	$6.50	$7.00	$8.00	$9.00	$10.00	$12.00	$15	$1,300
1909S, V.D.B. 484,000		425.00	475.00	525.00	700.00	800.00	950.00	1,100.00	1,350	
1909 . . . . .(2,618) . . .72,702,618		1.00	1.25	1.60	2.00	2.50	6.00	8.50	15	225
1909S 1,825,000		50.00	60.00	70.00	95.00	150.00	165.00	200.00	235	
1910 . . . . .(4,118) . .146,801,218		0.07	0.10	0.15	0.30	1.00	2.50	9.00	13	150
1910S 6,045,000		7.00	8.00	10.00	11.00	21.00	37.00	55.00	70	
1911 . . . . .(1,725) . .101,177,787		0.10	0.15	0.30	0.50	1.50	3.50	11.00	25	175
1911D 12,672,000		2.25	3.00	4.50	9.00	21.00	35.00	50.00	70	
1911S 4,026,000		15.00	19.00	22.00	26.00	35.00	55.00	110.00	150	
1912 . . . . .(2,172) . .68,153,060		0.15	0.25	0.70	2.00	2.50	8.00	17.00	25	150
1912D 10,411,000		2.75	3.50	4.25	10.00	25.00	40.00	75.00	120	
1912S 4,431,000		10.00	12.00	14.00	17.00	33.00	45.00	90.00	125	
1913 . . . . .(2,983) . . .76,532,352		0.15	0.20	0.40	1.25	6.00	10.00	16.00	25	160
1913D 15,804,000		0.75	1.00	1.50	3.50	20.00	26.00	50.00	100	
1913S 6,101,000		5.00	6.00	8.00	10.00	25.00	50.00	85.00	135	
1914 . . . . .(1,365) . . .75,238,432		0.20	0.30	0.75	2.00	6.50	17.00	25.00	35	180
1914D **(a)** 1,193,000		100.00	125.00	200.00	250.00	450.00	800.00	1,100.00	2,000	
1914S 4,137,000		10.00	12.00	14.00	19.00	40.00	90.00	175.00	260	
1915 . . . . .(1,150) . . .29,092,120		0.40	1.00	2.00	6.00	25.00	35.00	46.00	65	275
1915D 22,050,000		0.50	1.00	1.50	2.25	9.00	22.00	45.00	60	
1915S 4,833,000		8.00	9.00	11.00	14.00	30.00	60.00	100.00	150	
1916 . . . . . .(600) . .131,833,677		0.05	0.08	0.15	0.50	2.00	5.00	10.00	15	400
1916D 35,956,000		0.10	0.20	0.50	1.50	5.50	12.00	35.00	50	
1916S 22,510,000		0.35	0.50	1.00	1.75	8.00	15.00	38.00	70	
1917 196,429,785		0.05	0.07	0.10	0.25	0.60	3.00	10.00	15	
1917D 55,120,000		0.08	0.10	0.30	1.25	8.00	15.00	35.00	50	
1917S 32,620,000		0.08	0.10	0.25	0.50	2.75	12.00	35.00	65	

a. Beware of altered date or mintmark. No V.D.B. on shoulder of genuine 1914-D cent.

Designer's initials placed on Lincoln's shoulder next to rim, starting 1918.

Brilliant Uncirculated coins before 1934 are worth more than prices shown. Spotted, cleaned, or discolored pieces are worth less.

	Mintage	G-4	VG-8	F-12	VF-20	EF-40	AU-50	MS-60	MS-63
1918	288,104,634	$0.04	$0.05	$0.10	$0.20	$1.00	$3.00	$6.00	$15.00
1918D	47,830,000	0.10	0.15	0.60	1.25	6.00	12.00	32.00	65.00
1918S	34,680,000	0.10	0.15	0.50	1.00	4.00	15.00	35.00	75.00
1919	392,021,000	0.04	0.05	0.07	0.15	0.75	1.50	5.00	14.00
1919D	57,154,000	0.05	0.06	0.10	0.40	2.50	15.00	28.00	60.00
1919S	139,760,000	0.05	0.06	0.10	0.30	1.35	7.00	18.00	70.00
1920	310,165,000	0.03	0.05	0.07	0.15	0.50	1.50	6.00	12.00
1920D	49,280,000	0.05	0.06	0.10	0.50	3.50	12.00	33.00	55.00
1920S	46,220,000	0.05	0.06	0.10	0.30	2.00	15.00	42.00	100.00
1921	39,157,000	0.06	0.08	0.15	0.35	1.50	6.00	22.00	40.00
1921S	15,274,000	0.35	0.50	0.70	1.50	14.00	35.00	55.00	100.00
1922D	7,160,000	6.00	7.00	8.50	10.00	16.00	28.00	45.00	75.00
1922, No D **(b)**	......*	300.00	375.00	550.00	650.00	1,400.00	2,500.00	4,500.00	16,000.00
1923	74,723,000	0.04	0.05	0.07	0.15	1.00	2.50	7.00	14.00
1923S	8,700,000	0.50	0.60	0.75	2.00	14.00	35.00	100.00	225.00
1924	75,178,000	0.04	0.05	0.07	0.15	1.50	3.50	15.00	25.00
1924D	2,520,000	15.00	19.00	23.00	30.00	55.00	90.00	150.00	225.00
1924S	11,696,000	0.40	0.50	0.80	1.10	9.00	30.00	55.00	110.00
1925	139,949,000	0.03	0.04	0.05	0.15	0.50	2.00	5.00	10.00
1925D	22,580,000	0.04	0.06	0.10	0.30	4.50	11.00	27.00	38.00
1925S	26,380,000	0.04	0.06	0.10	0.25	3.00	14.00	40.00	80.00
1926	157,088,000	0.03	0.04	0.05	0.15	0.50	2.00	5.00	8.00
1926D	28,020,000	0.04	0.06	0.10	0.30	2.50	9.00	35.00	50.00
1926S	4,550,000	2.00	3.00	4.00	5.50	12.00	30.00	65.00	140.00
1927	144,440,000	0.03	0.04	0.05	0.20	0.50	1.00	5.00	10.00
1927D	27,170,000	0.10	0.15	0.50	1.00	2.00	6.00	26.00	42.00
1927S	14,276,000	0.25	0.30	0.50	1.25	4.00	11.00	35.00	70.00
1928	134,116,000	0.03	0.04	0.05	0.15	0.50	1.00	4.50	10.00
1928D	31,170,000	0.04	0.06	0.10	0.25	0.85	4.00	15.00	34.00
1928S	17,266,000	0.06	0.10	0.25	0.50	1.50	5.00	34.00	55.00
1929	185,262,000	0.03	0.04	0.05	0.15	0.35	1.50	4.00	6.00
1929D	41,730,000	0.04	0.06	0.10	0.25	1.00	2.00	12.00	15.00
1929S	50,148,000	0.03	0.05	0.10	0.15	0.60	1.75	7.00	11.00
1930	157,415,000	0.03	0.04	0.05	0.15	0.25	0.75	2.00	3.50
1930D	40,100,000	0.04	0.06	0.10	0.25	0.60	1.00	5.00	10.00
1930S	24,286,000	0.03	0.05	0.10	0.15	0.40	2.00	3.50	5.00
1931	19,396,000	0.15	0.20	0.30	0.40	0.60	2.00	10.00	15.00
1931D	4,480,000	1.25	1.75	2.00	2.50	4.50	12.00	30.00	40.00
1931S	866,000	50.00	60.00	65.00	75.00	80.00	85.00	90.00	100.00
1932	9,062,000	0.40	0.50	0.60	1.00	1.25	3.75	10.00	13.00
1932D	10,500,000	0.25	0.35	0.40	0.50	1.00	3.25	10.00	15.00
1933	14,360,000	0.30	0.40	0.50	0.70	1.25	3.75	10.00	15.00
1933D	6,200,000	0.75	1.00	1.25	1.50	3.00	5.00	12.00	15.00

* Included in number above. **b.** 1922 cents with a weak or missing mintmark were made from extremely worn dies that originally struck normal 1922-D cents. Three different die pairs were involved; two of them produced "Weak D" coins. One die pair (no. 2, identified by a "strong reverse") is acknowledged as striking "No D" coins. Weak D cents are worth considerably less. Beware of removed mintmark.

	Mintage	G-4	VG-8	F-12	VF-20	EF-40	AU-50	MS-60	MS-63	PF-63
1934	.219,080,000	$0.03	$0.03	$0.03	$0.03	$0.10	$1.00	$3.00	$4.50	
1934D	.28,446,000	0.04	0.06	0.08	0.15	0.50	2.00	9.00	15.00	
1935	.245,388,000	0.03	0.03	0.03	0.04	0.06	0.20	2.00	3.00	
1935D	.47,000,000	0.03	0.03	0.03	0.04	0.20	0.50	3.00	4.00	
1935S	.38,702,000	0.03	0.04	0.04	0.04	0.12	1.25	4.00	6.00	
1936 . . . . . (5,569) .	.309,632,000	0.03	0.03	0.03	0.04	0.06	0.25	1.00	3.00	$85
1936D	.40,620,000	0.03	0.03	0.03	0.04	0.08	0.20	1.00	3.00	
1936S	.29,130,000	0.03	0.03	0.03	0.04	0.10	0.20	1.00	3.00	
1937 . . . . (9,320) .	.309,170,000	0.02	0.03	0.03	0.03	0.05	0.20	0.50	3.00	34
1937D	.50,430,000	0.02	0.03	0.03	0.03	0.06	0.30	0.80	4.00	
1937S	.34,500,000	0.03	0.03	0.03	0.04	0.06	0.30	0.80	4.00	
1938 . . . (14,734) .	.156,682,000	0.02	0.03	0.03	0.03	0.05	0.30	0.75	2.00	25
1938D	.20,010,000	0.02	0.03	0.04	0.06	0.15	0.50	1.00	5.00	
1938S	.15,180,000	0.06	0.08	0.10	0.12	0.15	0.30	1.00	4.00	
1939 . . . (13,520) .	.316,466,000	0.02	0.03	0.03	0.03	0.03	0.20	0.30	2.50	23
1939D	.15,160,000	0.06	0.08	0.10	0.12	0.15	0.35	1.00	4.00	
1939S	.52,070,000	0.03	0.03	0.03	0.04	0.10	0.30	1.00	4.00	
1940 . . . . (15,872) .	.586,810,000	0.02	0.03	0.03	0.03	0.03	0.20	0.30	2.00	16
1940D	.81,390,000	0.02	0.03	0.03	0.03	0.03	0.20	0.40	2.00	
1940S	.112,940,000	0.02	0.03	0.03	0.03	0.04	0.20	0.40	2.75	
1941 . . . . (21,100) .	.887,018,000	0.02	0.03	0.03	0.03	0.03	0.20	0.30	2.00	15
1941D	.128,700,000	0.02	0.03	0.03	0.03	0.03	0.40	0.80	3.00	
1941S	.92,360,000	0.02	0.03	0.03	0.03	0.04	0.35	1.00	5.00	
1942 . . . . (32,600) .	.657,796,000	0.02	0.03	0.03	0.03	0.03	0.10	0.15	1.00	15
1942D	.206,698,000	0.02	0.03	0.03	0.03	0.03	0.10	0.15	2.00	
1942S	.85,590,000	0.02	0.03	0.03	0.03	0.10	1.00	2.00	8.00	

Variety 2 – Zinc-Coated Steel (1943)

	Mintage	F-12	VF-20	EF-40	MS-60	MS-63	MS-65
1943	.684,628,670	$0.05	$0.10	$0.15	$0.70	$1.25	$3.00
1943D	.217,660,000	0.05	0.10	0.15	0.90	2.00	4.50
1943S	.191,550,000	0.06	0.12	0.20	1.20	2.75	6.00

Variety 1 (Bronze) Resumed (1944–1958)

1944-D, D Over S

1955, Doubled-Die Error

	Mintage	VF-20	EF-40	MS-63	MS-65	PF-65
1944	.1,435,400,000	$0.03	$0.03	$0.15	$0.50	
1944D	.430,578,000	0.03	0.03	0.20	0.50	
1944D, D Over S . . . .*		75.00	90.00	225.00	600.00	
1944S	.282,760,000	0.03	0.03	0.15	1.50	

* Included in number above.

Chart continued on next page.

	Mintage	VF-20	EF-40	MS-63	MS-65	PF-65
1945	1,040,515,000	$0.03	$0.03	$0.20	$0.50	
1945D	266,268,000	0.03	0.03	0.15	0.50	
1945S	181,770,000	0.03	0.03	0.10	2.00	
1946	991,655,000	0.03	0.03	0.10	0.50	
1946D	315,690,000	0.03	0.03	0.15	1.00	
1946S	198,100,000	0.03	0.03	0.15	1.25	
1947	190,555,000	0.03	0.03	0.25	0.50	
1947D	194,750,000	0.03	0.03	0.12	0.50	
1947S	99,000,000	0.03	0.03	0.15	1.50	
1948	317,570,000	0.03	0.03	0.15	0.50	
1948D	172,637,500	0.03	0.03	0.12	0.60	
1948S	81,735,000	0.03	0.03	0.20	1.50	
1949	217,775,000	0.03	0.03	0.30	0.75	
1949D	153,132,500	0.03	0.03	0.20	0.75	
1949S	64,290,000	0.04	0.05	0.25	2.00	
1950 (51,386)	272,635,000	0.03	0.03	0.25	0.50	$30.00
1950D	334,950,000	0.03	0.03	0.10	0.50	
1950S	118,505,000	0.03	0.03	0.25	0.80	
1951 (57,500)	284,576,000	0.03	0.03	0.25	0.80	35.00
1951D	625,355,000	0.03	0.03	0.10	0.50	
1951S	136,010,000	0.03	0.03	0.30	0.60	
1952 (81,980)	186,775,000	0.03	0.03	0.15	0.60	25.00
1952D	746,130,000	0.03	0.03	0.15	0.60	
1952S	137,800,004	0.03	0.03	0.50	1.50	
1953 (128,800)	256,755,000	0.03	0.03	0.10	0.50	25.00
1953D	700,515,000	0.03	0.03	0.10	0.50	
1953S	181,835,000	0.03	0.04	0.12	0.50	
1954 (233,300)	71,640,050	0.03	0.06	0.10	0.50	11.00
1954D	251,552,500	0.03	0.03	0.05	0.30	
1954S	96,190,000	0.03	0.03	0.05	0.30	
1955 (378,200)	330,958,200	0.03	0.03	0.06	0.30	10.00
1955, Doubled-Die Obverse	*	550.00	750.00(a)	1,400.00	5,000.00	
1955D	563,257,500	0.03	0.03	0.05	0.25	
1955S	44,610,000	0.10	0.15	0.15	0.50	
1956 (669,384)	420,745,000	0.03	0.03	0.05	0.25	1.75
1956D	1,098,201,100	0.03	0.03	0.05	0.30	
1957 (1,247,952)	282,540,000	0.03	0.03	0.05	0.30	1.75
1957D	1,051,342,000	0.03	0.03	0.05	0.30	
1958 (875,652)	252,525,000	0.03	0.03	0.05	0.30	2.00
1958D	800,953,300	0.03	0.03	0.05	0.30	

* Included in number above. **a.** Value for MS-60 Uncirculated is $1,000.

LINCOLN, MEMORIAL REVERSE (1959 TO DATE)

Small Date   Large Date

	Mintage	MS-63	MS-65	PF-65
1959 (1,149,291)	609,715,000	$0.01	$0.10	$1.00

1969-S, Doubled-Die Error	Small Date, Numbers Aligned at Top	Large Date, Low 7 in Date	Enlarged Detail of 1972 Doubled-Die Error

	Mintage	MS-63	MS-65	PF-65
1959D 1,279,760,000		$0.01	$0.10	
1960, Lg Dt ..586,405,000		0.01	0.10	
..........(1,691,602)				$0.50
1960, Sm Dt ....*		1.00	2.50	
................*				9.00
1960D, Lg Dt ..1,580,884,000		0.01	0.10	
1960D, Sm Dt ....*		0.02	0.10	
1961 753,345,000		0.01	0.10	
..........(3,028,244)				0.50
1961D 1,753,266,700		0.01	0.10	
1962 606,045,000		0.01	0.10	
..........(3,218,019)				0.50
1962D 1,793,148,140		0.01	0.10	
1963 754,110,000		0.01	0.10	
..........(3,075,645)				0.50
1963D 1,774,020,400		0.01	0.10	
1964 2,648,575,000		0.01	0.10	
..........(3,950,762)				0.50
1964D 3,799,071,500		0.01	0.10	
1965 1,497,224,900		0.02	0.12	
1966 2,188,147,783		0.04	0.12	
1967 3,048,667,100		0.03	0.12	
1968 1,707,880,970		0.02	0.12	
1968D 2,886,269,600		0.01	0.10	
1968S 258,270,001		0.02	0.10	
..........(3,041,506)				0.50
1969 1,136,910,000		0.05	0.20	
1969D 4,002,832,200		0.03	0.10	
1969S 544,375,000		0.03	0.10	
..........(2,934,631)				0.50
1969S, DblDie Obv ....*		—	—	
1970 1,898,315,000		0.05	0.10	
1970D 2,891,438,900		0.02	0.10	
1970S, Sm Dt (High 7) ....**		20.00	30.00	
................**				25.00
1970S, Lg Dt (Low 7) ..690,560,004		0.03	0.10	
..........(2,632,810)				0.25

	Mintage	MS-63	MS-65	PF-65
1971 1,919,490,000		$0.05	$0.20	
1971D 2,911,045,600		0.03	0.20	
1971S 525,133,459		0.03	0.20	
..........(3,220,733)				$0.25
1972, DblDie Obv ....**		190.00	300.00	
1972 2,933,255,000		0.01	0.05	
1972D 2,665,071,400		0.02	0.10	
1972S 376,939,108		0.02	0.10	
..........(3,260,996)				0.25
1973 3,728,245,000		0.01	0.10	
1973D 3,549,576,588		0.01	0.10	
1973S 317,177,295		0.02	0.10	
..........(2,760,339)				0.25
1974 4,232,140,523		0.01	0.10	
1974D 4,235,098,000		0.01	0.10	
1974S 409,426,660		0.03	0.10	
..........(2,612,568)				0.25
1975 5,451,476,142		0.01	0.10	
1975D 4,505,275,300		0.01	0.10	
1975S ....(2,845,450)				1.50
1976 4,674,292,426		0.01	0.10	
1976D 4,221,592,455		0.02	0.10	
1976S ....(4,149,730)				1.25
1977 4,469,930,000		0.01	0.10	
1977D 4,194,062,300		0.01	0.10	
1977S ....(3,251,152)				1.00
1978 5,558,605,000		0.01	0.10	
1978D 4,280,233,400		0.01	0.10	
1978S ....(3,127,781)				1.00
1979 6,018,515,000		0.01	0.10	
1979D 4,139,357,254		0.01	0.10	
1979S, Filled S (3,677,175)				1.75
1979S, Clear S ....*				2.00
1980 7,414,705,000		0.01	0.10	
1980D 5,140,098,660		0.01	0.10	
1980S ....(3,554,806)				1.00
1981 7,491,750,000		0.01	0.10	
1981D 5,373,235,677		0.01	0.10	
1981S, Filled S (4,063,083)				1.50
1981S, Clear S ....*				20.00

* Included in number above. ** Included in number below.

Large Date				Small Date			
	Mintage	**MS-63**	**MS-65**	**PF-65**			

	Mintage	MS-63	MS-65	PF-65
1982,				
Lg Dt	10,712,525,000	$0.01	$0.10	
1982, Sm Dt . . . .*		0.02	0.12	

	Mintage	MS-63	MS-65	PF-65
1982D,				
Lg Dt . .6,012,979,368		$0.01	$0.10	
1982S . . . .(3,857,479)				$1.60

* Included in number above.

Copper-Plated Zinc (1982 to Date)

1995, Doubled Die showing strong doubling on word LIBERTY.

	Mintage	MS-63	MS-65	PF-65		Mintage	MS-63	MS-65	PF-65
1982, Lg Dt . . . .*		$0.01	$0.05		1991 5,165,940,000		$0.01	$0.05	
1982, Sm Dt . . . .*		0.01	0.05		1991D 4,158,446,076		0.01	0.05	
1982D, Lg Dt . . . .*		0.05	0.50		1991S . . . .(2,867,787)				$10.00
1982D, Sm Dt . . . .*		0.01	0.05		1992 4,648,905,000		0.01	0.05	
1983 7,752,355,000		0.01	0.05		1992, Close AM (a) . . . . .**		—	—	
1983D . . .6,467,199,428		0.01	0.05		1992D 4,448,673,300		0.01	0.05	
1983S . . . .(3,279,126)		0.01	0.05	$1.10	1992D, Close AM (a) . . . .**		—	—	
1984 8,151,079,000		0.01	0.05		1992S . . . .(4,176,560)				1.10
1984, Dbl Ear . . . .**		50.00	100.00		1993 5,684,705,000		0.01	0.05	
1984D 5,569,238,906		0.01	0.05		1993D 6,426,650,571		0.01	0.05	
1984S . . . .(3,065,110)				1.10	1993S . . . .(3,394,792)				2.00
1985 5,648,489,887		0.01	0.05		1994 6,500,850,000		0.01	0.05	
1985D 5,287,339,926		0.01	0.05		1994D 7,131,765,000		0.01	0.05	
1985S . . . .(3,362,821)				1.25	1994S . . . .(3,269,923)				2.00
1986 4,491,395,493		0.01	0.05		1995 6,411,440,000		0.01	0.05	
1986D 4,442,866,698		0.01	0.05		1995, DblDie Obv . . . .**		4.00	18.00	
1986S . . . .(3,010,497)				2.00	1995D 7,128,560,000		0.01	0.05	
1987 4,682,466,931		0.01	0.05		1995S . . . .(2,797,481)				2.00
1987D 4,879,389,514		0.01	0.05		1996 6,612,465,000		0.01	0.05	
1987S . . . .(4,227,728)				1.10	1996D 6,510,795,000		0.01	0.05	
1988 6,092,810,000		0.01	0.05		1996S . . . .(2,525,265)				1.25
1988D 5,253,740,443		0.01	0.05		1997 4,622,800,000		0.01	0.05	
1988S . . . .(3,262,948)				3.25	1997D 4,576,555,000		0.01	0.05	
1989 7,261,535,000		0.01	0.05		1997S . . . .(2,796,678)				2.00
1989D 5,345,467,111		0.01	0.05		1998 5,032,155,000		0.01	0.05	
1989S . . . .(3,220,194)				3.00	1998, Wide AM (a) . . . .**		2.00	4.00	
1990 6,851,765,000		0.01	0.05		1998D 5,225,353,500		0.01	0.05	
1990D 4,922,894,533		0.01	0.05		1998S . . . .(2,086,507)				2.00
1990S . . . .(3,299,559)				2.00					
1990, Pf, No S . . . .**			—						

* Included in previous section's mintages. ** Included in number above. **a.** Varieties were made using Proof dies that have a wide space between AM in AMERICA. The letters nearly touch on other Uncirculated cents.

	Mintage	MS-63	MS-65	PF-65
1999 5,237,600,000		$0.01	$0.05	
1999, Wide AM (a) . . . . . .**			—	
1999D 6,360,065,000		0.01	0.05	
1999S . . . .(3,347,966)				$2.00
1999S, Close AM (a) . . . .**			—	
2000 5,503,200,000		0.01	0.05	
2000, Wide AM (a) . . . . . .**		2.00	2.50	
2000D 8,774,220,000		0.01	0.05	
2000S . . . .(4,047,993)				1.00
2001 4,959,600,000		0.01	0.05	
2001D 5,374,990,000		0.01	0.05	
2001S . . . .(3,184,606)				1.00
2002 3,260,800,000		0.01	0.05	
2002D 4,028,055,000		0.01	0.05	
2002S . . . .(3,211,995)				1.00
2003 3,300,000,000		0.01	0.05	
2003D 3,548,000,000		0.01	0.05	

	Mintage	MS-63	MS-65	PF-65
2003S . . . .(3,298,439)				$1.00
2004 3,379,600,000		$0.01	$0.05	
2004D 3,456,400,000		0.01	0.05	
2004S . . . .(2,965,422)				1.00
2005 3,935,600,000		0.01	0.05	
2005D 3,764,450,500		0.01	0.05	
2005S . . . .(3,344,679)				1.00
2006 4,290,000,000		0.01	0.05	
2006D 3,944,000,000		0.01	0.05	
2006S . . . .(3,054,436)				1.00
2007 3,762,400,000		0.01	0.05	
2007D 3,638,800,000		0.01	0.05	
2007S . . . .(2,259,847)				1.00
2008 2,558,800,000		0.01	0.05	
2008D 2,849,600,000		0.01	0.05	
2008S . . . .(1,998,108)				1.00

** Included in number above. **a.** Varieties were made using Proof dies that have a wide space between AM in AMERICA. The letters nearly touch on other Uncirculated cents.

2009 Lincoln Bicentennial Cent Program

One-cent coins issued during 2009 are a unique tribute to President Abraham Lincoln, recognizing the bicentennial of his birth and the 100th anniversary of the first issuance of the Lincoln cent. These coins use four different design themes on the reverse to represent the four major aspects of President Lincoln's life. The obverse of each of these coins carries the traditional portrait of Lincoln that has been in use since 1909.

The special reverse designs, released as quarterly issues throughout 2009, are described as: Birth and Early Childhood in Kentucky (designer, Richard Masters; sculptor, Jim Licaretz); Formative Years in Indiana (designer and sculptor, Charles Vickers); Professional Life in Illinois (designer, Joel Iskowitz; sculptor, Don Everhart); and Presidency in Washington (designer, Susan Gamble; sculptor, Joseph Menna). Those issued for commercial circulation are made of the exact same copper-plated composition used since 1982. Special versions included in collector sets are made of the same metallic composition as was used for the original 1909 cents (95% copper, 5% tin and zinc).

2009 Lincoln cent reverse designs (U.S. Mint artist renderings)

	Mintage	MS-63	MS-65	PF-65
2009, Kentucky childhood		$0.05	$0.10	
2009D, Kentucky childhood		0.05	0.10	
2009S, Kentucky childhood				$2
2009, Indiana years		0.05	0.10	
2009D, Indiana years		0.05	0.10	

	Mintage	MS-63	MS-65	PF-65
2009S, Indiana years				$2
2009, Life in Illinois		$0.05	$0.10	
2009D, Life in Illinois		0.05	0.10	
2009S, Life in Illinois				2
2009, Presidency		0.05	0.10	
2009D, Presidency		0.05	0.10	
2009S, Presidency				2

TWO-CENT PIECE (1864–1873)

The Act of April 22, 1864, which changed the weight and composition of the cent, included a provision for the bronze two-cent piece. The weight was specified as 96 grains, the alloy being the same as for the cent. There are two varieties for the first year of issue, 1864: the Small Motto and the Large Motto. The differences are illustrated in the closeups below.

1864, Small Motto   **1864, Large Motto**

On the obverse the D in GOD is narrow on the Large Motto variety. The stem to the leaf shows plainly on the Small Motto variety.

G-4 Good: At least part of IN GOD visible.
VG-8 Very Good: WE weakly visible.
F-12 Fine: Complete motto visible. The word WE weak.
EF-40 Extremely Fine: The word WE bold.
AU-50 About Uncirculated: Traces of wear visible on leaf tips, arrow points, and the word WE.
MS-60 Uncirculated: No trace of wear. Light blemishes.
MS-63 Choice Uncirculated: Some distracting contact marks or blemishes in prime focal areas. Some impairment of luster possible.
PF-63 Choice Proof: Reflective surfaces with only a few blemishes in secondary focal places. No major flaws.

Brilliant red choice Uncirculated and Proof coins are worth more than prices shown. Cleaned or discolored pieces are worth less.

	Mintage	G-4	VG-8	F-12	VF-20	EF-40	AU-50	MS-60	MS-63	PF-63
1864, Small Motto ....*		$55	$70	$100	$200	$325	$400	$525	$750	$10,000
1864, Large Motto ..*(100+)* ..19,847,500		8	9	12	16	23	32	55	90	325
1865 ....*(500+)* ..13,640,000		8	9	12	16	23	32	55	90	275
1866 ....*(725+)* ...3,177,000		8	9	12	16	23	32	55	90	275
1867 ....*(625+)* ...2,938,750		8	9	12	16	23	32	55	90	275
1868 ....*(600+)* ...2,803,750		8	9	14	18	25	37	65	110	275
1869 ....*(600+)* ...1,546,500		9	10	14	19	32	60	100	110	275
1870 ....*(1,000+)* 861,250		11	13	19	25	45	80	125	150	375
1871 ....*(960+)* 721,250		13	15	22	30	65	90	165	190	400
1872 ....*(950+)* 65,000		120	160	180	230	350	400	500	800	600
1873 ....*(1,000+)*							700			1,000

* Included in number below.

SILVER THREE-CENT PIECES (TRIMES) (1851–1873)

This smallest of United States silver coins was authorized by Congress March 3, 1851. The first three-cent silver pieces had no lines bordering the six-pointed star. From 1854 through 1858 there were two lines, while issues of the last 15 years show only one line. Issues from 1854 through 1873 have an olive sprig over the III and a bundle of three arrows beneath.

G-4 Good: Star worn smooth. Legend and date readable.
VG-8 Very Good: Outline of shield defined. Legend and date clear.
F-12 Fine: Only star points worn smooth.
VF-20 Very Fine: Only partial wear on star ridges.
EF-40 Extremely Fine: Ridges on star points visible.
AU-50 About Uncirculated: Trace of wear visible at each star point. Center of shield possibly weak.
MS-60 Uncirculated: No trace of wear. Light blemishes.
MS-63 Choice Uncirculated: Some distracting contact marks or blemishes in prime focal areas. Some impairment of luster possible.
PF-63 Choice Proof: Reflective surfaces with only a few blemishes in secondary focal places. No major flaws.

Mintmark location.

No Outline Around Star (1851–1853)	Three Outlines to Star, Large Date (1854–1858)	Two Outlines to Star, Small Date (1859–1873)	1862, 2 Over 1

Well-struck specimens command higher prices.

	Mintage	G-4	VG-8	F-12	VF-20	EF-40	AU-50	MS-60	MS-63	PF-63
1851	5,447,400	$13	$16	$18	$24	$33	$70	$90	$150	—
1851O	720,000	16	20	25	47	75	110	180	260	
1852	18,663,500	13	16	18	24	33	70	85	150	—
1853	11,400,000	13	16	18	24	33	70	85	150	
1854	671,000	14	17	20	26	55	115	175	325	$6,500
1855	139,000	16	28	30	50	100	135	275	450	2,200
1856	1,458,000	13	16	20	26	50	100	150	320	1,800
1857	1,042,000	13	16	20	26	50	100	150	320	1,800
1858 ......(300+)	1,603,700	13	16	20	26	50	90	150	320	1,200
1859 ......(800)	364,200	13	16	20	26	35	75	90	175	275
1860 ......(1,000)	286,000	13	16	20	26	35	75	90	175	275
1861 ......(1,000)	497,000	13	16	20	26	35	75	90	175	275
1862, 2/1	*	13	16	20	26	35	90	110	225	
1862 ......(550)	343,000	13	16	20	26	35	75	90	175	285
1863 ......(460)	21,000				150	200	275	350	550	320
1864 ......(470)	12,000				150	200	275	350	550	310

	Mintage	VF-20	EF-40	AU-50	MS-60	MS-63	PF-63
1865 ......(500)	8,000	$175	$200	$300	$375	$525	$315
1866 ......(725)	22,000	150	175	275	350	500	315
1867 ......(625)	4,000	175	200	300	375	525	315
1868 ......(600)	3,500	175	200	300	375	600	315
1869 ......(600)	4,500	175	200	300	375	500	315
1870 ......(1,000)	3,000	175	200	300	375	500	325
1871 ......(960)	3,400	175	200	300	375	500	325
1872 ......(950)	1,000	200	225	300	375	600	350
1873, Proof only ......(600)			400				700

* Included in number below.

NICKEL THREE-CENT PIECES (1865–1889)

The three-cent pieces struck in nickel composition were designed to replace the silver three-cent coins. Composition is 75% copper and 25% nickel. All were coined at Philadelphia and have plain edges.

G-4 Good: Date and legends complete though worn. III smooth.

VG-8 Very Good: III half worn. Rims complete.

VF-20 Very Fine: Three-quarters of hair details visible.

EF-40 Extremely Fine: Slight, even wear.

AU-50 About Uncirculated: Slight wear on hair curls, above forehead, and on wreath and numeral III.

MS-60 Uncirculated: No trace of wear. Light blemishes.

MS-63 Choice Uncirculated: Some distracting contact marks or blemishes in prime focal areas. Some impairment of luster possible.

PF-63 Choice Proof: Reflective surfaces with only a few blemishes in secondary focal places. No major flaws.

Brilliant choice Uncirculated and Proof coins are worth more than prices shown. Spotted, cleaned, or discolored pieces are worth less.

	Mintage	G-4	VG-8	F-12	VF-20	EF-40	AU-50	MS-60	MS-63	PF-63
1865 ....(500+) ..11,382,000		$7	$9	$10	$12	$15	$25	$50	$90	$650
1866 ....(725+) ..4,801,000		7	9	10	12	15	25	50	90	160
1867 ....(625+) ..3,915,000		7	9	10	12	15	25	50	90	160
1868 ....(600+) ..3,252,000		7	9	10	12	15	25	50	90	160
1869 ....(600+) ..1,604,000		7	9	10	12	15	25	50	90	160
1870 ......(1,000+) ..1,335,000		7	9	10	12	15	25	50	90	160
1871 ....(960+) 604,000		7	9	10	12	15	25	50	100	160
1872 ....(950+) 862,000		7	9	10	12	15	25	50	100	160
1873 ....(1,100+) 390,000		7	9	10	12	15	25	50	90	160
1874 ....(700+) 790,000		8	10	11	13	17	27	60	110	160
1875 ....(700+) 228,000		9	11	12	14	20	32	80	110	160
1876 ....(1,150+) 162,000		9	11	12	15	22	38	110	125	175
1877, Pf only ..(510+)					550	600				900
1878, Pf only ..(2,350)					250	375				475
1879 ....(3,200) 38,000		20	25	30	40	60	75	130	200	200
1880 ....(3,955) 21,000		40	45	50	60	70	85	150	180	200
1881 ....(3,575) ..1,077,000		7	9	10	12	15	25	50	90	160
1882 ....(3,100) 22,200		35	45	50	60	80	100	150	200	225
1883 ....(6,609) 4,000		75	85	100	135	160	180	200	375	235
1884 ....(3,942) 1,700		155	175	190	250	275	300	400	550	275
1885 ....(3,790) 1,000		175	200	225	275	325	350	450	550	275
1886, Pf only ..(4,290)					175	200				250
1887 ....(2,960) 5,001		120	140	150	160	175	225	250	275	250
1887, 7/6 ....*					175	200				275
1888 ....(4,582) 36,501		20	23	27	35	45	60	140	175	185
1889 ....(3,436) 18,125		35	45	60	75	85	100	150	200	185

* Included in number above.

SHIELD (1866–1883)

The Shield type nickel was made possible by the Act of May 16, 1866. Its weight was set at 77-16/100 grains with the same composition as the nickel three-cent piece.

G-4 Good: All letters in motto readable.
VG-8 Very Good: Motto clear and stands out. Rims slightly worn but even. Part of shield lines visible.
F-12 Fine: Half of each olive leaf worn smooth.
EF-40 Extremely Fine: Slight wear to leaf tips and cross over shield.
AU-50 About Uncirculated: Traces of light wear on only the high design points. Half of mint luster present.
MS-60 Uncirculated: No trace of wear. Light blemishes.
MS-63 Choice Uncirculated: Some distracting blemishes in prime focal areas. Impaired luster possible.
PF-63 Choice Proof: Reflective surfaces. Only a few blemishes in secondary focal areas. No major flaws.

With Rays (1866–1867)   Without Rays (1867–1883)

Typical Example of
1883, 3 Over 2
Other varieties exist.

Brilliant choice Uncirculated and Proof coins are worth more than prices shown. Spotted, cleaned, or discolored pieces are worth less.

	Mintage	G-4	VG-8	F-12	EF-40	AU-50	MS-60	MS-63	PF-63
1866, Rays ....(600+) ..14,742,500		$13	$19	$22	$85	$110	$125	$200	$1,250
1867, Rays ....(25+) ...2,019,000		15	22	27	90	125	225	275	16,000
1867, No Rays ....(600+) ..28,890,500		9	10	11	20	25	70	120	220
1868 ....(600+) ..28,817,000		9	10	11	20	25	70	120	220
1869 ....(600+) ..16,395,000		9	10	11	20	25	70	120	220
1870 ....(1,000+) ...4,806,000		9	10	11	20	25	70	120	220
1871 ....(960+) 561,000		25	30	50	100	135	180	250	250
1872 ....(950+) ...6,036,000		10	11	13	24	50	90	125	220
1873, Close 3 ....(1,100+) 436,050		10	11	13	30	55	100	175	220
1873, Open 3 4,113,950		9	10	11	25	50	90	125	
1874 ....(700+) ...3,538,000		10	11	13	24	50	90	130	220
1875 ....(700+) ...2,097,000		12	14	20	40	55	100	140	225
1876 ....(1,150+) ...2,530,000		12	14	20	40	55	100	120	220
1877, Proof only ......(510+)		400	850					1,300
1878, Proof only ......(2,350)		275	450					900
1879 ....(3,200) 25,900		175	225	275	325	350	400	450	400
1880 ....(3,955) 16,000		190	240	290	500	800	1,600	2,500	450
1881 ....(3,575) 68,800		125	150	175	250	275	350	450	300
1882 ....(3,100) ..11,472,900		8	9	10	19	25	60	100	175
1883 ....(5,419) ...1,451,500		8	9	10	19	25	65	100	180
1883, 3 Over 2 ....*			45	100	175	375	450	600	

* Included in number above.

LIBERTY HEAD (1883–1912)

In 1883 the design was changed to the "Liberty head." This type first appeared without the word CENTS on the coin, merely a large letter V. These "CENTS-less" coins were goldplated by fraudsters and passed as $5 pieces. Later in that year the word CENTS was added.

G-4 Good: No details in head. LIBERTY obliterated.
VG-8 Very Good: Some letters in LIBERTY legible.
F-12 Fine: All letters in LIBERTY legible.
VF-20 Very Fine: LIBERTY bold, including letter L.
EF-40 Extremely Fine: LIBERTY sharp. Corn grains at bottom of wreath visible on reverse.
AU-50 About Uncirculated: Traces of light wear on only high points of design. Half of mint luster present.
MS-60 Uncirculated: No trace of wear. Contact marks possible. Surface may be spotted, or luster faded.
MS-63 Choice Uncirculated: No trace of wear. Light blemishes.
PF-63 Choice Proof: Reflective surfaces. Only a few blemishes in secondary focal areas. No major flaws.

Variety 1, Without CENTS (1883 Only) **Variety 2, With CENTS (1883–1913)** **Mintmark Location**

Brilliant choice Uncirculated and Proof coins are worth more than prices shown; spotted or cleaned coins, less.

	Mintage	G-4	VG-8	F-12	VF-20	EF-40	AU-50	MS-60	MS-63	PF-63
1883, Without CENTS . . .(5,219) . . .5,474,300		$2.25	$2.75	$3.10	$4	$4.75	$6.25	$18	$26	$165
1883, CENTS . .(6,783) . .16,026,200		6.00	7.00	12.00	20	35.00	45.00	75	100	140
1884 . . . .(3,942) . .11,270,000		7.00	12.00	14.00	20	35.00	50.00	100	130	130
1885 . . . .(3,790) . . .1,472,700		230.00	275.00	325.00	450	550.00	700.00	850	1,100	700
1886 . . . .(4,290) . . .3,326,000		100.00	125.00	200.00	250	310.00	395.00	450	800	375
1887 . . . .(2,960) . .15,260,692		4.00	7.00	11.00	20	40.00	45.00	75	125	150
1888 . . . .(4,582) . .10,167,901		10.00	15.00	25.00	50	65.00	90.00	135	180	150
1889 . . . .(3,336) . .15,878,025		3.00	5.00	11.00	20	35.00	50.00	75	125	140
1890 . . . .(2,740) . .16,256,532		2.50	4.00	10.00	15	25.00	30.00	75	125	140
1891 . . . .(2,350) . .16,832,000		2.50	4.00	10.00	15	25.00	30.00	75	125	140
1892 . . . .(2,745) . .11,696,897		2.50	4.00	10.00	15	25.00	30.00	75	125	140
1893 . . . .(2,195) . .13,368,000		2.50	4.00	10.00	15	30.00	35.00	80	135	140
1894 . . . .(2,632) . . .5,410,500		6.00	10.00	40.00	75	115.00	150.00	180	210	140
1895 . . . .(2,062) . . .9,977,822		1.50	2.50	7.00	10	25.00	30.00	75	130	140
1896 . . . .(1,862) . . .8,841,058		2.00	5.00	15.00	20	35.00	50.00	90	140	140
1897 . . . .(1,938) . .20,426,797		2.00	5.00	9.00	12	22.00	24.00	50	125	140
1898 . . . .(1,795) . .12,530,292		2.00	5.00	9.00	12	22.00	24.00	50	125	140
1899 . . . .(2,031) . .26,027,000		0.75	1.00	3.00	6	14.00	22.00	50	100	140
1900 . . . .(2,262) . .27,253,733		0.75	1.00	3.00	6	14.00	20.00	40	90	135
1901 . . . .(1,985) . .26,478,228		0.75	1.00	3.00	6	14.00	20.00	40	80	135
1902 . . . .(2,018) . .31,487,561		0.75	1.00	3.00	6	14.00	20.00	40	80	135
1903 . . . .(1,790) . .28,004,935		0.75	1.00	2.00	4	12.00	20.00	40	80	135
1904 . . . .(1,817) . .21,403,167		0.75	1.00	2.00	4	12.00	20.00	40	80	135
1905 . . . .(2,152) . .29,825,124		0.75	1.00	2.00	4	12.00	20.00	40	80	135
1906 . . . .(1,725) . .38,612,000		0.75	1.00	2.00	4	12.00	20.00	40	80	135
1907 . . . .(1,475) . .39,213,325		0.75	1.00	2.00	4	12.00	20.00	40	80	135
1908 . . . .(1,620) . .22,684,557		0.75	1.00	2.00	4	12.00	20.00	40	80	135

	Mintage	G-4	VG-8	F-12	VF-20	EF-40	AU-50	MS-60	MS-63	PF-63
1909 . . . .(4,763) . .11,585,763		$0.75	$1.00	$2	$4	$12	$22	$45	$95	$135
1910 . . . .(2,405) . .30,166,948		0.75	1.00	2	4	12	20	40	80	135
1911 . . . .(1,733) . .39,557,639		0.75	1.00	2	4	12	20	40	80	135
1912 . . . .(2,145) . .26,234,569		0.75	1.00	2	4	12	20	40	80	135
1912D 8,474,000		1.00	1.50	4	13	35	85	135	150	
1912S 238,000		65.00	100.00	125	225	425	650	750	950	
1913 Liberty Head (5 known)									2,000,000	

INDIAN HEAD OR BUFFALO (1913–1938)

The Buffalo nickel was designed by James E. Fraser, whose initial F is below the date. He modeled the bison after Black Diamond in the New York Central Park Zoo.

G-4 Good: Legends and date readable. Buffalo's horn does not show.
VG-8 Very Good: Horn worn nearly flat.
F-12 Fine: Horn and tail smooth but partially visible. Obverse rim intact.
VF-20 Very Fine: Much of horn visible. Indian's cheekbone worn.
EF-40 Extremely Fine: Horn lightly worn. Slight wear on Indian's hair ribbon.
AU-50 About Uncirculated: Traces of light wear on high points of design. Half of mint luster present.
MS-60 Uncirculated: No trace of wear. May have several blemishes.
MS-63 Choice Uncirculated: No trace of wear. Light blemishes.
Matte PF-63 Choice Proof: Crisp surfaces. Only a few blemishes in secondary focal areas. No major flaws.

Variety 1 – FIVE CENTS on Raised Ground (1913)

Brilliant choice Uncirculated coins are worth more than prices shown. Spotted, cleaned, weakly struck, or discolored pieces are worth less.

	Mintage	G-4	VG-8	F-12	VF-20	EF-40	AU-50	MS-60	MS-63	MATTE PF-63
1913, Variety 1 . .(1,520)	30,992,000	$4	$5	$6	$8	$11	$12	$21	$30	$750
1913D, Variety 1 5,337,000		6	8	10	14	18	23	35	45	
1913S, Variety 1 2,105,000		17	22	24	28	40	50	70	90	

Variety 2 – FIVE CENTS in Recess (1913–1938)

Mintmark Below FIVE CENTS   **1916, Doubled-Die Obverse**   **1918-D, 8 Over 7**

	Mintage	G-4	VG-8	F-12	VF-20	EF-40	AU-50	MS-60	MS-63	MATTE PF-63
1913, Variety 2 29,857,186		$4.25	$5.50	$6.50	$7.50	$11	$15	$22	$32	
. . . .(1,514)										$600
1913D, Variety 2 4,156,000		50.00	60.00	75.00	90.00	120	135	150	175	
1913S, Variety 2 1,209,000		150.00	165.00	210.00	240.00	325	375	500	625	
1914 20,664,463		10.00	11.00	12.00	14.00	16	22	35	50	
. . . .(1,275)										675

Chart continued on next page.

Brilliant choice Uncirculated coins are worth more than prices shown. Spotted, cleaned, weakly struck, or discolored pieces are worth less.

	Mintage	G-4	VG-8	F-12	VF-20	EF-40	AU-50	MS-60	MS-63	MATTE PF-63
1914D	.3,912,000	$35.00	$50.00	$65.00	$100.00	$150	$200	$235	$325	
1914S	.3,470,000	12.00	14.00	18.00	35.00	50	80	100	240	
1915	.20,986,220	2.50	2.50	4.00	5.00	12	30	45	50	
	.(1,050)									$700
1915D	.7,569,000	8.00	11.00	18.00	35.00	75	85	140	175	
1915S	.1,505,000	19.00	25.00	40.00	72.00	150	185	275	425	
1916	.63,497,466	2.00	2.50	3.00	3.50	5	10	28	35	
	.(600)									900
1916, DblDie Obv	.*	1,000.00	1,800.00	3,600.00	5,600.00	8,500	14,000	30,000	70,000	
1916D	.13,333,000	6.50	10.00	11.00	22.00	45	60	90	135	
1916S	.11,860,000	4.00	6.00	9.00	22.00	45	65	100	165	
1917	.51,424,019	2.00	2.50	3.00	4.00	7	16	30	60	
1917D	.9,910,000	7.00	10.00	14.00	42.00	75	110	175	375	
1917S	.4,193,000	9.00	13.00	20.00	50.00	85	135	225	600	
1918	.32,086,314	1.50	2.00	2.50	6.00	16	22	60	135	

	Mintage	G-4	VG-8	F-12	VF-20	EF-40	AU-50	MS-60	MS-63
1918D, 8 Over 7	.**	$550.00	$650.00	$1,300.00	$2,500.00	$4,500.00	$6,000	$15,000	$32,000
1918D	.8,362,000	8.00	14.00	18.00	70.00	130.00	175	235	600
1918S	.4,882,000	5.00	12.00	16.00	45.00	90.00	150	210	1,500
1919	.60,868,000	0.50	0.55	0.80	2.00	7.00	15	32	60
1919D (a)	.8,006,000	6.00	10.00	30.00	70.00	130.00	160	325	750
1919S (a)	.7,521,000	4.00	8.00	17.00	70.00	130.00	160	325	900
1920	.63,093,000	0.45	0.60	1.25	2.50	6.00	15	32	70
1920D (a)	.9,418,000	3.00	6.00	12.00	65.00	150.00	175	300	800
1920S	.9,689,000	1.50	4.00	10.00	50.00	120.00	150	230	900
1921	.10,663,000	0.80	2.00	3.00	10.00	25.00	35	70	140
1921S	.1,557,000	30.00	50.00	90.00	315.00	465.00	550	865	1,200
1923	.35,715,000	0.45	0.60	0.80	4.00	7.50	18	32	80
1923S (a)	.6,142,000	3.00	3.50	9.00	60.00	150.00	180	235	550
1924	.21,620,000	0.40	0.60	0.80	4.00	9.00	25	40	80
1924D	.5,258,000	3.50	4.00	10.00	40.00	120.00	140	190	500
1924S	.1,437,000	8.00	18.00	40.00	240.00	650.00	850	1,200	2,200
1925	.35,565,100	0.75	1.25	2.00	4.00	8.00	16	25	47
1925D	.4,450,000	4.00	5.00	18.00	45.00	85.00	125	210	325
1925S	.6,256,000	2.00	5.00	10.00	50.00	90.00	125	230	1,200
1926	.44,693,000	0.35	0.45	0.60	3.00	5.00	12	18	32
1926D	.5,638,000	3.00	6.00	10.00	50.00	90.00	140	160	235
1926S	.970,000	9.00	16.00	40.00	235.00	450.00	1,300	2,000	4,200
1927	.37,981,000	0.50	0.45	0.60	1.50	6.00	10	24	36
1927D	.5,730,000	0.85	2.00	2.50	15.00	40.00	55	85	160
1927S	.3,430,000	0.60	0.90	1.75	18.00	45.00	75	250	1,100
1928	.23,411,000	0.40	0.45	0.60	2.00	5.00	10	22	30
1928D	.6,436,000	0.45	0.85	1.75	6.00	20.00	23	28	48
1928S	.6,936,000	0.60	0.75	1.25	5.00	15.00	50	125	300
1929	.36,446,000	0.35	0.40	0.60	2.00	5.00	10	16	35
1929D	.8,370,000	0.45	0.60	0.80	3.00	15.00	18	32	65
1929S	.7,754,000	0.40	0.60	0.75	0.90	5.50	12	25	45

* Included in number above. ** Included in number below. **a.** Uncirculated pieces with full, sharp details are worth considerably more.

1937-D, "3-Legged" Variety

1938-D, D Over S

Brilliant choice Uncirculated coins are worth more than prices shown. Spotted, cleaned, weakly struck, or discolored pieces are worth less.

	Mintage	G-4	VG-8	F-12	VF-20	EF-40	AU-50	MS-60	MS-63	PF-63
1930	22,849,000	$0.40	$0.50	$0.70	$0.80	$5.00	$11.00	$16	$35	
1930S	5,435,000	0.40	0.50	0.70	0.80	6.00	15.00	25	60	
1931S	1,200,000	7.00	8.00	8.80	9.25	15.00	25.00	28	45	
1934	20,213,003	0.35	0.45	0.55	0.75	3.00	9.00	16	30	
1934D	7,480,000	0.50	0.75	1.25	3.00	8.00	21.00	35	55	
1935	58,264,000	0.35	0.45	0.55	0.75	1.25	4.25	10	22	
1935D	12,092,000	0.35	0.50	1.00	3.00	6.00	19.00	30	40	
1935S	10,300,000	0.35	0.45	0.55	0.75	2.00	7.50	15	36	
1936	(4,420) 118,997,000	0.35	0.45	0.55	0.75	1.25	4.00	10	23	$650
1936D	24,814,000	0.45	0.60	0.75	0.75	1.75	4.50	16	19	
1936S	14,930,000	0.35	0.45	0.55	0.75	1.25	4.50	11	16	
1937	(5,769) 79,480,000	0.35	0.45	0.55	0.75	1.25	2.75	13	16	550
1937D	17,826,000	0.35	0.45	0.55	0.75	1.25	4.00	11	16	
1937D, 3-Legged	*	250.00	350.00	450.00	550.00	650.00	750.00	1,250	2,800	
1937S	5,635,000	0.35	0.45	0.55	0.75	1.25	4.00	11	20	
1938D	7,020,000	1.00	1.10	1.50	1.75	2.00	4.00	11	15	
1938D, D Over S	*			4.00	5.00	8.00	12.00	25	35	

* Included in number above.

JEFFERSON (1938 TO DATE)

This nickel was originally designed by Felix Schlag. He won an award of $1,000 in a competition with some 390 artists. It established the definite public approval of portrait and pictorial rather than symbolic devices on our coinage. On October 8, 1942, the wartime five-cent piece composed of copper (56%), silver (35%), and manganese (9%) was introduced to eliminate nickel, a critical war material. A larger mintmark was placed above the dome. The letter P (Philadelphia) was used for the first time, indicating the change of alloy. The designer's initials FS were added below the bust starting in 1966. The mintmark position was moved to the obverse starting in 1968.

VG-8 Very Good: Second porch pillar from right nearly gone, other three still visible but weak.

F-12 Fine: Jefferson's cheekbone worn flat. Hair lines and eyebrow faint. Second pillar weak, especially at bottom.

VF-20 Very Fine: Second pillar plain and complete on both sides.

EF-40 Extremely Fine: Cheekbone, hair lines, eyebrow slightly worn but well defined. Base of triangle above pillars visible but weak.

MS-63 Select Uncirculated: No trace of wear. Slight blemishes.

MS-65 Choice Uncirculated: No trace of wear. Barely noticeable blemishes.

PF-65 Gem Proof: Brilliant surfaces. No noticeable blemishes or flaws. May have a few barely noticeable marks or hairlines.

Mintmark Located at Right of Building   Wartime Silver   Mintmark, Starting 1968

See next page for chart.

Uncirculated pieces with fully struck steps are valued higher.

	Mintage	VG-8	F-12	VF-20	EF-40	MS-63	MS-65	PF-65
1938 ....(19,365) ...19,496,000		$0.10	$0.12	$0.20	$0.25	$1.10	$5.00	$50
1938D 5,376,000		0.25	0.35	0.75	1.00	2.25	7.00	
1938S 4,105,000		0.40	0.60	0.85	1.50	2.75	8.00	
1939 ....(12,535) ..120,615,000		0.08	0.10	0.12	0.25	1.00	2.00	50
1939D 3,514,000		1.20	1.60	2.50	4.00	35.00	50.00	
1939S 6,630,000		0.25	0.30	0.50	1.35	12.00	20.00	
1940 ....(14,158) ..176,485,000				0.05	0.10	1.00	2.00	45
1940D 43,540,000				0.05	0.10	1.25	3.50	
1940S 39,690,000				0.05	0.10	1.25	3.50	
1941 ....(18,720) ..203,265,000				0.05	0.10	0.50	2.00	45
1941D 53,432,000				0.05	0.10	1.25	3.00	
1941S 43,445,000				0.05	0.10	1.50	3.50	
1942 ....(29,600) ..49,789,000				0.05	0.10	1.25	4.00	45
1942D 13,938,000		0.10	0.15	0.25	1.00	16.00	23.00	

Wartime Silver Alloy (1942–1945)

	Mintage	VG-8	F-12	VF-20	EF-40	MS-63	MS-65	PF-65
1942P ....(27,600) ...57,873,000		$0.60	$0.60	$0.60	$0.75	$4	$8.00	$100
1942S 32,900,000		0.60	0.60	0.60	0.75	4	9.00	
1943P, 3 Over 2 ....*			15.00	20.00	35.00	130	320.00	
1943P 271,165,000		0.60	0.60	0.60	0.75	3	6.00	
1943D 15,294,000		0.60	0.60	0.60	0.75	5	7.00	
1943S 104,060,000		0.60	0.60	0.60	0.75	3	6.00	
1944P 119,150,000		0.60	0.60	0.60	0.75	5	8.50	
1944D 32,309,000		0.60	0.60	0.60	0.75	5	8.00	
1944S 21,640,000		0.60	0.60	0.60	0.75	4	8.00	
1945P 119,408,100		0.60	0.60	0.60	0.75	3	8.00	
1945D 37,158,000		0.60	0.60	0.60	0.75	3	7.00	
1945S 58,939,000		0.60	0.60	0.60	0.75	3	7.00	

* Included in number below.

Prewar Composition, Mintmark Style Resumed (1946–1967)

1943, 3 Over 2	1954-S, S Over D	1955-D, D Over S

	Mintage	VF-20	EF-40	MS-63	MS-65	PF-65
1946 161,116,000		$0.05	$0.05	$0.60	$2.50	
1946D 45,292,200		0.05	0.05	0.60	2.50	
1946S 13,560,000		0.05	0.06	0.25	1.75	
1947 95,000,000		0.05	0.05	0.35	1.75	
1947D 37,822,000		0.05	0.05	0.35	1.75	
1947S 24,720,000		0.05	0.06	0.35	1.75	
1948 89,348,000		0.05	0.05	0.35	1.75	
1948D 44,734,000		0.05	0.06	0.50	2.00	
1948S 11,300,000		0.05	0.06	0.50	2.00	
1949 60,652,000		0.05	0.06	2.00	3.00	

NICKEL FIVE-CENT PIECES

	Mintage	VF-20	EF-40	MS-63	MS-65	PF-65
1949D	.36,498,000	$0.05	$0.05	$0.50	$2.00	
1949D, D Over S	*	18.00	30.00	100.00	160.00	
1949S	.9,716,000	0.05	0.10	0.40	2.00	
1950	(51,386) 9,796,000	0.05	0.10	0.50	2.50	$30.00
1950D	.2,630,030	2.00	2.25	8.00	11.00	
1951	(57,500) ..28,552,000	0.05	0.06	1.25	3.00	25.00
1951D	.20,460,000	0.05	0.06	2.00	3.50	
1951S	.7,776,000	0.05	0.10	0.50	2.50	
1952	(81,980) ..63,988,000	0.05	0.05	0.35	1.75	18.00
1952D	.30,638,000	0.05	0.05	2.00	3.00	
1952S	.20,572,000	0.05	0.05	0.55	1.50	
1953	(128,800) 46,644,000	0.05	0.05	0.10	0.35	16.00
1953D	.59,878,600	0.05	0.05	0.10	0.35	
1953S	.19,210,900	0.05	0.05	0.25	0.50	
1954	(233,300) ..47,684,050	0.05	0.05	0.50	1.00	8.00
1954D	.117,183,060	0.05	0.05	0.20	0.50	
1954S	.29,384,000	0.05	0.05	0.50	1.00	
1954S, S Over D	*	2.50	5.00	18.00	35.00	
1955	(378,200) ...7,888,000	0.06	0.08	0.40	0.50	6.00
1955D	.74,464,100	0.05	0.05	0.20	0.40	
1955D, D Over S (a)	*	3.00	5.00	23.00	35.00	
1956	(669,384) ...35,216,000		0.05	0.10	0.40	1.00
1956D	.67,222,940		0.05	0.10	0.40	
1957	(1,247,952) ...38,408,000		0.05	0.10	0.40	1.00
1957D	.136,828,900		0.05	0.20	0.60	
1958	(875,652) 17,088,000		0.05	0.20	0.60	1.50
1958D	.168,249,120		0.05	0.10	0.40	
1959	(1,149,291) ...27,248,000		0.05	0.10	0.20	0.75
1959D	.160,738,240		0.05	0.10	0.20	
1960	(1,691,602) 55,416,000		0.05	0.10	0.20	0.75
1960D	.192,582,180		0.05	0.10	0.20	
1961	(3,028,144) 73,640,100		0.05	0.10	0.20	0.75
1961D	.229,342,760		0.05	0.10	0.20	
1962	(3,218,019) ...97,384,000		0.05	0.10	0.20	0.75
1962D	.280,195,720		0.05	0.10	0.25	
1963	(3,075,645) ...175,776,000		0.05	0.10	0.20	0.75
1963D	.276,829,460		0.05	0.10	0.20	
1964	(3,950,762) ..1,024,672,000		0.05	0.10	0.20	0.75
1964D	.1,787,297,160		0.05	0.10	0.20	
1965	.136,131,380		0.05	0.10	0.20	

* Included in number above. **a.** Varieties exist. Values are for the variety illustrated.

1966 Through 2003

	Mintage	MS-63	MS-65	PF-65
1966	.156,208,283	$0.10	$0.20	
1967	.107,325,800	0.10	0.20	
1968D	.91,227,880	0.10	0.20	
1968S	.100,396,004	0.10	0.20	
	(3,041,506)			$0.75
1969D	.202,807,500	0.10	0.20	
1969S	.120,165,000	0.10	0.20	
	(2,934,631)			0.75

	Mintage	MS-63	MS-65	PF-65
1970D	.515,485,380	$0.10	$0.20	
1970S	.238,832,004	0.10	0.20	
	(2,632,810)			$0.75
1971	.106,884,000	0.25	0.50	
1971D	.316,144,800	0.10	0.20	
1971S	(3,220,733)			1.00
1972	.202,036,000	0.10	0.20	
1972D	.351,694,600	0.10	0.20	

Chart continued on next page.

	Mintage	MS-63	MS-65	PF-65
1972S	(3,260,996)			$1.00
1973	384,396,000	$0.10	$0.20	
1973D	261,405,000	0.10	0.20	
1973S	(2,760,339)			1.00

	Mintage	MS-63	MS-65	PF-65
1974	601,752,000	$0.10	$0.20	
1974D	277,373,000	0.10	0.20	
1974S	(2,612,568)			$1.00

	Mintage	MS-65	PF-65
1975	181,772,000	$0.35	
1975D	401,875,300	0.20	
1975S	(2,845,450)		$0.85
1976	367,124,000	0.20	
1976D	563,964,147	0.20	
1976S	(4,149,730)		0.85
1977	585,376,000	0.20	
1977D	297,313,422	0.50	
1977S	(3,251,152)		0.75
1978	391,308,000	0.20	
1978D	313,092,780	0.20	
1978S	(3,127,781)		0.75
1979	463,188,000	0.20	
1979D	325,867,672	0.20	
1979S, Filled S	(3,677,175)		0.75
1979S, Clear S	*		1.00
1980P	593,004,000	0.20	
1980D	502,323,448	0.20	
1980S	(3,554,806)		0.75
1981P	657,504,000	0.20	
1981D	364,801,843	0.20	
1981S	(4,063,083)		0.85
1982P	292,355,000	2.00	
1982D	373,726,544	1.50	
1982S	(3,857,479)		1.00
1983P	561,615,000	1.50	
1983D	536,726,276	1.25	
1983S	(3,279,126)		1.00
1984P	746,769,000	1.25	
1984D	517,675,146	0.20	
1984S	(3,065,110)		1.50
1985P	647,114,962	0.25	
1985D	459,747,446	0.25	
1985S	(3,362,821)		1.25
1986P	536,883,483	0.25	
1986D	361,819,140	0.60	
1986S	(3,010,497)		2.50
1987P	371,499,481	0.20	
1987D	410,590,604	0.20	
1987S	(4,227,728)		1.00
1988P	771,360,000	0.20	
1988D	663,771,652	0.20	
1988S	(3,262,948)		2.00
1989P	898,812,000	0.20	

	Mintage	MS-65	PF-65
1989D	570,842,474	$0.20	
1989S	(3,220,194)		$1.50
1990P	661,636,000	0.20	
1990D	663,938,503	0.20	
1990S	(3,299,559)		1.75
1991P	614,104,000	0.20	
1991D	436,496,678	0.20	
1991S	(2,867,787)		2.00
1992P	399,552,000	1.00	
1992D	450,565,113	0.20	
1992S	(4,176,560)		1.50
1993P	412,076,000	0.20	
1993D	406,084,135	0.20	
1993S	(3,394,792)		1.50
1994P	722,160,000	0.20	
1994D	715,762,110	0.20	
1994S	(3,269,923)		1.50
1995P	774,156,000	0.40	
1995D	888,112,000	0.20	
1995S	(2,797,481)		2.00
1996P	829,332,000	0.20	
1996D	817,736,000	0.20	
1996S	(2,525,265)		1.00
1997P	470,972,000	0.20	
1997D	466,640,000	0.20	
1997S	(2,796,678)		1.75
1998P	688,272,000	0.20	
1998D	635,360,000	0.20	
1998S	(2,086,507)		1.75
1999P	1,212,000,000	0.20	
1999D	1,066,720,000	0.20	
1999S	(3,347,966)		2.00
2000P	846,240,000	0.20	
2000D	1,509,520,000	0.20	
2000S	(4,047,993)		1.75
2001P	675,704,000	0.20	
2001D	627,680,000	0.20	
2001S	(3,184,606)		1.75
2002P	539,280,000	0.20	
2002D	691,200,000	0.20	
2002S	(3,211,995)		1.50
2003P	441,840,000	0.20	
2003D	383,040,000	0.20	
2003S	(3,298,439)		1.50

* Included in number above.

"Westward Journey" Nickels

The Westward Journey Nickel Series™ (2004–2006) commemorates the bicentennial of the Louisiana Purchase and the journey of Meriwether Lewis and William Clark to explore that vast territory. **2004**—*Obverse:* traditional portrait of Jefferson. *Reverses:* Louisiana Purchase / Peace Medal reverse, by Mint sculptor Norman E. Nemeth. Keelboat reverse, by Mint sculptor Al Maletsky. **2005**—*Obverse:* new portrait of Jefferson, designed by Joe Fitzgerald after a 1789 marble bust by Jean-Antoine Houdon, and rendered by Mint sculptor Don Everhart. *Reverses:* American Bison reverse, designed by Jamie Franki and produced by Norman E. Nemeth. "Ocean in View" reverse, designed by Joe Fitzgerald and produced by Mint sculptor Donna Weaver. **2006**—*Obverse:* facing portrait of Jefferson, designed by Jamie Franki and sculpted by Donna Weaver. *Reverse:* traditional depiction of Monticello.

2004 Obverse | Peace Medal | Keelboat | 2005 Obverse

American Bison | Ocean in View | 2006 Obverse | Monticello

	Mintage	MS-65	PF-65
2004P, Peace Medal	361,440,000	$0.25	
2004D, Peace Medal	372,000,000	0.25	
2004S, Peace Medal	(2,965,422)		$1.10
2004P, Keelboat	366,720,000	0.25	
2004D, Keelboat	344,880,000	0.25	
2004S, Keelboat	(2,965,422)		1.10
2005P, American Bison	448,320,000	0.25	
2005D, American Bison	487,680,000	0.25	
2005S, American Bison	(3,344,679)		1.10
2005P, Ocean in View	394,080,000	0.25	
2005D, Ocean in View	411,120,000	0.25	
2005S, Ocean in View	(3,344,679)		1.10
2006P, Monticello	693,120,000	0.25	
2006D, Monticello	809,280,000	0.25	
2006S, Monticello	(3,054,436)		1.10
2007P	571,680,000	0.20	
2007D	626,160,000	0.20	
2007S	(2,259,847)		1.10
2008P	279,840,000	0.20	
2008D	345,600,000	0.20	
2008S	(1,198,108)		1.10
2009P		0.20	
2009D		0.20	
2009S			1.10

The half dime types present the same general characteristics as larger United States silver coins. Authorized by the Act of April 2, 1792, they were not coined until February, 1795, although dated 1794. At first the weight was 20.8 grains, and fineness .8924. By the Act of January 18, 1837, the weight was slightly reduced to 20-5/8 grains and the fineness changed to .900. Finally, the weight was reduced to 19.2 grains by the Act of February 21, 1853.

FLOWING HAIR (1794–1795)

AG-3 About Good: Details clear enough to identify.
G-4 Good: Eagle, wreath, bust outlined but lack details.
VG-8 Very Good: Some details on face. All lettering legible.
F-12 Fine: Hair ends visible. Hair at top smooth.
VF-20 Very Fine: Hair lines at top visible. Hair about ear defined.
EF-40 Extremely Fine: Hair above forehead and at neck well defined but shows some wear.
AU-50 About Uncirculated: Slight wear on high waves of hair, near ear and face, and on head and tips of eagle's wings.
MS-60 Uncirculated: No trace of wear. Light blemishes.
MS-63 Choice Uncirculated: Some distracting marks or blemishes in prime focal areas. Some impairment of luster possible.

Weakly struck Uncirculated coins are worth less than values shown.

	Mintage	AG-3	G-4	VG-8	F-12	VF-20	EF-40	AU-50	MS-60	MS-63
1794 86,416		$375	$750	$900	$1,250	$1,800	$3,500	$5,500	$9,500	$17,500
1795 . . . .*		250	600	700	900	1,500	2,500	3,500	7,000	12,000

* Included in number above.

DRAPED BUST (1796–1797)

AG-3 About Good: Details clear enough to identify.
G-4 Good: Date, stars, LIBERTY readable. Bust of Liberty outlined, but no details.
VG-8 Very Good: Some details visible.
F-12 Fine: Hair and drapery lines worn, but visible.
VF-20 Very Fine: Only left side of drapery indistinct.
EF-40 Extremely Fine: Details visible in all hair lines.
AU-50 About Uncirculated: Slight wear on bust, shoulder, and hair; wear on eagle's head and top of wings.
MS-60 Uncirculated: No trace of wear. Light blemishes.
MS-63 Choice Uncirculated: Some distracting marks or blemishes in prime focal areas. Impaired luster possible.

Small Eagle Reverse (1796–1797)

	Mintage	AG-3	G-4	VG-8	F-12	VF-20	EF-40	AU-50	MS-60	MS-63
1796, 6 Over 5 10,230		$285	$500	$625	$1,000	$1,800	$3,000	$5,500	$11,000	$20,000
1796 . . . .*		230	480	600	900	1,400	2,750	4,500	6,250	13,000
1796, LIBERTY . . . .*		230	480	600	900	1,400	2,750	4,500	6,500	15,000
1797, 15 Stars 44,527		230	480	600	900	1,400	2,500	4,000	6,250	12,000
1797, 16 Stars . . . .*		230	480	690	800	1,400	2,500	4,000	6,250	12,000
1797, 13 Stars . . . .*		230	500	700	1,000	1,600	3,400	5,500	13,000	17,000

* Included in number above.

Heraldic Eagle Reverse (1800–1805)

1800 LIBEKTY

	Mintage	AG-3	G-4	VG-8	F-12	VF-20	EF-40	AU-50	MS-60	MS-63
1800	24,000	$150	$300	$450	$700	$1,000	$1,500	$3,000	$4,500	$9,500
1800, LIBEKTY	16,000	150	300	450	700	1,000	1,500	3,000	4,500	9,500
1801	27,760	150	300	500	800	1,100	1,700	3,500	6,000	10,500
1802	3,060	8,000	12,000	16,000	27,000	50,000	70,000	—	—	—
1803	37,850	175	400	500	850	1,150	1,750	3,750	6,200	10,500
1805	15,600	175	400	500	850	1,500	2,600	7,500	—	—

CAPPED BUST (1829–1837)

G-4 Good: Bust of Liberty outlined, no detail. Date and legend legible.
VG-8 Very Good: Complete legend and date plain. At least three letters of LIBERTY on edge of cap show clearly.
F-12 Fine: All letters in LIBERTY visible.
VF-20 Very Fine: Full rims. Ear and shoulder clasp show plainly.
EF-40 Extremely Fine: Ear very distinct; eyebrow and hair well defined.
AU-50 About Uncirculated: Traces of light wear on many of the high points. At least half of mint luster still present.
MS-60 Uncirculated: No trace of wear. Light blemishes.
MS-63 Choice Uncirculated: No trace of wear. Light blemishes. Attractive mint luster.

	Mintage	G-4	VG-8	F-12	VF-20	EF-40	AU-50	MS-60	MS-63
1829	1,230,000	$15	$20	$25	$42	$75	$100	$175	$400
1830	1,240,000	15	20	25	42	75	100	175	400
1831	1,242,700	15	20	25	42	75	100	175	400
1832	965,000	15	20	25	42	75	100	175	400
1833	1,370,000	15	20	25	42	75	100	175	400
1834	1,480,000	15	20	25	42	75	100	175	400
1835	2,760,000	15	20	25	42	75	100	175	400
1836	1,900,000	15	20	25	42	75	100	175	400
1837, Small 5c	871,000	19	25	35	70	110	185	475	1,000
1837, Large 5c	*	15	20	25	42	75	100	175	400

* Included in number above.

LIBERTY SEATED (1837–1873)

G-4 Good: LIBERTY on shield smooth. Date and letters legible.
VG-8 Very Good: At least three letters in LIBERTY visible.
F-12 Fine: Entire LIBERTY visible, weak spots.
VF-20 Very Fine: Entire LIBERTY strong and even.
EF-40 Extremely Fine: LIBERTY and scroll edges distinct.
AU-50 About Uncirculated: Traces of light wear on many of the high points. At least half of mint luster still present.
MS-60 Uncirculated: No trace of wear. Light blemishes.
MS-63 Choice Uncirculated: No trace of wear. Light blemishes. Attractive mint luster.

Variety 1 – No Stars on Obverse (1837–1838)

See next page for chart.

	Mintage	G-4	VG-8	F-12	VF-20	EF-40	AU-50	MS-60	MS-63
1837 1,405,000		$15	$20	$30	$60	$100	$175	$400	$500
18380, No Stars 70,000		35	60	100	200	325	500	850	3,400

Variety 2 – Stars on Obverse (1838–1853)

From 1838 through 1859 the mintmark is located above the bow on the reverse. Large, medium, or small mintmark varieties occur for several dates.

	Mintage	G-4	VG-8	F-12	VF-20	EF-40	AU-50	MS-60	MS-63
1838 2,255,000		$7	$8	$11	$14	$30	$65	$150	$180
1839 1,069,150		7	8	11	14	30	65	150	180
18390 1,060,000		9	11	13	20	35	65	185	800
1840 1,344,085		7	8	11	14	30	65	150	180
18400 935,000		9	11	13	20	35	85	275	950
1841 1,150,000		7	8	11	14	30	65	100	125
18410 815,000		8	10	15	20	45	115	325	650
1842 815,000		7	8	13	16	32	65	90	125
18420 350,000		13	15	27	75	210	375	525	850
1843 1,165,000		7	8	11	14	30	65	90	130
1844 430,000		7	8	11	14	30	65	90	130
18440 220,000		32	45	85	225	485	1,450	2,400	6,000
1845 1,564,000		7	8	11	14	30	65	90	130
1846 27,000		100	160	300	375	1,000	2,100	6,000	9,500
1847 1,274,000		7	8	11	14	30	65	110	220
1848 668,000		7	8	11	14	30	65	100	130
18480 600,000		9	11	15	23	45	110	190	270
1849, 9 Over 6 . . . .*		10	12	16	23	45	110	200	600
1849, 9 Over 8 . . . .*		10	13	25	40	75	125	275	700
1849, Normal Date . .1,309,000		7	8	11	14	30	65	100	200
18490 140,000		12	17	33	90	200	400	1,000	1,900
1850 955,000		7	8	11	15	35	60	90	145
18500 690,000		8	10	13	21	45	135	325	700
1851 781,000		7	8	11	15	35	60	90	125
18510 860,000		8	10	12	18	45	100	225	350
1852 1,000,500		7	8	11	14	28	60	90	125
18520 260,000		12	17	27	55	110	210	385	775
1853, No Arrows 135,000		14	18	27	55	110	175	325	475
18530, No Arrows 160,000		80	125	160	300	650	1,200	2,600	5,500

* Included in number below.

Variety 3 – Arrows at Date (1853–1855)

As on the dimes, quarters, and halves, arrows were placed at the sides of the date for a short period starting in 1853 to denote the reduction of weight.

	Mintage	G-4	VG-8	F-12	VF-20	EF-40	AU-50	MS-60	MS-63	PF-63
1853 13,210,020		$7	$8	$10	$14	$30	$55	$110	$130	
18530 2,200,000		8	9	12	19	32	70	135	400	
1854 5,740,000		7	8	10	14	30	60	110	140	$4,000

| | | | | | | | | **HALF DIMES**

	Mintage	G-4	VG-8	F-12	VF-20	EF-40	AU-50	MS-60	MS-63	PF-63
1854O	1,560,000	$8	$9	$11	$18	$30	$70	$135	$350	
1855	1,750,000	7	8	10	14	30	55	110	130	$3,500
1855O	600,000	7	10	11	24	80	110	275	485	

Variety 2 Resumed (1856–1859: Weight Standard of 1853)

1858 Over Inverted Date

	Mintage	G-4	VG-8	F-12	VF-20	EF-40	AU-50	MS-60	MS-63	PF-63
1856	4,880,000	$7	$8	$9	$12	$25	$50	$80	$120	$2,000
1856O	1,100,000	7	8	10	20	40	100	210	450	
1857	7,280,000	7	8	9	12	25	50	80	120	1,750
1857O	1,380,000	7	8	10	16	30	80	175	210	
1858	3,500,000	7	8	9	12	25	50	80	120	750
1858, Over Inverted Date	*	15	20	30	50	95	150	300	600	
1858O	1,660,000	7	8	10	18	28	60	125	200	
1859	340,000	8	9	12	20	50	90	130	175	650
1859O	560,000	8	9	12	20	50	90	130	150	

* Included in number above.

Variety 4 – Legend on Obverse (1860–1873)

	Mintage	G-4	VG-8	F-12	VF-20	EF-40	AU-50	MS-60	MS-63	PF-63
1860	(1,000) 799,000	$7	$8	$10	$12	$19	$30	$75	$100	$300
1860O	1,060,000	7	8	10	12	19	35	100	135	
1861	(1,000) 3,360,000	7	8	10	12	19	30	75	100	300
1862	(550) 1,492,000	9	12	18	20	25	40	110	125	300
1863	(460) 18,000	60	70	95	125	200	270	300	400	350
1863S	100,000	11	15	18	21	60	160	350	450	
1864	(470) 48,000	110	175	210	275	400	500	550	600	350
1864S	90,000	18	20	35	50	110	180	310	700	
1865	(500) 13,000	100	125	180	210	275	300	400	600	350
1865S	120,000	11	15	18	22	60	200	450	850	
1866	(725) 10,000	100	115	150	200	300	320	375	600	320
1866S	120,000	10	15	18	22	60	180	200	400	
1867	(625) 8,000	175	200	250	300	350	400	475	620	350
1867S	120,000	9	13	18	25	60	140	210	500	
1868	(600) 88,600	20	25	40	70	120	200	300	400	350
1868S	280,000	7	9	11	13	19	40	125	250	
1869	(600) 208,000	7	9	11	13	19	60	120	150	300
1869S	230,000	7	9	11	13	19	50	150	350	
1870	(1,000) 535,000	7	9	10	11	19	30	70	120	300
1870S (unique)							—			
1871	(960) 1,873,000	7	9	10	11	19	30	70	120	300
1871S	161,000	8	11	15	25	40	75	135	210	
1872	(950) 2,947,000	7	9	10	11	19	30	70	120	300
1872S	837,000	7	9	10	11	19	30	70	120	
1873	(600) 7,126,000	7	9	10	11	19	30	70	120	300
1873S	324,000	7	9	10	11	19	30	70	120	

The designs of the dimes, first coined in 1796, followed closely those of the half dimes up through the Liberty Seated type. The dimes in each instance weigh twice as much as the half dimes.

DRAPED BUST (1796–1807)
Small Eagle Reverse (1796–1797)

AG-3 About Good: Details clear enough to identify.
G-4 Good: Date legible. Bust outlined, but no detail.
VG-8 Very Good: All but deepest drapery folds worn smooth. Hair lines nearly gone and curls lacking in detail.
F-12 Fine: All drapery lines visible. Hair partly worn.
VF-20 Very Fine: Only left side of drapery indistinct.
EF-40 Extremely Fine: Hair well outlined with details visible.
AU-50 About Uncirculated: Traces of light wear on many of the high points. At least half of mint luster still present.
MS-60 Uncirculated: No trace of wear. Light blemishes.
MS-63 Choice Uncirculated: Some distracting marks or blemishes in prime focal areas. Impaired luster possible.

| | 1797, 16 Stars | | 1797, 13 Stars | | | | | | |

	Mintage	AG-3	G-4	VG-8	F-12	VF-20	EF-40	AU-50	MS-60	MS-63
1796 22,135		$400	$800	$1,100	$1,500	$2,200	$3,750	$6,000	$7,000	$15,000
1797, All kinds 25,261										
1797, 16 Stars		400	800	1,100	1,600	2,500	4,000	6,250	8,000	17,500
1797, 13 Stars		400	800	1,100	1,600	2,500	4,000	6,250	8,000	17,000

Heraldic Eagle Reverse (1798–1807)

	Mintage	AG-3	G-4	VG-8	F-12	VF-20	EF-40	AU-50	MS-60	MS-63
1798, All kinds 27,550										
1798, 98 Over 97, 16 Stars on Reverse		$125	$275	$400	$475	$700	$1,250	$2,100	$3,200	$7,000
1798, 98 Over 97, 13 Stars on Reverse		250	800	1,000	1,500	3,000	4,000	—	—	
1798		125	225	300	425	600	1,100	1,600	2,500	7,000
1800 21,760		125	225	300	425	600	1,100	1,600	2,700	7,000
1801 34,640		125	250	300	500	900	1,800	3,200	5,000	14,000
1802 10,975		160	375	500	850	1,300	3,000	4,500	12,000	
1803 33,040		110	225	300	400	600	1,500	3,500	5,500	
1804 8,265		250	500	800	1,300	2,100	5,000	12,000	18,000	
1805 120,780		100	200	275	350	500	900	1,100	2,800	4,200
1807 165,000		100	200	275	350	500	900	1,100	2,800	4,200

CAPPED BUST (1809–1837)

G-4 Good: Date, letters, and stars discernible. Bust outlined, no details.
VG-8 Very Good: Legends and date plain. Some letters in LIBERTY visible.
F-12 Fine: Clear LIBERTY. Ear and shoulder clasp visible. Part of rim visible on both sides.
VF-20 Very Fine: LIBERTY distinct. Full rim. Ear and clasp plain and distinct.
EF-40 Extremely Fine: LIBERTY sharp. Ear distinct. Hair above eye well defined.
AU-50 About Uncirculated: Traces of light wear on only the high points of the design. Half of mint luster present.
MS-60 Uncirculated: No trace of wear. Light blemishes.
MS-63 Choice Uncirculated: Some distracting marks or blemishes in prime focal areas. Impaired luster possible.

Variety 1 – Wide Border (1809–1828)

1823, 3 Over 2   **1824, 4 Over 2**   **1828, Large Date**   **1828, Small Date**

	Mintage	G-4	VG-8	F-12	VF-20	EF-40	AU-50	MS-60	MS-63
1809	51,065	$55	$85	$150	$250	$500	$800	$1,900	$2,900
1811, 11 Over 09	65,180	40	60	125	225	500	800	1,700	2,750
1814	421,500	13	16	28	70	200	275	500	1,200
1820	942,587	13	16	25	60	200	275	500	1,200
1821	1,186,512	13	16	25	60	200	275	500	1,200
1822	100,000	175	300	425	700	1,400	2,400	5,000	8,500
1823, 3 Over 2, All kinds	440,000								
1823, 3 Over 2, Small E's		13	16	25	60	200	275	550	1,100
1823, 3 Over 2, Large E's		13	16	25	60	200	275	550	1,100
1824, 4 Over 2	510,000	14	18	40	140	300	600	1,000	1,800
1825	*	13	16	20	50	175	275	500	1,100
1827	1,215,000	13	16	20	50	175	275	500	1,100
1828, Large Date, Curl Base 2	125,000	16	30	50	140	300	600	1,000	1,800

* Included in number above.

Variety 2 – Modified Design (1828–1837)

1829, Small 10c   **1829, Large 10c**   **1830, 30 Over 29**

	Mintage	G-4	VG-8	F-12	VF-20	EF-40	AU-50	MS-60	MS-63
1828, Sm Date, Square Base 2	*	$13	$18	$30	$65	$200	$325	$625	$1,100
1829, Small 10c	770,000	12	14	17	35	120	180	400	750
1829, Medium 10c	*	12	14	17	35	120	180	350	650
1829, Large 10c	*	12	16	22	50	135	200	400	675
1830, 30 Over 29	510,000	17	25	45	90	250	275	500	1,100

* Included in number above.

Chart continued on next page.

	Mintage	G-4	VG-8	F-12	VF-20	EF-40	AU-50	MS-60	MS-63
1830, Large 10c	*	$12	$14	$17	$35	$120	$180	$350	$675
1830, Small 10c	*	12	14	17	35	120	180	350	675
1831	771,350	12	14	17	35	120	180	350	675
1832	522,500	12	14	17	35	120	180	350	675
1833	485,000	12	14	17	35	120	180	350	675
1834	635,000	12	14	17	35	120	180	350	675
1835	1,410,000	12	14	17	35	120	180	350	675
1836	1,190,000	12	14	17	35	120	180	350	675
1837	359,500	12	14	17	35	120	180	350	675

* Included in mintage for 1830, 30 Over 29 (previous page).

LIBERTY SEATED (1837–1891)
Variety 1 – No Stars on Obverse (1837–1838)

G-4 Good: LIBERTY on shield smooth. Date and letters legible.
F-12 Fine: LIBERTY visible, weak spots.
VF-20 Very Fine: LIBERTY strong and even.
EF-40 Extremely Fine: LIBERTY and scroll edges distinct.
AU-50 About Uncirculated: Wear on Liberty's shoulder and hair high points.
MS-60 Uncirculated: No trace of wear. Light blemishes.
MS-63 Choice Uncirculated: Some distracting marks or blemishes in focal areas. Impaired luster possible.

No Drapery From Elbow
No Stars on Obverse

Mintmarks on Liberty Seated dimes on reverse, within or below the wreath. Size of mintmark varies on many dates.

	Mintage	G-4	F-12	VF-20	EF-40	AU-50	MS-60	MS-63
1837	682,500	$18	$35	$125	$220	$325	$600	$850
1838O	406,034	21	60	160	300	550	1,300	3,000

Variety 2 – Stars on Obverse (1838–1853)

No Drapery From Elbow, Tilted Shield (1838–1840)

Drapery From Elbow, Upright Shield (1840–1891)

1838, Small Stars   1838, Large Stars   Obverse   Reverse

	Mintage	G-4	F-12	VF-20	EF-40	AU-50	MS-60	MS-63
1838, All kinds	1,992,500							
1838, Small Stars		$9	$18	$35	$70	$175	$400	$600
1838, Large Stars		8	11	14	40	100	150	350
1838, Partial Drapery		9	18	35	75	210	425	1,000
1839	1,053,115	8	11	14	40	100	150	350
1839O	1,291,600	9	13	16	45	120	175	500
1840, No Drapery	981,500	8	11	14	40	100	150	350
1840O, No Drapery	1,175,000	9	13	20	50	120	475	950
1840, Drapery	377,500	13	30	55	125	170	425	2,200

	Mintage	G-4	F-12	VF-20	EF-40	AU-50	MS-60	MS-63
1841	1,622,500	$8	$11	$14	$20	$50	$135	$250
1841O	2,007,500	9	13	15	28	90	425	900
1842	1,887,500	8	11	14	20	50	135	250
1842O	2,020,000	9	13	17	100	500	1,300	2,600
1843	1,370,000	8	11	14	20	50	135	300
1843O	150,000	16	45	100	250	800	2,000	—
1844	72,500	100	225	350	600	800	1,400	4,000
1845	1,755,000	8	11	14	20	50	135	300
1845O	230,000	9	20	80	185	475	1,300	—
1846	31,300	30	75	150	400	900	1,800	6,500
1847	245,000	9	16	27	55	120	400	1,000
1848	451,500	8	11	16	35	60	210	400
1849	839,000	8	11	14	20	50	150	425
1849O	300,000	8	17	50	110	300	1,000	2,400
1850	1,931,500	8	11	14	20	50	125	300
1850O	510,000	9	13	33	65	150	425	975
1851	1,026,500	8	11	14	20	50	160	325
1851O	400,000	9	17	35	100	175	1,000	1,400
1852	1,535,500	8	11	14	20	50	150	300
1852O	430,000	10	20	50	100	175	800	1,300
1853, No Arrows	95,000	20	40	75	135	175	350	400

Variety 3 – Arrows at Date (1853–1855)

Arrows at Date (1853–1855)

	Mintage	G-4	F-12	VF-20	EF-40	AU-50	MS-60	MS-63	PF-63
1853, With Arrows	12,078,010	$7	$8	$12	$22	$60	$150	$300	
1853O	1,100,000	7	8	17	45	120	475	1,300	
1854	4,470,000	7	8	12	22	60	150	300	$5,250
1854O	1,770,000	7	8	13	35	75	285	500	
1855	2,075,000	7	8	12	22	60	175	400	5,250

Variety 2 Resumed (1856–1860)

Small Date, Arrows Removed (1856–1860)

	Mintage	G-4	F-12	VF-20	EF-40	AU-50	MS-60	MS-63	PF-63
1856, All kinds	5,780,000								
1856, Large Date		$7	$8	$11	$18	$40	$140	$275	
1856, Small Date		7	8	11	18	40	140	275	$1,800
1856O	1,180,000	7	8	11	24	90	300	650	
1856S	70,000	35	125	200	425	650	1,400	—	

Chart continued on next page.

	Mintage	G-4	F-12	VF-20	EF-40	AU-50	MS-60	MS-63	PF-63
1857 5,580,000		$7	$8	$10	$18	$40	$135	$275	$1,800
18570 1,540,000		7	8	11	18	70	190	275	
1858 . . . .(300+) . . .1,540,000		7	8	10	18	40	135	275	900
18580 290,000		8	15	35	75	125	300	450	
1858S 60,000		35	90	150	325	600	1,350		
1859 . . . .(800+) 429,200		7	8	11	25	50	135	275	700
18590 480,000		7	9	18	37	100	180	375	
1859S 60,000		35	110	175	450	850	4,000		
1860S 140,000		12	20	50	125	350	950	1,800	

Variety 4 – Legend on Obverse (1860–1873)

	Mintage	G-4	F-12	VF-20	EF-40	AU-50	MS-60	MS-63	PF-63
1860 . . . .(1,000) . . .606,000		$7	$8	$10	$18	$40	$135	$250	$400
18600 40,000		155	350	675	1,600	2,500	5,500	—	
1861 . . . .(1,000) . .1,883,000		7	8	10	18	40	100	180	400
1861S 172,500		13	40	80	160	210	600	1,800	
1862 . . . .(550) . . .847,000		7	8	10	16	25	100	120	350
1862S 180,750		11	21	50	100	125	600	1,000	
1863 . . . .(460) 14,000		100	200	300	350	400	550	600	400
1863S 157,500		11	20	40	70	125	450	1,200	
1864 . . . .(470) 11,000		80	170	210	350	425	550	600	400
1864S 230,000		8	17	32	60	110	500	550	
1865 . . . .(500) 10,000		75	200	250	310	375	525	600	400
1865S 175,000		8	17	32	100	250	800	1,900	
1866 . . . .(725) 8,000		120	235	375	400	600	700	800	400
1866S 135,000		11	20	40	100	135	550	1,100	
1867 . . . .(625) 6,000		175	275	400	475	550	675	800	450
1867S 140,000		9	20	40	100	220	600	900	
1868 . . . .(600) . . .464,000		7	8	16	31	60	175	375	300
1868S 260,000		7	13	30	50	75	185	450	
1869 . . . .(600) . . .256,000		7	13	25	40	70	185	400	300
1869S 450,000		7	11	17	35	65	185	375	
1870 . . . .(1,000) . . .470,500		7	8	11	18	40	110	200	300
1870S 50,000		100	150	200	280	350	750	1,000	
1871 . . . .(960) . . .906,750		7	8	11	15	65	140	180	300
1871CC 20,100		450	1,200	1,700	3,800	5,000	—	—	
1871S 320,000		7	8	11	15	65	110	200	
1872 . . . .(950) . .2,395,500		7	8	11	13	35	75	110	300
1872CC 35,480		200	575	1,400	2,800	7,000	—	—	
1872S 190,000		10	35	50	95	175	500	1,000	
1873, Close 3 . .(1,100) . .1,506,900		7	8	11	13	30	100	125	300
1873, Open 3 60,000		9	20	30	60	90	195	550	
1873CC (unique) 12,400							—		

Variety 5 – Arrows at Date (1873–1874)

In 1873, the dime was increased in weight from 2.49 grams to 2.50 grams. Arrows at the date in 1873 and 1874 indicate this change.

	Mintage	G-4	F-12	VF-20	EF-40	AU-50	MS-60	MS-63	PF-63
1873 . . . . . .(800) . .	2,377,700	$7	$11	$22	$55	$120	$275	$450	$700
1873CC	18,791	400	1,400	3,000	7,500	14,000	—	—	
1873S	455,000	8	16	28	65	175	450	950	
1874 . . . . . .(700) . .	2,939,300	7	11	22	55	125	285	450	700
1874CC	10,817	1,100	2,500	5,500	8,500	13,500	—		
1874S	240,000	11	27	45	90	220	400	900	

Variety 4 Resumed (1875–1891)

	Mintage	G-4	F-12	VF-20	EF-40	AU-50	MS-60	MS-63	PF-63
1875 . . . . . .(700) . .	10,350,000	$6	$7	$9	$13	$30	$75	$110	$250
1875CC	4,645,000	6	7	10	15	32	125	185	
1875S	9,070,000	6	7	9	13	30	75	110	
1876 . . . .(1,150) . .	11,450,000	6	7	9	13	30	75	110	250
1876CC	8,270,000	6	7	9	15	32	100	175	
1876S	10,420,000	6	7	9	13	30	75	110	
1877 . . . . . .(510) . .	7,310,000	6	7	9	13	30	75	110	275
1877CC	7,700,000	6	7	9	13	30	100	160	
1877S	2,340,000	6	7	9	13	30	75	110	
1878 . . . . . .(800) . .	1,677,200	6	7	9	13	30	80	110	250
1878CC	200,000	20	50	75	150	200	450	700	
1879 . . . .(1,100)	14,000	70	120	180	210	275	325	350	250
1880 . . . .(1,355)	36,000	50	100	125	175	225	275	350	250
1881 . . . . . .(975)	24,000	50	100	125	175	225	300	350	250
1882 . . . .(1,100) . .	3,910,000	6	7	9	13	30	75	110	250
1883 . . . .(1,039) . .	7,674,673	6	7	9	13	30	75	110	250
1884 . . . . . .(875) . .	3,365,505	6	7	9	13	30	75	110	250
1884S	564,969	9	13	20	35	110	325	575	
1885 . . . . . .(930) . .	2,532,497	6	7	9	13	30	75	110	250
1885S	43,690	150	335	600	1,000	2,000	2,600	4,200	
1886 . . . . . .(886) . .	6,376,684	6	7	9	13	30	75	110	250
1886S	206,524	10	20	30	50	90	275	500	
1887 . . . . . .(710) . .	11,283,229	6	7	9	13	30	75	110	250
1887S	4,454,450	6	7	9	13	30	75	110	
1888 . . . . . .(832) . .	5,495,655	6	7	9	13	30	75	110	250
1888S	1,720,000	6	7	9	15	40	120	300	
1889 . . . . . .(711) . .	7,380,000	6	7	9	13	30	75	110	250
1889S	972,678	7	10	20	35	60	200	400	
1890 . . . . . .(590) . .	9,910,951	6	7	9	13	30	75	110	250
1890S	1,423,076	7	9	17	30	60	135	275	
1891 . . . . . .(600) . .	15,310,000	6	7	9	13	30	75	110	275
1891O	4,540,000	6	7	9	15	40	110	150	
1891S	3,196,116	6	7	9	13	35	100	125	

BARBER OR LIBERTY HEAD (1892–1916)

This type was designed by Charles E. Barber, chief engraver of the Mint. His initial B is at the truncation of the neck. He also designed the quarters and half dollars of the same period.

G-4 Good: Date and letters plain. LIBERTY obliterated.
VG-8 Very Good: Some letters visible in LIBERTY.
F-12 Fine: Letters in LIBERTY visible, though some weak.
VF-20 Very Fine: Letters of LIBERTY evenly plain.
EF-40 Extremely Fine: All letters in LIBERTY sharp, distinct. Headband edges distinct.
AU-50 About Uncirculated: Slight traces of wear on hair cheekbone and on leaf tips in wreath.
MS-60 Uncirculated: No trace of wear. Light blemishes.
MS-63 Choice Uncirculated: Some distracting blemishes in prime focal areas. Impaired luster possible.

Mintmark location is on reverse, below wreath.

	Mintage	G-4	VG-8	F-12	VF-20	EF-40	AU-50	MS-60	MS-63	PF-63
1892 . . . . . .(1,245) . .12,120,000		$2.00	$4.00	$9	$14	$16.00	$35	$80	$120	$275
1892O 3,841,700		5.00	7.00	15	24	35.00	45	100	175	
1892S 990,710		35.00	45.00	85	125	160.00	180	240	400	
1893, 3/2 . . . .*						120.00	160	350	1,000	500
1893 . . . . . .(792) . . .3,339,940		4.00	6.00	10	15	24.00	35	100	140	275
1893O 1,760,000		15.00	25.00	65	80	90.00	125	175	350	
1893S 2,491,401		7.00	14.00	18	25	40.00	75	150	375	
1894 . . . . . .(972) . . .1,330,000		8.00	20.00	55	75	90.00	100	175	350	275
1894O 720,000		30.00	45.00	100	150	210.00	360	825	1,400	
1894S 24								600,000		
1895 . . . . . .(880) 690,000		35.00	45.00	100	250	290.00	325	400	810	310
1895O 440,000		180.00	210.00	450	720	1,400.00	1,700	3,000	4,250	
1895S 1,120,000		20.00	30.00	75	100	125.00	175	300	625	
1896 . . . . . .(762) . .2,000,000		4.00	10.00	28	36	50.00	60	100	275	280
1896O 610,000		35.00	75.00	160	200	280.00	325	575	1,300	
1896S 575,056		40.00	70.00	150	200	275.00	310	500	825	
1897 . . . . . .(731) . .10,868,533		1.50	1.75	3	5	12.00	22	80	125	275
1897O 666,000		35.00	50.00	140	200	250.00	325	500	950	
1897S 1,342,844		8.00	16.00	50	75	90.00	125	250	650	
1898 . . . . . .(735) . .16,320,000		1.50	1.75	3	6	12.00	30	65	100	275
1898O 2,130,000		3.00	4.00	30	60	80.00	120	275	650	
1898S 1,702,507		2.00	5.00	16	25	40.00	75	180	600	
1899 . . . . . .(846) . .19,580,000		1.50	1.75	3	6	12.50	30	65	100	275
1899O 2,650,000		4.50	6.00	35	45	70.00	100	210	575	
1899S 1,867,493		4.00	4.50	8	16	20.00	55	160	425	
1900 . . . . . .(912) . .17,600,000		1.50	1.75	3	6	12.00	30	65	100	275

* Included in number below.

	Mintage	G-4	VG-8	F-12	VF-20	EF-40	AU-50	MS-60	MS-63	PF-63
1900O 2,010,000		$8.00	$20.00	$45	$50.00	$120	$160	$320	$500	
1900S 5,168,270		1.75	2.00	5	7.00	13	35	120	220	
1901 . . . . . .(813) . .18,859,665		1.50	1.75	3	6.00	12	32	65	100	$275
1901O 5,620,000		1.75	2.00	5	9.00	30	50	250	460	
1901S 593,022		45.00	70.00	185	250.00	300	350	635	875	
1902 . . . . . .(777) . .21,380,000		1.40	1.50	2	4.00	12	30	65	100	275
1902O 4,500,000		1.70	2.00	6	12.00	25	50	180	450	
1902S 2,070,000		3.00	6.00	18	30.00	45	70	180	450	
1903 . . . . . .(755) . .19,500,000		1.40	1.50	2	4.00	12	30	65	100	275
1903O 8,180,000		1.75	2.10	7	9.00	18	35	160	295	
1903S 613,300		40.00	60.00	200	250.00	400	500	750	1,000	
1904 . . . . . .(670) . .14,600,357		1.40	1.50	2	4.00	12	30	65	90	275
1904S 800,000		20.00	35.00	75	100.00	150	250	425	850	
1905 . . . . . .(727) . .14,551,623		1.40	1.50	2	4.00	12	30	65	90	275
1905O 3,400,000		1.75	3.00	13	25.00	50	75	150	250	
1905S 6,855,199		1.50	2.00	4	7.00	18	40	140	200	
1906 . . . . . .(675) . .19,957,731		1.40	1.50	2	5.00	12	30	65	90	275
1906D 4,060,000		1.50	2.00	4	8.00	13	32	95	200	
1906O 2,610,000		2.00	5.00	20	35.00	45	65	120	175	
1906S 3,136,640		1.50	2.00	5	10.00	16	50	125	210	
1907 . . . . . .(575) . .22,220,000		1.40	1.50	2	4.00	12	30	65	90	275
1907D 4,080,000		1.50	2.50	5	8.00	18	60	150	475	
1907O 5,058,000		1.50	3.50	15	18.00	24	45	100	185	
1907S 3,178,470		1.50	2.50	6	12.00	20	45	200	400	
1908 . . . . . .(545) . .10,600,000		1.40	1.50	2	4.00	12	30	65	90	275
1908D 7,490,000		1.40	1.50	4	6.00	14	35	70	150	
1908O 1,789,000		1.75	5.00	22	35.00	50	80	150	275	
1908S 3,220,000		1.50	3.00	6	8.00	16	75	175	350	
1909 . . . . . .(650) . .10,240,000		1.40	1.50	2	3.50	12	30	65	90	275
1909D 954,000		3.50	10.00	35	50.00	75	100	275	600	
1909O 2,287,000		1.75	3.00	6	10.00	20	60	120	275	
1909S 1,000,000		3.00	8.50	40	50.00	90	165	275	650	
1910 . . . . . .(551) . .11,520,000		1.40	1.50	2	3.50	12	30	65	90	275
1910D 3,490,000		1.75	3.00	5	6.00	18	45	125	225	
1910S 1,240,000		2.00	4.00	21	34.00	60	90	250	370	
1911 . . . . . .(543) . .18,870,000		1.50	1.75	2	3.50	12	30	65	90	275
1911D 11,209,000		1.40	1.50	2	3.50	12	30	65	90	
1911S 3,520,000		1.50	3.00	8	8.00	16	45	120	220	
1912 . . . . . .(700) . .19,349,300		1.40	1.50	2	3.50	12	30	65	90	275
1912D 11,760,000		1.40	1.50	2	3.50	12	30	65	100	
1912S 3,420,000		1.75	3.00	5	8.00	16	50	100	165	
1913 . . . . . .(622) . .19,760,000		1.40	1.50	2	3.50	12	30	65	90	275
1913S 510,000		9.00	18.00	45	80.00	125	175	260	375	
1914 . . . . . .(425) . .17,360,230		1.40	1.50	2	3.50	12	30	65	90	275
1914D 11,908,000		1.40	1.50	2	3.50	12	30	65	90	
1914S 2,100,000		1.40	2.10	6	8.00	12	30	110	190	
1915 . . . . . .(450) . . .5,620,000		1.40	1.50	2	3.50	12	30	65	90	400
1915S 960,000		2.00	3.00	15	20.00	30	65	140	275	
1916 18,490,000		1.40	1.50	2	3.50	12	30	65	90	
1916S 5,820,000		1.40	1.50	2	3.50	12	30	65	90	

WINGED LIBERTY HEAD
OR MERCURY (1916–1945)

Although this coin is commonly called the *Mercury* dime, the main device is in fact a representation of Liberty. The wings crowning her cap are intended to symbolize liberty of thought. The designer's monogram AW is at the right of the neck.

G-4 Good: Letters and date clear. Lines and bands in fasces obliterated.

VG-8 Very Good: Half of sticks discernible in fasces.

F-12 Fine: All sticks in fasces defined. Diagonal bands worn nearly flat.

VF-20 Very Fine: Diagonal bands definitely visible.

EF-40 Extremely Fine: Only slight wear on diagonal bands. Braids and hair before ear clearly visible.

AU-50 About Uncirculated: Slight trace of wear. Most mint luster present.

MS-63 Choice Uncirculated: No trace of wear. Light blemishes. Attractive mint luster.

MS-65 Gem Uncirculated: Only light, scattered marks that are not distracting. Strong luster, good eye appeal.

Mintmark location is on reverse, left of fasces.

Uncirculated values shown are for average pieces with minimum blemishes; those with sharp strikes and split bands on reverse are worth much more.

	Mintage	G-4	VG-8	F-12	VF-20	EF-40	MS-60	MS-63	MS-65
1916	22,180,080	$1.50	$2.10	$3.50	$4.25	$5.50	$18	$24	$50
1916D	264,000	500.00	800.00	1,200.00	1,600.00	2,750.00	8,000	9,000	16,000
1916S	10,450,000	3.00	4.00	5.00	6.00	10.00	20	35	125
1917	55,230,000	1.30	1.40	1.25	3.00	4.00	15	26	85
1917D	9,402,000	2.25	3.25	5.00	8.00	22.00	65	180	700
1917S	27,330,000	1.30	1.40	3.00	3.50	6.00	30	90	250
1918	26,680,000	1.30	1.40	3.00	6.00	13.00	40	90	225
1918D	22,674,800	1.30	1.40	3.00	6.00	12.00	55	120	250
1918S	19,300,000	1.30	1.40	2.00	5.00	8.50	45	150	375
1919	35,740,000	1.30	1.40	1.75	3.00	6.00	22	55	175
1919D	9,939,000	1.30	1.40	4.00	10.00	20.00	110	250	1,000
1919S	8,850,000	1.30	1.40	3.00	8.00	20.00	110	270	650
1920	59,030,000	1.30	1.40	1.50	3.50	5.00	27	35	150
1920D	19,171,000	1.30	1.40	2.00	6.00	11.00	85	220	450
1920S	13,820,000	1.30	1.40	2.00	6.00	10.00	65	175	650
1921	1,230,000	30.00	40.00	80.00	175.00	300.00	650	900	1,700
1921D	1,080,000	35.00	70.00	100.00	200.00	400.00	675	1,000	1,750
1923	50,130,000	1.30	1.40	1.75	3.00	4.00	15	25	65
1923S	6,440,000	1.30	1.40	4.00	8.00	32.00	80	220	600
1924	24,010,000	1.30	1.40	1.75	3.00	7.00	23	60	120
1924D	6,810,000	1.30	1.40	3.50	8.00	26.00	95	280	600
1924S	7,120,000	1.30	1.40	3.00	5.00	24.00	90	290	625
1925	25,610,000	1.30	1.40	1.75	3.00	4.50	28	45	125
1925D	5,117,000	2.50	3.25	6.00	22.00	60.00	180	425	950
1925S	5,850,000	1.30	1.40	3.00	7.00	30.00	90	275	800
1926	32,160,000	1.30	1.40	1.50	3.00	4.50	25	35	130
1926D	6,828,000	1.30	1.40	3.00	6.00	17.00	60	150	350
1926S	1,520,000	3.50	6.25	12.00	32.00	140.00	600	850	1,800
1927	28,080,000	1.30	1.40	1.75	3.00	4.00	13	32	80
1927D	4,812,000	1.30	1.40	3.00	12.00	35.00	110	225	725

	Mintage	G-4	VG-8	F-12	VF-20	EF-40	MS-60	MS-63	MS-65
1927S	.4,770,000	$1.30	$1.40	$2.00	$4.00	$15.00	$120	$275	$800
1928	.19,480,000	1.30	1.40	1.75	3.00	4.50	25	30	70
1928D	.4,161,000	1.30	1.40	4.00	10.00	24.00	85	180	475
1928S	.7,400,000	1.30	1.40	1.75	2.50	8.00	35	160	265
1929	.25,970,000	1.30	1.40	1.75	2.25	3.00	13	20	40
1929D	.5,034,000	1.30	1.40	1.75	4.00	8.00	17	22	40
1929S	.4,730,000	1.30	1.40	1.75	2.50	5.00	18	25	60
1930	.6,770,000	1.30	1.40	1.75	2.50	4.00	15	25	60
1930S	.1,843,000	1.30	1.40	3.00	3.80	8.00	30	65	110
1931	.3,150,000	1.30	1.40	1.75	3.00	5.00	20	40	80
1931D	.1,260,000	4.00	5.00	7.00	11.00	18.00	48	75	140
1931S	.1,800,000	2.00	2.50	3.00	5.00	8.50	38	75	150

	Mintage	VG-8	F-12	VF-20	EF-40	MS-60	MS-63	MS-65	PF-63
1934	.24,080,000	$1.30	$1.30	$1.40	$1.40	$10.00	$15	$25	
1934D	.6,772,000	1.30	1.30	1.40	1.40	20.00	30	45	
1935	.58,830,000	1.30	1.30	1.40	1.40	6.50	9	18	
1935D	.10,477,000	1.30	1.30	1.40	1.40	20.00	25	50	
1935S	.15,840,000	1.30	1.30	1.40	1.40	12.00	16	25	
1936	.(4,130) ..87,500,000	1.30	1.30	1.40	1.40	5.00	12	16	$1,200
1936D	.16,132,000	1.30	1.30	1.40	1.40	14.00	20	30	
1936S	.9,210,000	1.30	1.30	1.40	1.40	12.00	15	18	
1937	.(5,756) ..56,860,000	1.30	1.30	1.40	1.40	4.00	9	15	425
1937D	.14,146,000	1.30	1.30	1.40	1.40	14.00	16	24	
1937S	.9,740,000	1.30	1.30	1.40	1.40	12.00	15	22	
1938	.(8,728) ..22,190,000	1.30	1.30	1.40	1.40	7.00	9	15	250
1938D	.5,537,000	1.30	1.30	1.40	1.40	9.00	10	16	
1938S	.8,090,000	1.30	1.30	1.40	1.40	8.00	9	15	
1939	.(9,321) ..67,740,000	1.30	1.30	1.40	1.40	4.50	8	12	225
1939D	.24,394,000	1.30	1.30	1.40	1.40	4.50	8	14	
1939S	.10,540,000	1.30	1.30	1.40	1.40	12.00	15	25	
1940	.(11,827) ..65,350,000	1.30	1.30	1.40	1.40	4.50	7	15	210
1940D	.21,198,000	1.30	1.30	1.40	1.40	4.50	9	16	
1940S	.21,560,000	1.30	1.30	1.40	1.40	4.50	8	16	
1941	.(16,557) 175,090,000	1.30	1.30	1.40	1.40	4.50	7	15	200
1941D	.45,634,000	1.30	1.30	1.40	1.40	4.50	9	16	
1941S	.43,090,000	1.30	1.30	1.40	1.40	4.50	8	16	
1942, 2 Over 1	.............*	275.00	375.00	400.00	500.00	1,200.00	2,200	8,500	
1942	.(22,329) 205,410,000	1.30	1.30	1.40	1.40	4.50	7	15	200
1942D, 2 Over 1	.............*	275.00	375.00	400.00	500.00	1,200.00	2,400	4,500	
1942D	.60,740,000	1.30	1.30	1.40	1.40	5.50	9	16	
1942S	.49,300,000	1.30	1.30	1.40	1.40	6.50	9	16	
1943	.191,710,000	1.30	1.30	1.40	1.40	4.50	6	15	
1943D	.71,949,000	1.30	1.30	1.40	1.40	5.50	7	16	
1943S	.60,400,000	1.30	1.30	1.40	1.40	5.50	7	15	
1944	.231,410,000	1.30	1.30	1.40	1.40	4.50	6	15	
1944D	.62,224,000	1.30	1.30	1.40	1.40	4.50	6	15	
1944S	.49,490,000	1.30	1.30	1.40	1.40	4.50	6	15	
1945	.159,130,000	1.30	1.30	1.40	1.40	4.50	6	15	
1945D	.40,245,000	1.30	1.30	1.40	1.40	4.50	6	16	
1945S	.41,920,000	1.30	1.30	1.40	1.40	4.50	7	16	
1945S, Micro S	.............*	1.30	1.30	1.40	1.50	9.00	15	45	

*Included in regular mintage.

ROOSEVELT (1946 TO DATE)

John R. Sinnock (whose initials JS are at the truncation of the neck) designed this dime showing a portrait of Franklin D. Roosevelt. The design has heavier lettering and a more modernistic character than preceding types.

VF-20 Very Fine: Moderate wear on high points of design. All major details are clear.
EF-40 Extremely Fine: All lines of torch, flame, and hair very plain.
MS-63 Choice Uncirculated: Some distracting contact marks or blemishes in prime focal areas. Impaired luster possible.
MS-65 Gem Uncirculated: Only light, non-distracting scattered marks. Strong luster, good eye appeal.
PF-65 Gem Proof: Nearly perfect.

Mintmark on reverse
(1946–1964).

Mintmark on obverse
starting 1968.

Silver Coinage (1946–1964)

	Mintage	VF-20	EF-40	MS-63	MS-65	PF-65
1946	255,250,000	$1.20	$1.20	$1.50	$6.00	
1946D	61,043,500	1.20	1.20	1.50	7.00	
1946S	27,900,000	1.20	1.20	2.25	10.00	
1947	121,520,000	1.20	1.20	3.00	6.00	
1947D	46,835,000	1.20	1.20	3.25	6.00	
1947S	34,840,000	1.20	1.20	3.00	6.00	
1948	74,950,000	1.20	1.20	2.00	6.00	
1948D	52,841,000	1.20	1.20	3.00	6.00	
1948S	35,520,000	1.20	1.20	2.75	6.00	
1949	30,940,000	1.20	1.20	12.50	16.00	
1949D	26,034,000	1.20	1.20	5.00	9.00	
1949S	13,510,000	1.20	1.20	20.00	25.00	
1950	(51,386) 50,130,114	1.20	1.20	6.00	7.00	$25
1950D	46,803,000	1.20	1.20	3.00	6.00	
1950S	20,440,000	1.20	1.20	18.00	22.00	
1951	(57,500) 103,880,102	1.20	1.20	1.50	5.00	25
1951D	56,529,000	1.20	1.20	1.50	5.00	
1951S	31,630,000	1.20	1.20	6.00	10.00	
1952	(81,980) 99,040,093	1.20	1.20	1.50	5.00	16
1952D	122,100,000	1.20	1.20	1.50	3.00	
1952S	44,419,500	1.20	1.20	4.00	6.00	
1953	(128,800) 53,490,120	1.20	1.20	1.50	4.00	16
1953D	136,433,000	1.20	1.20	1.50	4.00	
1953S	39,180,000	1.20	1.20	1.50	4.00	
1954	(233,300) 114,010,203	1.20	1.20	1.50	4.00	10
1954D	106,397,000	1.20	1.20	1.50	4.00	
1954S	22,860,000	1.20	1.20	1.50	4.00	
1955	(378,200) 12,450,181	1.20	1.20	1.50	5.00	8
1955D	13,959,000	1.20	1.20	1.50	4.00	
1955S	18,510,000	1.20	1.20	1.50	4.00	
1956	(669,384) 108,640,000	1.20	1.20	1.50	4.00	2
1956D	108,015,100	1.20	1.20	1.50	3.50	
1957	(1,247,952) 160,160,000	1.20	1.20	1.50	3.50	2

	Mintage	VF-20	EF-40	MS-63	MS-65	PF-65
1957D	113,354,330	$1.20	$1.20	$1.50	$3.25	
1958	(875,652) 31,910,000	1.20	1.20	1.50	4.00	$2
1958D	136,564,600	1.20	1.20	1.50	4.00	
1959	(1,149,291) 85,780,000	1.20	1.20	1.50	3.50	2
1959D	164,919,790	1.20	1.20	1.50	3.50	
1960	(1,691,602) 70,390,000	1.20	1.20	1.50	3.50	2
1960D	200,160,400	1.20	1.20	1.50	3.00	
1961	(3,028,244) 93,730,000	1.20	1.20	1.50	3.00	2
1961D	209,146,550	1.20	1.20	1.50	3.00	
1962	(3,218,019) 72,450,000	1.20	1.20	1.50	3.00	2
1962D	334,948,380	1.20	1.20	1.50	3.00	
1963	(3,075,645) ...123,650,000	1.20	1.20	1.50	3.00	2
1963D	421,476,530	1.20	1.20	1.50	3.00	
1964	(3,950,762) ...929,360,000	1.20	1.20	1.50	3.00	2
1964D	1,357,517,180	1.20	1.20	1.50	3.00	

Clad Coinage and Silver Proofs (1965 to Date)

	Mintage	MS-63	MS-65	PF-65		Mintage	MS-63	MS-65	PF-65
1965	1,652,140,570	$0.15	$0.75		1977S	(3,251,152)			$0.50
1966	1,382,734,540	0.15	0.65		1978	663,980,000		$0.15	
1967	2,244,007,320	0.15	0.50		1978D	282,847,540		0.15	
1968	424,470,400	0.15	0.50		1978S	(3,127,781)			0.40
1968D	480,748,280	0.15	0.50		1979	315,440,000	$0.15	0.25	
1968S	(3,041,506)			$0.50	1979D	390,921,184	0.15	0.25	
1969	145,790,000	0.25	0.50		1979S, Filled S	(3,677,175)			0.50
1969D	563,323,870	0.15	0.20		1979S, Clear S	..........*			1.40
1969S	(2,394,631)			0.50	1980P	735,170,000	0.15	0.25	
1970	345,570,000	0.15	0.25		1980D	719,354,321	0.15	0.25	
1970D	754,942,100	0.15	0.25		1980S	(3,554,806)			0.40
1970S	(2,632,810)			0.50	1981P	676,650,000	0.15	0.25	
1971	162,690,000	0.18	0.30		1981D	712,284,143	0.15	0.25	
1971D	377,914,240	0.16	0.20		1981S	(4,063,083)			0.40
1971S	(3,220,733)			0.50	1982, No Mmk		85.00	115.00	
1972	431,540,000	0.15	0.25		1982P	519,475,000	1.50	2.00	
1972D	330,290,000	0.15	0.25		1982D	542,713,584	0.60	1.10	
1972S	(3,260,996)			0.50	1982S	(3,857,479)			0.60
1973	315,670,000	0.15	0.25		1983P	647,025,000	1.25	1.50	
1973D	455,032,426	0.15	0.25		1983D	730,129,224	0.35	0.60	
1973S	(2,760,339)			0.50	1983S	(3,279,126)			0.50
1974	470,248,000	0.15	0.25		1984P	856,669,000	0.15	0.25	
1974D	571,083,000	0.15	0.25		1984D	704,803,976	0.20	0.35	
1974S	(2,612,568)			0.50	1984S	(3,065,110)			0.65
1975	585,673,900	0.15	0.25		1985P	705,200,962	0.15	0.25	
1975D	313,705,300	0.15	0.25		1985D	587,979,970	0.15	0.25	
1975S	(2,845,450)			0.70	1985S	(3,362,821)			0.50
1976	568,760,000	1.50	0.25		1986P	682,649,693	0.25	0.35	
1976D	695,222,774		0.15		1986D	473,326,970	0.25	0.35	
1976S	(4,149,730)			0.70	1986S	(3,010,497)			1.00
1977	796,930,000	0.15	0.25		1987P	762,709,481	0.15	0.35	
1977D	376,607,228	0.15	0.25		1987D	653,203,402	0.15	0.35	

* Included in number above.

Chart continued on next page.

	Mintage	MS-63	MS-65	PF-65
1987S	. . . .(4,227,728)			$0.60
1988P	1,030,550,000	$0.12	$0.20	
1988D	962,385,489	0.12	0.20	
1988S	. . . .(3,262,948)			1.00
1989P	1,298,400,000	0.10	0.20	
1989D	896,535,597	0.10	0.20	
1989S	. . . . (3,220,194)			1.00
1990P	1,034,340,000	0.10	0.20	
1990D	839,995,824	0.10	0.20	
1990S	. . . .(3,299,559)			0.75
1991P	927,220,000	0.10	0.20	
1991D	601,241,114	0.12	0.20	
1991S	. . . .(2,867,787)			1.20
1992P	593,500,000	0.10	0.15	
1992D	616,273,932	0.10	0.15	
1992S	. . . .(2,858,981)			2.00
1992S, Silver	. . .(1,317,579)			3.00
1993P	766,180,000	0.10	0.15	
1993D	750,110,166	0.10	0.15	
1993S	. . . .(2,633,439)			2.00
1993S, Silver	. . . .(761,353)			2.50
1994P	1,189,000,000	0.10	0.15	
1994D	1,303,268,110	0.10	0.15	
1994S	. . . .(2,484,594)			2.00
1994S, Silver	. . . .(785,329)			2.75
1995P	1,125,500,000	0.10	0.20	
1995D	1,274,890,000	0.15	0.25	
1995S	. . . .(2,117,496)			4.00
1995S, Silver	. . . .(679,985)			6.50
1996P	1,421,163,000	0.10	0.20	
1996D	1,400,300,000	0.10	0.20	
1996W	1,457,000	6.00	10.00	
1996S	. . . .(1,750,244)			2.00
1996S, Silver	. . . .(775,021)			3.00
1997P	991,640,000	0.10	0.15	
1997D	979,810,000	0.10	0.15	
1997S	. . . .(2,055,000)			3.00
1997S, Silver	. . . .(741,678)			10.00
1998P	1,163,000,000	0.10	0.15	
1998D	1,172,250,000	0.10	0.15	
1998S	. . . .(2,086,507)			2.00
1998S, Silver	. . . .(878,792)			3.00
1999P	2,164,000,000	0.10	0.15	
1999D	1,397,750,000	$0.10	$0.15	
1999S	. . . .(2,543,401)			$1.00
1999S, Silver	. . . .(804,565)			3.50
2000P	1,842,500,000	0.10	0.15	
2000D	1,818,700,000	0.10	0.15	
2000S	. . . .(3,082,572)			1.00
2000S, Silver	. . . .(965,421)			2.00
2001P	1,369,590,000	0.10	0.15	
2001D	1,412,800,000	0.10	0.15	
2001S	. . . .(2,294,909)			0.50
2001S, Silver	. . . .(889,697)			2.00
2002P	1,187,500,000	0.10	0.15	
2002D	1,379,500,000	0.10	0.15	
2002S	. . . .(2,319,766)			0.75
2002S, Silver	. . . .(892,229)			2.00
2003P	1,085,500,000	0.10	0.15	
2003D	986,500,000	0.10	0.15	
2003S	. . . .(2,172,684)			0.60
2003S, Silver	. . .(1,125,755)			1.50
2004P	1,328,000,000	0.10	0.15	
2004D	1,159,500,000	0.10	0.15	
2004S	. . . .(1,789,488)			0.60
2004S, Silver	. . .(1,175,934)			1.50
2005P	1,412,000,000	0.10	0.15	
2005D	1,423,500,000	0.10	0.15	
2005S	. . . .(2,275,000)			0.60
2005S, Silver	. . .(1,069,679)			1.70
2006P	1,381,000,000	0.10	0.15	
2006D	1,447,000,000	0.10	0.15	
2006S	. . . .(2,000,428)			0.60
2006S, Silver	. . .(1,054,008)			1.70
2007P	1,047,500,000	0.10	0.15	
2007D	1,042,000,000	0.10	0.15	
2007S	. . . .(1,384,797)			0.50
2007S, Silver	. . . .(875,050)			1.50
2008P	391,000,000	0.10	0.15	
2008D	624,500,000	0.10	0.15	
2008S	. . . .(1,377,424)			0.50
2008S, Silver	. . . .(620,664)			1.50
2009P	. . . .	0.10	0.15	
2009D	. . . .	0.10	0.15	
2009S	. . . .			0.50
2009S, Silver	. . . .			1.50

* Included in number above.

LIBERTY SEATED (1875–1878)

The twenty-cent piece was a short-lived coin authorized by the Act of March 3, 1875. The edge of the coin is plain. Most of the 1876-CC coins were melted at the Mint and never released. The mintmark is on the reverse below the eagle.

G-4 Good: LIBERTY on shield obliterated. Letters and date legible.

VG-8 Very Good: One or two letters in LIBERTY barely visible. Other details bold.

F-12 Fine: Some letters of LIBERTY possibly visible.

VF-20 Very Fine: LIBERTY readable, but partly weak.

EF-40 Extremely Fine: LIBERTY mostly sharp. Only slight wear on high points of coin.

AU-50 About Uncirculated: Slight trace of wear on breast, head, and knees.

MS-60 Uncirculated: No trace of wear. Light blemishes.

MS-63 Choice Uncirculated: Some distracting blemishes in prime focal areas. Some impairment of luster possible.

PF-63 Choice Proof: Reflective surfaces with only a few blemishes in secondary focal places. No major flaws.

		G-4	VG-8	F-12	VF-20	EF-40	AU-50	MS-60	MS-63	PF-63
1875 . . . .(2,790) 36,910		$75	$90	$110	$175	$225	$250	$425	$725	$1,250
1875CC 133,290		150	175	250	275	375	425	775	1,600	
1875S 1,155,000		52	57	65	85	125	155	275	600	
1876 . . . .(1,260) 14,640		90	125	150	200	250	300	450	750	1,350
1876CC 10,000								80,000		
1877 . . . .(350)					1,000	1,200				2,200
1878 . . . .(600)					900	1,000				1,800

Authorized in 1792, this denomination was not issued until four years later. The first type weighed 104 grains, the standard until modified to 103-1/8 grains by the Act of January 18, 1837. As with the dime and half dime, the weight was reduced and arrows placed at the date in 1853. Rays were placed in the field of the reverse during that year only.

DRAPED BUST (1796–1807)

AG-3 About Good: Details clear enough to identify.
G-4 Good: Date readable. Bust outlined, but no detail.
VG-8 Very Good: All but deepest drapery folds worn smooth. Hairlines nearly gone and curls lacking in detail.
F-12 Fine: All drapery lines visible. Hair partly worn.
VF-20 Very Fine: Only left side of drapery indistinct.
EF-40 Extremely Fine: Hair well outlined and detailed.
AU-50 About Uncirculated: Slight trace of wear on shoulder and highest waves of hair.
MS-60 Uncirculated: No trace of wear. Light blemishes.
MS-63 Choice Uncirculated: Some distracting marks or blemishes in focal areas. Impaired luster possible.

Small Eagle Reverse (1796)

	Mintage	AG-3	G-4	VG-8	F-12	VF-20	EF-40	AU-50	MS-60	MS-63
1796	6,146	$2,750	$5,000	$6,750	$14,000	$18,000	$25,000	$30,000	$42,000	$65,000

Heraldic Eagle Reverse (1804–1807)

	Mintage	AG-3	G-4	VG-8	F-12	VF-20	EF-40	AU-50	MS-60	MS-63
1804	6,738	$775	$1,500	$2,000	$3,000	$5,000	$9,500	$18,000	$25,000	$55,000
1805	121,394	55	110	140	210	425	950	1,700	3,000	5,750
1806, 6 Over 5	*	60	120	150	300	500	1,100	1,800	3,500	8,750
1806	206,124	55	110	140	210	425	900	1,700	3,000	5,500
1807	220,643	55	110	140	210	425	900	1,700	3,000	5,500

* Included in number below.

CAPPED BUST (1815–1838)
Variety 1 – Large Diameter (1815–1828)

AG-3 About Good: Details clear enough to identify.
G-4 Good: Date, letters, stars legible. Hair under Liberty's headband smooth. Cap lines worn smooth.
VG-8 Very Good: Rim well defined. Main details visible. Full LIBERTY on cap. Hair above eye nearly smooth.
F-12 Fine: All hair lines visible, but only partial detail visible in drapery. Shoulder clasp distinct.
VF-20 Very Fine: All details visible, but some wear evident. Clasp and ear sharp.
EF-40 Extremely Fine: All details distinct. Hair well outlined.
AU-50 About Uncirculated: Slight trace of wear on tips of curls and above the eye, and on the wing and claw tips.
MS-60 Uncirculated: No trace of wear. Light blemishes.
MS-63 Choice Uncirculated: Some distracting marks or blemishes in focal areas. Impaired luster possible.

	Mintage	AG-3	G-4	VG-8	F-12	VF-20	EF-40	AU-50	MS-60	MS-63
1815	89,235	$15	$40	$45	$65	$175	$500	$650	$1,300	$2,300
1818, 8 Over 5	*	15	40	45	65	175	475	650	1,500	2,500
1818, Normal Date	361,174	15	40	45	65	160	475	650	1,200	2,300
1819	144,000	15	40	45	65	160	475	650	1,200	2,300
1820	127,444	15	40	45	65	160	475	650	1,200	2,300
1821	216,851	15	40	45	65	160	475	650	1,200	2,300
1822	64,080	15	40	45	50	80	175	490	700	1,400	2,800
1822, 25 Over 50c	*	300	700	1,400	2,400	3,250	5,500	10,000	17,500	
1823, 3 Over 2	17,800	6,500	14,000	17,500	22,000	25,000	35,000	65,000	—	
1824, 4 Over 2	**	25	45	65	160	300	800	2,000	4,750	
1825	168,000	15	40	45	65	160	475	650	1,300	2,300
1827, Original (Curl Base 2 in 25c)	4,000								100,000	
1827, Restrike (Square Base 2 in 25c)	*								40,000	
1828	102,000	15	40	45	60	150	425	700	1,300	2,600
1828, 25 Over 50c	*	30	60	110	225	475	850	1,600	4,000	

* Included in regular mintage. ** Included in 1825 mintage.

Variety 2 – Reduced Diameter, Motto Removed (1831–1838)

G-4 Good: Bust of Liberty well defined. Hair under headband smooth. Date, letters, stars legible. Scant rims.
VG-8 Very Good: Details apparent but worn on high spots. Rims strong. Full LIBERTY.
F-12 Fine: All hair lines visible. Drapery partly worn. Shoulder clasp distinct.
VF-20 Very Fine: Only top spots worn. Clasp sharp. Ear distinct.
EF-40 Extremely Fine: Hair details and clasp bold and clear.

AU-50 About Uncirculated: Slight trace of wear on hair around forehead, on cheek, and at top and bottom tips of eagle's wings and left claw.
MS-60 Uncirculated: No trace of wear. Light blemishes.
MS-63 Choice Uncirculated: Some distracting contact marks or blemishes in prime focal areas. Impaired luster possible.

	Mintage	G-4	VG-8	F-12	VF-20	EF-40	AU-50	MS-60	MS-63
1831	398,000	$32	$40	$45	$65	$150	$275	$485	$1,600
1832	320,000	32	40	45	65	150	275	485	1,600
1833	156,000	32	40	50	70	185	300	650	2,000
1834	286,000	32	40	45	65	150	275	485	1,600
1835	1,952,000	32	40	45	65	150	275	485	1,600
1836	472,000	32	40	45	65	150	275	485	1,600
1837	252,400	32	40	45	65	150	275	485	1,600
1838	366,000	32	40	45	65	150	275	485	1,600

LIBERTY SEATED (1838–1891)

G-4 Good: Scant rim. LIBERTY on shield worn off. Date and letters legible.
VG-8 Very Good: Rim fairly defined, at least three letters in LIBERTY evident.
F-12 Fine: LIBERTY complete, but partly weak.
VF-20 Very Fine: LIBERTY strong.
EF-40 Extremely Fine: Complete LIBERTY and edges of scroll. Clasp clear.
AU-50 About Uncirculated: Slight wear on Liberty's knees and breast and on eagle's neck, wing tips, and claws.
MS-60 Uncirculated: No trace of wear. Light blemishes.
MS-63 Choice Uncirculated: Some distracting marks or blemishes in focal areas. Impaired luster possible.

Variety 1 – No Motto Above Eagle (1838–1853)

Small Date

Large Date

Mintmark location is on reverse, below eagle.

	Mintage	G-4	VG-8	F-12	VF-20	EF-40	AU-50	MS-60	MS-63
1838	466,000	$10	$13	$20	$36	$110	$220	$625	$1,750
1839	491,146	10	13	20	35	110	220	625	1,750
1840	188,127	9	12	21	32	70	110	400	1,100
1840O	425,200	11	15	27	45	125	225	650	2,000
1841	120,000	18	30	45	65	110	125	425	850
1841O	452,000	10	12	19	32	80	120	350	700
1842, Small Date (Proof only)									28,000
1842, Large Date	88,000	30	40	75	130	175	250	750	1,500
1842O, Small Date	*	150	250	475	775	1,500	3,500	7,500	
1842O, Large Date	769,000	10	11	17	31	70	125	650	1,800
1843	645,600	9	10	16	22	40	60	225	600
1843O	968,000	10	13	20	45	100	275	900	2,200
1844	421,200	9	10	16	22	40	60	225	600
1844O	740,000	10	11	18	32	80	120	550	1,400
1845	922,000	9	10	16	22	40	60	225	625
1846	510,000	9	10	16	22	40	60	225	600
1847	734,000	9	10	16	22	40	60	225	600
1847O	368,000	12	17	27	50	110	275	900	2,500
1848	146,000	11	17	28	50	80	125	450	1,100
1849	340,000	10	12	20	27	70	100	400	700
1849O	(a)	175	260	450	950	1,600	2,400	6,000	—
1850	190,800	13	17	25	35	65	100	400	750
1850O	412,000	13	17	25	35	65	180	550	1,100
1851	160,000	15	20	28	50	85	100	400	725
1851O	88,000	65	100	200	300	650	1,100	2,900	
1852	177,060	16	21	30	55	90	110	375	650
1852O	96,000	80	120	175	300	600	1,500	3,500	9,000
1853, Recut Date, No Arrows or Rays	44,200	110	140	175	275	500	750	1,300	2,000

* Included in number below. **a.** Mintage for 1849-O included with 1850-O.

Variety 2 – Arrows at Date, Rays Around Eagle (1853)

1853, 3 Over 4

QUARTER DOLLARS

	Mintage	G-4	VG-8	F-12	VF-20	EF-40	AU-50	MS-60	MS-63
1853 15,210,020		$9	$12	$15	$20	$65	$125	$450	$975
1853, 3 Over 4 . . . .*		20	35	55	110	160	250	900	2,250
1853O 1,332,000		9	12	17	30	115	450	1,300	4,000

* Included in number above.

Variety 3 – Arrows at Date, No Rays (1854–1855)

	Mintage	G-4	VG-8	F-12	VF-20	EF-40	AU-50	MS-60	MS-63
1854 12,380,000		$9	$11	$14	$18	$35	$100	$250	$600
1854O 1,484,000		9	11	16	20	40	110	325	850
1855 2,857,000		9	11	14	18	35	100	275	650
1855O 176,000		17	25	45	110	150	340	1,200	3,500
1855S 396,400		17	25	35	60	125	300	850	2,000

Variety 1 Resumed (1856–1865; Weight Standard of 1853)

	Mintage	G-4	VG-8	F-12	VF-20	EF-40	AU-50	MS-60	MS-63	PF-63
1856 7,264,000		$9	$11	$14	$19	$27	$60	$170	$300	$2,600
1856O 968,000		9	11	14	21	40	100	500	825	
1856S 286,000		15	20	35	80	160	300	1,000	3,750	
1857 9,644,000		9	11	14	19	26	60	150	300	1,800
1857O 1,180,000		9	11	14	19	37	110	500	1,200	
1857S 82,000		25	40	70	150	250	400	1,200	3,250	
1858 . . . . . .(300+) . . .7,368,000		9	11	14	19	26	60	150	300	1,000
1858O 520,000		9	11	14	25	50	150	650	1,750	
1858S 121,000		19	32	50	100	200	650	4,000	—	
1859 . . . .(800) . . .1,343,200		9	11	14	19	26	60	150	425	625
1859O 260,000		9	14	20	26	50	150	500	1,600	
1859S 80,000		35	55	90	160	700	4,400	—	—	
1860 . . . . . .(1,000) . . .804,400		9	11	14	19	26	60	175	300	550
1860O 388,000		9	11	14	20	32	150	450	850	
1860S 56,000		90	150	200	500	2,000	6,000	—	—	
1861 . . . . . .(1,000) . . .4,853,600		9	11	14	19	26	60	175	350	550
1861S 96,000		25	50	100	190	500	3,500	—	—	
1862 . . . .(550) 932,000		9	11	14	19	26	60	175	350	550
1862S 67,000		20	32	80	110	250	450	1,200	3,500	
1863 . . . .(460) 191,600		14	18	30	45	70	120	300	425	550
1864 . . . .(470) 93,600		30	35	45	70	110	180	300	600	550
1864S 20,000		110	160	300	425	900	1,800	—	—	
1865 . . . .(500) 58,800		25	30	45	70	110	180	350	600	550
1865S 41,000		30	40	60	140	225	450	1,200	1,900	

Variety 4 – Motto Above Eagle (1866–1873)

	Mintage	G-4	VG-8	F-12	VF-20	EF-40	AU-50	MS-60	MS-63	PF-63
1866 . . . .(725) 16,800		$150	$200	$225	$350	$550	$700	$850	$1,200	$425
1866S 28,000		75	110	200	350	500	900	1,600	2,500	

Chart continued on next page.

	Mintage	G-4	VG-8	F-12	VF-20	EF-40	AU-50	MS-60	MS-63	PF-63
1867 . . . .(625) 20,000		$80	$100	$175	$210	$260	$350	$500	$1,100	$425
1867S 48,000		85	120	170	250	500	1,000	3,500	—	
1868 . . . .(600) 29,400		40	60	80	100	125	210	400	700	425
1868S 96,000		30	40	50	90	200	350	1,100	2,800	
1869 . . . .(600) 16,000		90	110	170	200	275	400	600	1,100	425
1869S 76,000		30	45	80	125	225	450	1,000	2,000	
1870 . . . .(1,000) 86,400		20	25	40	60	90	175	400	500	425
1870CC 8,340		1,100	2,500	3,600	6,500	12,000	20,000	—		
1871 . . . .(960) . . .118,200		11	16	22	40	60	125	225	425	400
1871CC 10,890		700	1,300	2,000	6,000	10,000	18,000	—		
1871S 30,900		100	150	200	320	450	900	1,300	2,000	
1872 . . . .(950) . . .182,000		11	16	22	40	60	100	300	700	400
1872CC 22,850		200	350	600	1,100	2,500	4,500	16,000		
1872S 83,000		235	450	600	800	1,200	2,000	3,500		
1873 . . . .(650) . . .212,600		11	16	22	35	50	90	200	425	400
1873CC 4,000					—		—			

Variety 5 – Arrows at Date (1873–1874)

	Mintage	G-4	VG-8	F-12	VF-20	EF-40	AU-50	MS-60	MS-63	PF-63
1873 . . . .(540) . .1,271,160		$10	$11	$16	$35	$90	$175	$425	$700	$800
1873CC 12,462		700	1,200	1,800	4,000	8,250	12,000	25,000	40,000	
1873S 156,000		11	14	23	45	110	200	600	1,000	
1874 . . . .(700) . . .471,200		10	11	16	35	90	175	450	750	800
1874S 392,000		11	13	20	45	110	175	450	750	

Variety 4 Resumed (1875–1891)

1877-S, S Over Horizontal S

	Mintage	G-4	VG-8	F-12	VF-20	EF-40	AU-50	MS-60	MS-63	PF-63
1875 . . . .(700) . . .4,292,800		$9	$11	$14	$18	$25	$60	$125	$200	$350
1875CC 140,000		25	35	65	125	200	300	700	1,100	
1875S 680,000		10	16	23	35	70	125	275	500	
1876 . . . . . .(1,150) . .17,816,000		9	11	14	19	25	60	125	200	350
1876CC 4,944,000		11	16	18	23	35	75	200	400	
1876S 8,596,000		9	11	14	18	25	60	125	200	
1877 . . . .(510) . .10,911,200		9	11	14	18	25	60	125	200	350
1877CC 4,192,000		10	16	18	23	35	75	200	350	
1877S 8,996,000		9	11	14	19	25	60	125	200	

	Mintage	G-4	VG-8	F-12	VF-20	EF-40	AU-50	MS-60	MS-63	PF-63
1877S, S Over Horizontal S ......*		$11	$16	$35	$50	$90	$125	$300	$500	
1878 ....(800) ..2,260,000		9	11	14	19	25	60	125	200	$350
1878CC 996,000		11	16	20	30	55	95	250	400	
1878S 140,000		45	80	100	125	200	425	700	1,250	
1879 ....(1,100) 13,600		40	50	75	80	100	135	200	375	350
1880 ....(1,355) 13,600		40	50	75	80	100	135	200	375	350
1881 ....(975) 12,000		50	65	85	100	120	190	225	400	400
1882 ....(1,100) 15,200		45	50	80	100	110	150	275	375	350
1883 ....(1,039) 14,400		45	50	80	100	110	150	275	375	350
1884 ....(875) 8,000		90	100	120	125	150	200	350	450	350
1885 ....(930) 13,600		40	50	75	100	110	200	300	400	350
1886 ....(886) 5,000		95	110	150	175	275	375	475	500	400
1887 ....(710) 10,000		80	90	100	125	175	200	300	400	350
1888 ....(832) 10,001		70	80	90	135	200	225	300	375	350
1888S 1,216,000		9	11	14	18	25	65	150	275	
1889 ....(711) 12,000		50	60	90	110	120	200	300	400	350
1890 ....(590) 80,000		20	25	35	50	80	125	275	375	350
1891 ....(600) ..3,920,000		8	9	11	15	22	65	150	250	350
1891O 6,800		50	65	110	325	475	525	1,600	2,200	
1891S 2,216,000		9	11	14	18	25	65	150	250	

* Included in 1877S regular mintage (previous page).

BARBER OR LIBERTY HEAD (1892–1916)

Like other silver coins of this type, the quarter dollars minted from 1892 to 1916 were designed by Charles E. Barber. His initial B is found at the truncation of the neck of Miss Liberty.

G-4 Good: Date and legends legible. LIBERTY worn off headband.
VG-8 Very Good: Some letters in LIBERTY legible.
F-12 Fine: LIBERTY completely legible but not sharp.
VF-20 Very Fine: All letters in LIBERTY evenly plain.
EF-40 Extremely Fine: LIBERTY bold, its ribbon distinct.
AU-50 About Uncirculated: Slight trace of wear above forehead, on cheek, and on eagle's head, wings, and tail.
MS-60 Uncirculated: No trace of wear. Light blemishes.
MS-63 Choice Uncirculated: Some distracting marks or blemishes in focal areas. Impaired luster possible.

PF-63 Choice Proof: Reflective surfaces with only a few blemishes in secondary focal places. No major flaws.

	Mintage	G-4	VG-8	F-12	VF-20	EF-40	AU-50	MS-60	MS-63	PF-63
1892 ......(1,245) ...8,236,000		$3.60	$3.75	$9	$13	$27	$50	$115	$125	$300
1892O 2,460,000		4.00	5.00	11	18	35	60	150	200	
1892S 964,079		10.00	18.00	30	40	70	130	200	425	
1893 ....(792) ...5,444,023		3.60	3.75	9	13	30	50	115	165	300
1893O 3,396,000		3.60	4.00	10	14	35	60	160	220	
1893S 1,454,535		6.00	10.00	20	40	70	130	200	500	
1894 ....(972) ...3,432,000		3.60	3.75	10	15	30	60	110	200	300
1894O 2,852,000		3.60	3.75	10	20	35	90	160	300	
1894S 2,648,821		3.60	3.75	11	20	35	90	160	300	
1895 ....(880) ...4,440,000		3.60	3.75	10	14	30	60	110	200	300
1895O 2,816,000		3.75	5.00	15	27	45	90	185	400	
1895S 1,764,681		5.00	8.50	25	50	65	120	225	450	
1896 ....(762) ...3,874,000		3.60	3.75	9	14	32	60	125	200	300
1896O 1,484,000		10.00	18.00	50	110	150	275	450	750	

Chart continued on next page.

	Mintage	G-4	VG-8	F-12	VF-20	EF-40	AU-50	MS-60	MS-63	PF-63
1896S	188,039	$300.00	$500.00	$825.00	$1,350	$2,000	$2,700	$3,350	$7,500	
1897	. . . .(731) . . .8,140,000	3.60	3.75	9.00	13	28	50	90	125	$300
1897O	1,414,800	5.00	12.00	40.00	100	130	275	425	750	
1897S	542,229	15.00	22.00	90.00	120	130	275	425	750	
1898	. . . .(735) . .11,100,000	3.60	3.75	9.00	13	30	50	90	125	300
1898O	1,868,000	5.00	9.00	22.00	55	110	150	300	650	
1898S	1,020,592	4.00	7.00	15.00	20	35	90	200	600	
1899	. . . .(846) . .12,624,000	3.60	3.75	9.00	13	26	50	90	125	300
1899O	2,644,000	4.00	5.00	9.00	16	32	100	200	400	
1899S	708,000	5.00	12.00	18.00	35	45	125	225	550	
1900	. . . .(912) . .10,016,000	3.60	3.75	9.00	13	25	60	90	125	300
1900O	3,416,000	4.00	9.00	20.00	30	50	150	250	400	
1900S	1,858,585	3.60	4.00	11.00	16	30	50	175	450	
1901	. . . .(813) . . .8,892,000	3.60	4.00	8.00	14	30	60	100	120	300
1901O	1,612,000	18.00	25.00	55.00	100	175	250	400	900	
1901S	72,664	2,800.00	4,250.00	6,500.00	8,500	12,000	14,000	18,500	25,000	
1902	. . . .(777) . .12,196,967	3.60	3.75	8.00	14	30	50	90	125	300
1902O	4,748,000	3.60	4.00	12.00	25	50	90	200	600	
1902S	1,524,612	4.50	7.00	18.00	30	60	100	220	475	
1903	. . . .(755) . . .9,759,309	3.60	3.75	8.00	14	30	50	90	175	300
1903O	3,500,000	3.60	4.00	11.00	20	32	100	150	600	
1903S	1,036,000	4.00	6.00	14.00	25	45	100	210	400	
1904	. . . .(670) . . .9,588,143	3.60	3.75	8.00	14	25	50	90	125	300
1904O	2,456,000	3.60	4.00	16.00	30	90	175	350	600	
1905	. . . .(727) . . .4,967,523	3.60	3.75	8.50	14	30	50	90	150	300
1905O	1,230,000	4.00	10.00	35.00	60	110	160	200	550	
1905S	1,884,000	3.60	4.25	16.00	22	42	90	175	500	
1906	. . . .(675) . . .3,655,760	3.60	3.75	8.00	14	25	50	90	125	300
1906D	3,280,000	3.60	3.75	9.00	15	26	60	110	200	
1906O	2,056,000	3.60	3.75	12.00	17	30	90	135	250	
1907	. . . .(575) . . .7,132,000	3.60	3.75	8.00	14	25	50	90	125	300
1907D	2,484,000	3.60	3.75	9.00	15	26	60	125	350	
1907O	4,560,000	3.60	3.75	8.00	14	25	55	100	250	
1907S	1,360,000	4.00	5.00	16.00	22	50	100	200	400	
1908	. . . .(545) . . .4,232,000	3.60	3.75	8.00	14	25	50	90	125	300
1908D	5,788,000	3.60	3.75	8.00	14	25	50	110	200	
1908O	6,244,000	3.60	3.75	8.00	14	25	50	100	125	
1908S	784,000	6.00	13.00	35.00	60	150	200	350	550	
1909	. . . .(650) . . .9,268,000	3.60	3.75	8.00	14	25	50	90	125	300
1909D	5,114,000	3.60	3.75	8.00	14	25	60	110	160	
1909O	712,000	6.00	13.00	30.00	70	125	225	400	850	
1909S	1,348,000	3.60	3.75	10.00	16	30	90	150	350	
1910	. . . .(551) . . .2,244,000	3.60	3.75	8.00	14	25	60	90	150	300
1910D	1,500,000	3.60	3.75	15.00	18	35	110	175	400	
1911	. . . .(543) . . .3,720,000	3.60	3.75	8.00	14	25	50	90	125	300
1911D	933,600	3.60	3.75	30.00	90	130	225	325	600	
1911S	988,000	3.60	3.75	18.00	30	60	120	175	350	
1912	. . . .(700) . . .4,400,000	3.60	3.75	8.00	14	25	50	90	125	300
1912S	708,000	3.60	4.50	15.00	18	35	100	175	400	
1913	. . . .(613) 484,000	6.00	9.00	25.00	67	185	210	550	600	375
1913D	1,450,800	3.60	4.00	11.00	17	35	75	140	185	
1913S	40,000	650.00	900.00	2,000.00	2,750	3,100	3,800	4,750	6,000	

	Mintage	G-4	VG-8	F-12	VF-20	EF-40	AU-50	MS-60	MS-63	PF-63
1914 . . . .(380) . . .6,244,230		$3.60	$3.75	$8.00	$14	$25	$50	$90	$125	$375
1914D 3,046,000		3.60	3.75	8.00	14	25	50	90	125	
1914S 264,000		30.00	40.00	85.00	125	200	300	450	675	
1915 . . . .(450) . . .3,480,000		3.60	3.75	8.00	14	25	50	90	125	375
1915D 3,694,000		3.60	3.75	8.00	14	25	50	90	125	
1915S 704,000		3.60	3.75	9.00	15	32	90	125	200	
1916 1,788,000		3.60	3.75	8.00	14	25	50	90	125	
1916D 6,540,800		3.60	3.75	8.00	14	25	50	90	125	

STANDING LIBERTY (1916–1930)

This design is by Hermon A. MacNeil, whose initial M is above and to the right of the date. Liberty bears a shield of protection in her left arm, while the right hand holds the olive branch of peace. There was a modification in 1917. The reverse had a new arrangement of stars and the eagle was higher. After 1924 the date was "recessed," thereby giving it greater protection from the effects of circulation.

G-4 Good: Date and lettering legible. Top of date worn. Liberty's right leg and toes worn off. Much wear evident on left leg and drapery lines.

VG-8 Very Good: Distinct date. Toes faintly visible. Drapery lines visible above Liberty's left leg.

F-12 Fine: High curve of right leg flat from thigh to ankle. Only slight wear evident on left leg. Drapery lines over right thigh seen only at sides of leg.

VF-20 Very Fine: Garment line across right leg worn, but visible at sides.

EF-40 Extremely Fine: Flattened only at high spots. Liberty's toes are sharp. Drapery lines across right leg evident.

AU-50 About Uncirculated: Slight trace of wear on head, kneecap, shield's center, and highest point on eagle's body.

MS-60 Uncirculated: No trace of wear, but contact marks, surface spots, or faded luster possible.

MS-63 Choice Uncirculated: No trace of wear. Light blemishes. Attractive mint luster.

Variety 1 – No Stars Below Eagle (1916–1917)

Mintmark location is on obverse, to left of date.

	Mintage	G-4	VG-8	F-12	VF-20	EF-40	AU-50	MS-60	MS-63
1916 52,000		$1,800	$2,500	$4,200	$6,000	$7,500	$8,000	$10,000	$12,500
1917, Variety 1 8,740,000		13	18	26	32	50	100	140	180
1917D, Variety 1 1,509,200		15	19	27	35	60	110	150	200
1917S, Variety 1 1,952,000		16	22	28	40	75	125	170	250

Variety 2 – Stars Below Eagle (1917–1930)
Pedestal Date (1917–1924)

See next page for chart.

1918-S, 8 Over 7

	Mintage	G-4	VG-8	F-12	VF-20	EF-40	AU-50	MS-60	MS-63
1917, Variety 2	13,880,000	$11	$13	$16	$18	$27	$55	$100	$140
1917D, Variety 2	6,224,400	18	22	32	40	60	85	125	175
1917S, Variety 2	5,552,000	18	22	32	40	65	90	125	175
1918	14,240,000	8	9	15	17	25	50	100	145
1918D	7,380,000	13	16	26	34	50	85	125	200
1918S, Normal Date	11,072,000	9	11	17	20	30	50	120	175
1918S, 8 Over 7	*	825	1,000	1,650	2,500	3,500	7,000	10,000	21,000
1919	11,324,000	18	22	27	35	40	60	100	125
1919D	1,944,000	50	70	100	150	225	300	375	800
1919S	1,836,000	50	70	100	150	275	325	400	900
1920	27,860,000	8	10	15	20	25	40	100	125
1920D	3,586,400	25	30	40	45	65	100	125	450
1920S	6,380,000	9	12	16	20	30	50	110	400
1921	1,916,000	85	110	160	200	275	425	600	850
1923	9,716,000	8	10	15	17	20	40	100	150
1923S	1,360,000	150	200	240	400	500	700	975	1,700
1924	10,920,000	8	10	12	15	20	50	100	150
1924D	3,112,000	25	35	50	65	100	125	150	175
1924S	2,860,000	12	15	20	25	60	125	170	500

* Included in number above.

Recessed Date (1925–1930)

	Mintage	G-4	VG-8	F-12	VF-20	EF-40	AU-50	MS-60	MS-63
1925	12,280,000	$3.30	$3.60	$4	$6	$16	$35	$70	$140
1926	11,316,000	3.30	3.60	4	6	16	35	70	140
1926D	1,716,000	3.50	4.00	8	16	26	50	100	170
1926S	2,700,000	3.40	3.60	6	11	50	125	200	400
1927	11,912,000	3.30	3.60	4	6	16	35	70	140
1927D	976,000	6.00	8.00	13	30	65	90	160	200
1927S	396,000	15.00	21.00	45	175	640	1,600	2,500	4,200
1928	6,336,000	3.30	3.60	4	6	16	35	70	135
1928D	1,627,600	3.40	3.60	4	6	16	35	70	135
1928S	2,644,000	3.40	3.60	4	6	16	35	70	140
1929	11,140,000	3.30	3.60	4	6	16	35	70	140
1929D	1,358,000	3.40	3.60	4	6	16	35	70	140
1929S	1,764,000	3.30	3.60	4	6	16	35	70	140
1930	5,632,000	3.30	3.60	4	6	16	35	70	135
1930S	1,556,000	3.30	3.60	4	6	16	35	70	135

WASHINGTON (1932 TO DATE)

This type was intended to be a commemorative issue marking the 200th anniversary of Washington's birth. John Flanagan, a New York sculptor, was the designer. The initials JF are found at the base of the neck. The mintmark is on the reverse below the wreath for coins from 1932 to 1964. Starting in 1968, the mintmark was moved to the obverse at the right of the ribbon.

F-12 Fine: Hair lines about Washington's ear visible. Tiny feathers on eagle's breast faintly visible.
VF-20 Very Fine: Most hair details visible. Wing feathers clear.
EF-40 Extremely Fine: Hair lines sharp. Wear spots confined to top of eagle's legs and center of breast.
MS-60 Uncirculated: No trace of wear, but many contact marks, surface spotting, or faded luster possible.
MS-63 Choice Uncirculated: No trace of wear. Light blemishes. Attractive mint luster.
MS-64 Uncirculated: A few scattered contact marks. Good eye appeal and attractive luster.
MS-65 Gem Uncirculated: Only light, scattered, non-distracting marks. Strong luster, good eye appeal.
PF-65 Gem Proof: Hardly any blemishes, and no flaws.

Silver Coinage (1932–1964)

	Mintage	VG-8	F-12	VF-20	EF-40	MS-60	MS-63	MS-65	PF-65
1932	5,404,000	$3.50	$3.50	$3.50	$4.00	$13	$23	$200	
1932D	436,800	75.00	90.00	120.00	175.00	525	1,750	12,000	
1932S	408,000	75.00	90.00	100.00	130.00	275	700	3,750	
1934	31,912,052	3.00	3.00	3.00	3.50	9	17	45	
1934D	3,527,200	3.00	3.00	3.50	10.00	100	175	650	
1935	32,484,000	3.00	3.00	3.00	3.50	9	15	45	
1935D	5,780,000	3.00	3.00	3.25	8.00	100	140	400	
1935S	5,660,000	3.00	3.00	3.00	5.00	40	60	140	
1936 ....(3,837)	41,300,000	3.00	3.00	3.00	3.50	8	16	40	$850
1936D	5,374,000	3.00	3.00	3.00	18.00	180	350	725	
1936S	3,828,000	3.00	3.00	3.00	4.00	40	75	200	
1937 ....(5,542)	19,696,000	3.00	3.00	3.00	3.50	8	15	48	325
1937D	7,189,600	3.00	3.00	3.00	4.00	25	45	70	
1937S	1,652,000	3.00	3.00	3.50	10.00	70	100	150	
1938 ....(8,045)	9,472,000	3.00	3.00	3.00	4.00	30	50	120	200
1938S	2,832,000	3.00	3.00	3.00	4.50	35	60	125	
1939 ....(8,795)	33,540,000	3.00	3.00	3.00	3.50	5	12	25	175
1939D	7,092,000	3.00	3.00	3.00	3.50	14	20	50	
1939S	2,628,000	3.00	3.00	3.00	5.00	45	65	150	

	Mintage	F-12	VF-20	EF-40	MS-60	MS-63	MS-65	PF-65
1940 ....(11,246)	35,704,000	$3.00	$3.00	$3.00	$5.00	$12	$30	$150
1940D	2,797,600	3.00	3.25	7.50	50.00	80	140	
1940S	8,244,000	3.00	3.00	3.00	7.00	13	25	
1941 ....(15,287)	79,032,000	3.00	3.00	3.00	3.50	6	20	100
1941D	16,714,800	3.00	3.00	3.50	12.00	22	25	
1941S	16,080,000	3.00	3.00	3.00	7.50	18	25	
1942 ....(21,123)	102,096,000	3.00	3.00	3.00	3.25	4	10	100
1942D	17,487,200	3.00	3.00	3.00	6.00	12	20	
1942S	19,384,000	3.00	3.00	4.00	27.00	45	90	
1943	99,700,000	3.00	3.00	3.00	3.50	4	20	
1943D	16,095,600	3.00	3.00	3.00	8.00	16	20	
1943S	21,700,000	3.00	3.00	3.00	8.00	19	25	
1944	104,956,000	3.00	3.00	3.00	3.25	4	18	
1944D	14,600,800	3.00	3.00	3.00	4.00	10	18	
1944S	12,560,000	3.00	3.00	3.00	5.00	12	18	
1945	74,372,000	3.00	3.00	3.00	3.25	4	18	
1945D	12,341,600	3.00	3.00	3.00	6.00	12	20	
1945S	17,004,001	3.00	3.00	3.00	3.75	5	15	
1946	53,436,000	3.00	3.00	3.00	3.25	4	16	
1946D	9,072,800	3.00	3.00	3.00	3.50	4	15	
1946S	4,204,000	3.00	3.00	3.00	3.50	4	16	
1947	22,556,000	3.00	3.00	3.00	3.50	5	15	

Chart continued on next page.

	Mintage	F-12	VF-20	EF-40	MS-60	MS-63	MS-65	PF-65
1947D	.15,338,400	$3.00	$3.00	$3.00	$3.50	$4.00	$15.00	
1947S	.5,532,000	3.00	3.00	3.00	3.50	4.00	15.00	
1948	.35,196,000	3.00	3.00	3.00	3.50	4.00	15.00	
1948D	.16,766,800	3.00	3.00	3.00	3.50	5.00	30.00	
1948S	.15,960,000	3.00	3.00	3.00	3.50	5.00	18.00	
1949	.9,312,000	3.00	3.00	3.75	10.00	18.00	30.00	
1949D	.10,068,400	3.00	3.00	3.25	6.00	11.00	22.00	
1950	.(51,386)...24,920,126	3.00	3.00	3.00	3.50	5.00	13.00	$30.00
1950D	.21,075,600	3.00	3.00	3.00	3.50	5.00	13.00	
1950D, D Over S	.*		25.00	75.00	125.00	175.00	500.00	
1950S	.10,284,004	3.00	3.00	3.25	5.00	6.00	25.00	
1950S, S Over D	.*		25.00	80.00	140.00	200.00	400.00	
1951	.(57,500)...43,448,102	3.00	3.00	3.00	3.50	4.00	14.00	27.50
1951D	.35,354,800	3.00	3.00	3.00	3.50	4.00	14.00	
1951S	.9,048,000	3.00	3.00	3.25	5.00	12.00	18.00	
1952	.(81,980)...38,780,093	3.00	3.00	3.00	3.50	4.00	11.00	25.00
1952D	.49,795,200	3.00	3.00	3.00	3.50	4.00	16.00	
1952S	.13,707,800	3.00	3.00	3.25	5.00	10.00	16.00	
1953	.(128,800)...18,536,120	3.00	3.00	3.00	3.50	4.00	16.00	22.00
1953D	.56,112,400	3.00	3.00	3.00	3.50	4.00	15.00	
1953S	.14,016,000	3.00	3.00	3.00	3.50	4.00	12.00	
1954	.(233,300)...54,412,203	3.00	3.00	3.00	3.50	4.00	13.00	12.00
1954D	.42,305,500	3.00	3.00	3.00	3.50	3.75	17.00	
1954S	.11,834,722	3.00	3.00	3.00	3.50	3.75	15.00	
1955	.(378,200)...18,180,181	3.00	3.00	3.00	3.50	3.75	12.00	12.00
1955D	.3,182,400	3.00	3.00	3.00	3.50	3.85	20.00	
1956	.(669,384)...44,144,000	3.00	3.00	3.00	3.50	3.75	8.00	4.00
1956D	.32,334,500	3.00	3.00	3.00	3.50	3.75	10.00	
1957	.(1,247,952)...46,532,000	3.00	3.00	3.00	3.50	3.75	10.00	4.00
1957D	.77,924,160	3.00	3.00	3.00	3.50	3.75	10.00	
1958	.(875,652)...6,360,000	3.00	3.00	3.00	3.50	3.75	9.00	4.00
1958D	.78,124,900	3.00	3.00	3.00	3.50	3.75	9.00	
1959	.(1,149,291)...24,384,000	3.00	3.00	3.00	3.50	3.75	9.00	4.00
1959D	.62,054,232	3.00	3.00	3.00	3.50	3.75	12.00	
1960	.(1,691,602)...29,164,000	3.00	3.00	3.00	3.50	3.75	6.50	4.00
1960D	.63,000,324	3.00	3.00	3.00	3.50	3.75	6.50	
1961	.(3,028,244)...37,036,000	3.00	3.00	3.00	3.50	3.75	6.50	4.00
1961D	.83,656,928	3.00	3.00	3.00	3.50	3.75	6.50	
1962	.(3,218,019)...36,156,000	3.00	3.00	3.00	3.50	3.75	6.50	4.00
1962D	.127,554,756	3.00	3.00	3.00	3.50	3.75	6.50	
1963	.(3,075,645)...74,316,000	3.00	3.00	3.00	3.50	3.75	6.50	4.00
1963D	.135,288,184	3.00	3.00	3.00	3.50	3.75	6.50	
1964	.(3,950,762)..560,390,585	3.00	3.00	3.00	3.50	3.75	6.50	4.00
1964D	.704,135,528	3.00	3.00	3.00	3.50	3.75	6.50	

* Included in number above.

Clad Coinage and Silver Proofs (1965 to Date)

	Mintage	MS-63	MS-65	PF-65		Mintage	MS-63	MS-65	PF-65
1965	.1,819,717,540	$0.30	$2.00		1968D	.101,534,000	$0.30	$1.00	
1966	.821,101,500	0.30	1.00		1968S	.(3,041,506)			$1
1967	.1,524,031,848	0.30	1.00		1969	.176,212,000	0.75	1.50	
1968	.220,731,500	0.50	1.50		1969D	.114,372,000	0.50	1.50	

	Mintage	MS-63	MS-65	PF-65
1969S	(2,934,631)			$1
1970	136,420,000	$0.25	$1.75	
1970D	417,341,364	0.25	1.00	
1970S	(2,632,810)			1
1971	109,284,000	0.30	1.00	
1971D	258,634,428	0.30	0.50	
1971S	(3,220,733)			1
1972	215,048,000	0.30	1.00	

	Mintage	MS-63	MS-65	PF-65
1972D	311,067,732	$0.30	$1.50	
1972S	(3,260,996)			$1
1973	346,924,000	0.30	1.50	
1973D	232,977,400	0.30	2.00	
1973S	(2,760,339)			1
1974	801,456,000	0.30	1.00	
1974D	353,160,300	0.30	1.50	
1974S	(2,612,568)			1

Bicentennial Coinage Dated 1776–1976

	Mintage	MS-63	MS-65	PF-65
1776–1976, Copper-Nickel Clad	809,784,016	$0.30	$1	
1776–1976D, Copper-Nickel Clad	860,118,839	0.30	1	
1776–1976S, Copper-Nickel Clad	(7,059,099)			$1
1776–1976S, Silver Clad	7,000,000	1.40	2	
1776–1976S, Silver Clad	(4,000,000)			2

Note: Mintage figures for 1976-S coins are approximate; many were melted in 1982.

Eagle Reverse Resumed (1977–1998)
(Dies Slightly Modified to Lower Relief)

	Mintage	MS-63	MS-65	PF-65
1977	468,556,000	$0.27		
1977D	256,524,978	0.27	$1.00	
1977S	(3,251,152)			$1
1978	521,452,000	0.27	1.50	
1978D	287,373,152	0.27	1.50	
1978S	(3,127,781)			1
1979	515,708,000	0.28	1.50	
1979D	489,789,780	0.27	1.25	
1979S	(3,677,175)			
Filled S				1
Clear S				1
1980P	635,832,000	0.27	1.50	
1980D	518,327,487	0.27	1.25	
1980S	(3,554,806)			1
1981P	601,716,000	0.27	1.50	
1981D	575,722,833	0.27	1.00	
1981S	(4,063,083)			1
1982P	500,931,000	1.00	8.00	
1982D	480,042,788	0.70	6.00	
1982S	(3,857,479)			1
1983P	673,535,000	4.00	20.00	
1983D	617,806,446	3.00	14.00	
1983S	(3,279,126)			1

	Mintage	MS-63	MS-65	PF-65
1984P	676,545,000	$0.30	$2.00	
1984D	546,483,064	0.50	2.00	
1984S	(3,065,110)			$1.00
1985P	775,818,962	0.50	6.00	
1985D	519,962,888	0.35	2.50	
1985S	(3,362,821)			1.00
1986P	551,199,333	1.00	4.00	
1986D	504,298,660	1.50	9.00	
1986S	(3,010,497)			1.00
1987P	582,499,481	0.27	2.50	
1987D	655,594,696	0.27	1.00	
1987S	(4,227,728)			1.00
1988P	562,052,000	0.50	5.00	
1988D	596,810,688	0.27	4.00	
1988S	(3,262,948)			1.00
1989P	512,868,000	0.30	4.25	
1989D	896,535,597	0.27	1.00	
1989S	(3,220,194)			1.00
1990P	613,792,000	0.27	4.00	
1990D	927,638,181	0.28	4.00	
1990S	(3,299,559)			1.75
1991P	570,968,000	0.30	4.00	
1991D	630,966,693	0.30	1.50	

Chart continued on next page.

Mintage	MS-63	MS-65	PF-65
1991S . . . .(2,867,787)			$1.25
1992P 384,764,000	$0.35	$4.25	
1992D 389,777,107	0.35	4.25	
1992S . . . .(2,858,981)			1.25
1992S, Silver . . .(1,317,579)			3.50
1993P 639,276,000	0.30	1.75	
1993D 645,476,128	0.30	1.75	
1993S . . . .(2,633,439)			1.25
1993S, Silver . . . .(761,353)			3.50
1994P 825,600,000	0.30	4.00	
1994D 880,034,110	0.30	4.00	
1994S . . . .(2,484,594)			1.00
1994S, Silver . . . .(785,329)			4.00
1995P 1,004,336,000	0.30	4.00	
1995D 1,103,216,000	0.30	2.50	

Mintage	MS-63	MS-65	PF-65
1995S . . . .(2,117,496)			$4.00
1995S, Silver . . . .(679,985)			4.00
1996P 925,040,000	$0.25	$2.00	
1996D 906,868,000	0.25	2.00	
1996S . . . .(1,750,244)			1.75
1996S, Silver . . . .(775,021)			4.00
1997P 595,740,000	0.25	1.25	
1997D 599,680,000	0.25	1.25	
1997S . . . .(2,055,000)			3.00
1997S, Silver . . . .(741,678)			3.50
1998P 896,268,000	0.25	1.00	
1998D 821,000,000	0.25	1.00	
1998S . . . .(2,086,507)			2.50
1998S, Silver . . .(878,792)			3.50

State Quarters (1999–2008)

The United States Mint 50 State Quarters® Program, which began in 1999, produced a series of 50 quarter dollar coins with special designs honoring each state. Five different designs were issued each year during the period 1999 to 2008. States were commemorated in the order of their entrance into statehood.

These are all legal tender coins of standard weight and composition. The obverse side depicting President George Washington was modified to include some of the wording previously used on the reverse. The modification was authorized by special legislation, and carried out by Mint Sculptor-Engraver William Cousins, whose initials were added to the truncation of Washington's neck adjacent to those of the original designer, John Flanagan.

Each state theme was proposed and approved by the governor of the state. Final designs were created by Mint personnel.

Circulation coins are made at the Philadelphia and Denver mints. Proof coins are made in San Francisco. Both copper-nickel and silver Proof coins were made each year.

Mintage	AU-50	MS-63	PF-65
Delaware			
1999P 373,400,000	$0.25	$0.50	
1999D 401,424,000	0.25	0.50	
1999S . . . . . .(3,713,359)			$1.75
1999S, Silver . .(804,565)			7.00
Pennsylvania			
1999P 349,000,000	0.25	0.50	
1999D 358,332,000	0.25	0.50	
1999S . . . . . .(3,713,359)			1.75
1999S, Silver . .(804,565)			6.00

Mintage	AU-50	MS-63	PF-65
New Jersey			
1999P 363,200,000	$0.25	$0.30	
1999D 299,028,000	0.25	0.35	
1999S . . . . . .(3,713,359)			$1.75
1999S, Silver . .(804,565)			6.00
Georgia			
1999P 451,188,000	0.25	0.30	
1999D 488,744,000	0.25	0.30	
1999S . . . . . .(3,713,359)			1.75
1999S, Silver . .(804,565)			6.00

	Mintage	AU-50	MS-63	PF-65
Connecticut				
1999P 688,744,000		0.25	0.30	
1999D 657,880,000		0.25	0.30	

	Mintage	AU-50	MS-63	PF-65
Connecticut				
1999S . . . . . .(3,713,359)				1.75
1999S, Silver . .(804,565)				7.00

	Mintage	AU-50	MS-63	PF-65
Massachusetts				
2000P 628,600,000		$0.25	$0.30	
2000D 535,184,000		0.25	0.30	
2000S . . . . . .(4,020,172)				$1.50
2000S, Silver . .(965,421)				3.50
Maryland				
2000P 678,200,000		0.25	0.30	
2000D 556,532,000		0.25	0.30	
2000S . . . . . .(4,020,172)				1.50
2000S, Silver . .(965,421)				3.50
South Carolina				
2000P 742,576,000		0.25	0.32	
2000D 566,208,000		0.25	0.32	

	Mintage	AU-50	MS-63	PF-65
South Carolina				
2000S . . . . . .(4,020,172)				$1.50
2000S, Silver . .(965,421)				3.50
New Hampshire				
2000P 673,040,000		$0.25	$0.30	
2000D 495,976,000		0.25	0.30	
2000S . . . . . .(4,020,172)				1.50
2000S, Silver . .(965,421)				3.50
Virginia				
2000P 943,000,000		0.25	0.30	
2000D 651,616,000		0.25	0.30	
2000S . . . . . .(4,020,172)				1.50
2000S, Silver . .(965,421)				3.50

	Mintage	AU-50	MS-63	PF-65
New York				
2001P 655,400,000		$0.25	$0.30	
2001D 619,640,000		0.25	0.30	
2001S . . . . . .(3,094,140)				$1.50
2001S, Silver . .(889,697)				3.50
North Carolina				
2001P 627,600,000		0.25	0.30	
2001D 427,876,000		0.25	0.30	
2001S . . . . . .(3,094,140)				1.50
2001S, Silver . .(889,697)				3.50
Rhode Island				
2001P 423,000,000		0.25	0.30	
2001D 447,100,000		0.25	0.30	

	Mintage	AU-50	MS-63	PF-65
Rhode Island				
2001S . . . . . .(3,094,140)				$1.50
2001S, Silver . .(889,697)				3.50
Vermont				
2001P 423,400,000		$0.25	$0.30	
2001D 459,404,000		0.25	0.30	
2001S . . . . . .(3,094,140)				1.50
2001S, Silver . .(889,697)				3.50
Kentucky				
2001P 353,000,000		0.25	0.30	
2001D 370,564,000		0.25	0.30	
2001S . . . . . .(3,094,140)				1.50
2001S, Silver . .(889,697)				3.50

	Mintage	AU-50	MS-63	PF-65
Tennessee				
2002P 361,600,000	$0.30	$0.40	
2002D 286,468,000	0.30	0.40	
2002S . . . . . .(3,084,245)			$1.50
2002S, Silver . .(892,229)			3.50
Ohio				
2002P 217,200,000	0.25	0.30	
2002D 414,832,000	0.25	0.30	
2002S . . . . . .(3,084,245)			1.50
2002S, Silver . .(892,229)			3.50
Louisiana				
2002P 362,000,000	0.25	0.30	
2002D 402,204,000	0.25	0.30	

	Mintage	AU-50	MS-63	PF-65
Louisiana				
2002S . . . . . .(3,084,245)			$1.50
2002S, Silver . .(892,229)			3.50
Indiana				
2002P 362,600,000	$0.25	$0.30	
2002D 327,200,000	0.25	0.30	
2002S . . . . . .(3,084,245)			1.50
2002S, Silver . .(892,229)			3.50
Mississippi				
2002P 290,000,000	0.25	0.30	
2002D 289,600,000	0.25	0.30	
2002S . . . . . .(3,084,245)			1.50
2002S, Silver . .(892,229)			3.50

	Mintage	AU-50	MS-63	PF-65
Illinois				
2003P 225,800,000	$0.25	$0.30	
2003D 237,400,000	0.25	0.30	
2003S . . . .(3,408,516)			$1.50
2003S, Silver . .(1,125,755)			3.50
Alabama				
2003P 225,000,000	0.25	0.30	
2003D 232,400,000	0.25	0.30	
2003S . . . .(3,408,516)			1.50
2003S, Silver . .(1,125,755)			3.50
Maine				
2003P 217,400,000	0.25	0.30	
2003D 231,400,000	0.25	0.30	

	Mintage	AU-50	MS-63	PF-65
Maine				
2003S . . . .(3,408,516)			$1.50
2003S, Silver . .(1,125,755)			3.50
Missouri				
2003P 225,000,000	$0.25	$0.30	
2003D 228,200,000	0.25	0.30	
2003S . . . .(3,408,516)			1.50
2003S, Silver . .(1,125,755)			3.50
Arkansas				
2003P 228,000,000	0.25	0.30	
2003D 229,800,000	0.25	0.30	
2003S . . . .(3,408,516)			1.50
2003S, Silver . .(1,125,755)			3.50

QUARTER DOLLARS

	Mintage	AU-50	MS-63	PF-65
Michigan				
2004P 233,800,000	$0.25	$0.30	
2004D 225,800,000	0.25	0.30	
2004S . . . . . .(2,740,684)			$1.50
2004S, Silver . .(1,769,786)			3.50
Florida				
2004P 240,200,000	0.25	0.30	
2004D 241,600,000	0.25	0.30	
2004S . . . . . .(2,740,684)			1.50
2004S, Silver . .(1,769,786)			3.50
Texas				
2004P 278,800,000	0.25	0.30	
2004D 263,000,000	0.25	0.30	

	Mintage	AU-50	MS-63	PF-65
Texas				
2004S . . . . . .(2,740,684)			$1.50
2004S, Silver . .(1,769,786)			3.50
Iowa				
2004P 213,800,000	$0.25	$0.30	
2004D 251,400,000	0.25	0.30	
2004S . . . . . .(2,740,684)			1.50
2004S, Silver . .(1,769,786)			3.50
Wisconsin				
2004P 226,400,000	0.25	0.30	
2004D 226,800,000	0.25	0.30	
2004S . . . . . .(2,740,684)			1.50
2004S, Silver . .(1,769,786)			3.50

	Mintage	AU-50	MS-63	PF-65
California				
2005P 257,200,000	$0.25	$0.30	
2005D 263,200,000	0.25	0.30	
2005S . . . . . .(3,262,960)			$1.50
2005S, Silver . .(1,678,649)			3.50
Minnesota				
2005P 239,600,000	0.25	0.30	
2005D 248,400,000	0.25	0.30	
2005S . . . . . .(3,262,960)			1.50
2005S, Silver . .(1,678,649)			3.50
Oregon				
2005P 316,200,000	0.25	0.30	
2005D 404,000,000	0.25	0.30	

	Mintage	AU-50	MS-63	PF-65
Oregon				
2005S . . . . . .(3,262,960)			$1.50
2005S, Silver . .(1,678,649)			3.50
Kansas				
2005P 263,400,000	$0.25	$0.30	
2005D 300,000,000	0.25	0.30	
2005S . . . . . .(3,262,960)			1.50
2005S, Silver . .(1,678,649)			3.50
West Virginia				
2005P 365,400,000	0.25	0.30	
2005D 356,200,000	0.25	0.30	
2005S . . . . . .(3,262,960)			1.50
2005S, Silver . .(1,678,649)			3.50

	Mintage	AU-50	MS-63	PF-65
Nevada				
2006P 277,000,000		$0.25	$0.30	
2006D 312,800,000		0.25	0.30	
2006S . . . . . .(2,882,428)				$1.50
2006S, Silver . .(1,585,008)				3.50
Nebraska				
2006P 318,000,000		0.25	0.30	
2006D 273,000,000		0.25	0.30	
2006S . . . . . .(2,882,428)				1.50
2006S, Silver . .(1,585,008)				3.50
Colorado				
2006P 274,800,000		0.25	0.30	
2006D 294,200,000		0.25	0.30	

	Mintage	AU-50	MS-63	PF-65
Colorado				
2006S . . . . . .(2,882,428)				$1.50
2006S, Silver . .(1,585,008)				3.50
North Dakota				
2006P 305,800,000		$0.25	$0.30	
2006D 359,000,000		0.25	0.30	
2006S . . . . . .(2,882,428)				1.50
2006S, Silver . .(1,585,008)				3.50
South Dakota				
2006P 245,000,000		0.25	0.30	
2006D 265,800,000		0.25	0.30	
2006S . . . . . .(2,882,428)				1.50
2006S, Silver . .(1,585,008)				3.50

	Mintage	AU-50	MS-63	PF-65
Montana				
2007P *257,000,000*		$0.25	$0.30	
2007D *256,240,000*		0.25	0.30	
2007S . . . . . .*(2,002,812)*				$1.50
2007S, Silver . .*(1,094,993)*				3.50
Washington				
2007P *265,200,000*		0.25	0.30	
2007D *280,000,000*		0.25	0.30	
2007S . . . . . .*(2,002,812)*				1.50
2007S, Silver . .*(1,094,993)*				3.50
Idaho				
2007P *294,600,000*		0.25	0.30	
2007D *286,800,000*		0.25	0.30	

	Mintage	AU-50	MS-63	PF-65
Idaho				
2007S . . . . . .*(2,002,812)*				$1.50
2007S, Silver . .*(1,094,993)*				3.50
Wyoming				
2007P *243,600,000*		$0.25	$0.30	
2007D *320,800,000*		0.25	0.30	
2007S . . . . . .*(2,002,812)*				1.50
2007S, Silver . .*(1,094,993)*				3.50
Utah				
2007P		0.25	0.30	
2007D		0.25	0.30	
2007S . . . . . .*(2,002,812)*				1.50
2007S, Silver . .*(1,094,993)*				3.50

QUARTER DOLLARS

	Mintage	AU-50	MS-63	PF-65
Oklahoma				
2008P	$0.25	$0.30		
2008D	0.25	0.30		
2008S			$1.50	
2008S, Silver			3.50	
New Mexico				
2008P	0.25	0.30		
2008D	0.25	0.30		
2008S			1.50	
2008S, Silver			3.50	
Arizona				
2008P	0.25	0.30		
2008D	0.25	0.30		

	Mintage	AU-50	MS-63	PF-65
Arizona				
2008S				$1.50
2008S, Silver				3.50
Alaska				
2008P	$0.25	$0.30		
2008D	0.25	0.30		
2008S				1.50
2008S, Silver				3.50
Hawaii				
2008P	0.25	0.30		
2008D	0.25	0.30		
2008S				1.50
2008S, Silver				3.50

Some statehood quarters were accidentally made with "dis-oriented" dies and are valued higher than ordinary pieces. Normal United States coins have dies oriented in "coin alignment," such that the reverse appears upside down when the coin is rotated from right to left. Values for the rotated-die quarters vary according to the amount of shifting. The most valuable are those that are shifted 180 degrees, so that both sides appear upright when the coin is turned over (called *medal alignment*).

Manufacturing varieties showing die doubling or other minor, unintentional characteristics are of interest to collectors and are often worth premium prices.

District of Columbia and U.S. Territories Quarters (2009)

At the ending of the U.S. Mint 50 State Quarters® Program a new series of quarter-dollar reverse designs was authorized to recognize the District of Columbia and the five U.S. territories: the Commonwealth of Puerto Rico, Guam, American Samoa, the U.S. Virgin Islands, and the Commonwealth of the Northern Mariana Islands. Each of these coins, issued sequentially during 2009, has the same portrait of George Washington as in the past, and is made of the same weight and composition. Each coin commemorates the history, geography, or traditions of the place it represents.

See next page for chart.

	Mintage	AU-50	MS-63	PF-65
District of Columbia				
2009P		$0.25	$0.30	
2009D		0.25	0.30	
2009S				$1.50
2009S, Silver				3.50
Puerto Rico				
2009P		0.25	0.30	
2009D		0.25	0.30	
2009S				1.50
2009S, Silver				3.50
Guam				
2009P		0.25	0.30	
2009D		0.25	0.30	
2009S				1.50
2009S, Silver				3.50

	Mintage	AU-50	MS-63	PF-65
American Samoa				
2009P		$0.25	$0.30	
2009D		0.25	0.30	
2009S				$1.50
2009S, Silver				3.50
U.S. Virgin Islands				
2009P		0.25	0.30	
2009D		0.25	0.30	
2009S				1.50
2009S, Silver				3.50
Northern Mariana Islands				
2009P		0.25	0.30	
2009D		0.25	0.30	
2009S				1.50
2009S, Silver				3.50

America's Beautiful National Parks Quarters (2010–2020)

Following up on the popularity of the 50 State Quarters® Program, Congress has authorized the production of new circulating commemorative quarters from 2010 to 2020. The coins will honor a site of "natural or historic significance" from each of the 50 states, five U.S. territories, and the District of Columbia. They will continue to bear George Washington's portrait on the obverse.

Five designs will be released each year, in the order the coins' featured locations were designated national parks or national sites. At the discretion of the secretary of the Treasury, this series could be extended an additional 11 years by featuring a second national park or site from each state, district, and territory.

The half dollar, authorized by the Act of April 2, 1792, was not minted until December, 1794. The weight of the half dollar was 208 grains and its fineness .8924 when first issued. This standard was not changed until 1837 when the Act of January 18, 1837 specified 206-1/4 grains, .900 fine. This fineness continued in use until 1965.

Arrows at the date in 1853 indicate the reduction of weight to 192 grains. During that year only, rays were added to the reverse. Arrows remained in 1854 and 1855. In 1873 the weight was raised by .9 grains and arrows were again placed at the date.

FLOWING HAIR (1794–1795)

AG-3 About Good: Clear enough to identify.
G-4 Good: Date and letters sufficient to be legible. Main devices outlined, but lacking in detail.
VG-8 Very Good: Major details discernible. Letters well formed but worn.
F-12 Fine: Hair ends distinguishable. Top hair lines visible, but otherwise worn smooth.
VF-20 Very Fine: Some detail visible in hair in center; other details more bold.
EF-40 Extremely Fine: Hair above head and down neck detailed, with slight wear.
AU-50 About Uncirculated: All hair visible; slight wear on bust of Liberty and on top edges of eagle's wings, head, and breast.

2 Leaves Under Wings   3 Leaves Under Wings

	Mintage	AG-3	G-4	VG-8	F-12	VF-20	EF-40	AU-50
1794 23,464		$900	$1,300	$2,200	$4,000	$8,000	$17,000	$37,500
1795 .299,680		160	335	475	900	2,000	5,000	8,500
1795, Recut Date . . . .*		160	335	475	900	2,000	5,000	8,500
1795, 3 Leaves Under Each Wing . . . .*		500	800	1,000	2,000	3,000	6,500	12,000

* Included in number above.

DRAPED BUST (1796–1807)

AG-3 About Good: Clear enough to identify.
G-4 Good: Date and letters sufficiently clear to be legible. Main devices outlined, but lacking in detail.
VG-8 Very Good: Major details discernible. Letters well formed but worn.
F-12 Fine: Hair ends distinguishable. Top hair lines visible, but otherwise worn smooth.
VF-20 Very Fine: Right side of drapery slightly worn. Left side to curls smooth.
EF-40 Extremely Fine: All lines in drapery on bust distinctly visible around to hair curls.
AU-50 About Uncirculated: Slight trace of wear on cheek, hair, and shoulder.

Small Eagle Reverse (1796–1797)

1796, 16 Stars   **1797, 15 Stars**

See next page for chart.

	Mintage	AG-3	G-4	VG-8	F-12	VF-20	EF-40	AU-50
1796, All kinds 3,918								
1796, 15 Stars		$7,500	$15,000	$17,000	$24,000	$34,000	$50,000	$75,000
1796, 16 Stars		8,000	16,000	18,000	26,000	36,000	52,500	80,000
1797, 15 Stars		7,500	15,000	17,000	24,000	34,000	50,000	75,000

Heraldic Eagle Reverse (1801–1807)

1805, 5 Over 4

1806, 6 Over 5

	Mintage	G-4	VG-8	F-12	VF-20	EF-40	AU-50	MS-60
1801 30,289		$300	$500	$1,000	$1,500	$4,000	$6,000	$16,000
1802 29,890		300	500	1,000	1,500	4,000	6,000	15,000
1803 188,234		75	90	150	250	600	1,900	4,200
1805, All kinds 211,722								
1805, 5 Over 4		100	150	275	375	1,100	2,600	10,000
1805, Normal Date		80	100	120	225	600	1,600	4,000
1806, All kinds 839,576								
1806, Normal Date		80	100	120	200	450	1,200	2,800
1806, 6 Over 5		80	100	120	200	450	1,200	2,800
1806, 6 Over Inverted 6		90	120	200	450	900	2,200	4,750
1807 301,076		80	100	120	200	450	1,200	2,800

CAPPED BUST, LETTERED EDGE (1807–1836)

John Reich designed this capped head concept of Liberty. Reich's design of Liberty facing left was used on all U.S. silver denominations for the next 30 years.

G-4 Good: Date and letters legible. Bust worn smooth with outline distinct.

VG-8 Very Good: LIBERTY faint. Legends distinguishable. Clasp at shoulder visible; curl above it nearly smooth.

F-12 Fine: Clasp and adjacent curl clearly outlined with slight details.

VF-20 Very Fine: Clasp at shoulder clear. Wear visible on highest point of curl. Hair over brow distinguishable.

EF-40 Extremely Fine: Clasp and adjacent curl fairly sharp. Brow and hair above distinct. Curls well defined.

AU-50 About Uncirculated: Trace of wear on hair over eye and over ear.

MS-60 Uncirculated: No trace of wear. Light blemishes. Possible slide marks from storage handling.

MS-63 Choice Uncirculated: Some distracting contact marks or blemishes in prime focal areas. Impaired luster possible.

First Style (1807–1808)

	Mintage	G-4	VG-8	F-12	VF-20	EF-40	AU-50	MS-60	MS-63
1807	750,500	$40	$60	$100	$200	$550	$1,200	$2,200	$4,000
1808, 8 Over 7	*	30	40	60	90	200	600	1,200	3,000
1808	1,368,600	24	30	35	55	125	255	825	1,600

* Included in number below.

Remodeled Portrait and Eagle (1809–1836)

	Mintage	G-4	VG-8	F-12	VF-20	EF-40	AU-50	MS-60	MS-63
1809	1,405,810	$22	$26	$35	$50	$100	$250	$700	$1,600
1810	1,276,276	22	26	35	45	100	225	675	1,500
1811	1,203,644	22	26	34	40	85	185	600	1,100

1812, 2 Over 1 — 1813, 50 C. Over UNI — 1814, 4 Over 3

	Mintage	G-4	VG-8	F-12	VF-20	EF-40	AU-50	MS-60	MS-63
1812, All kinds	1,628,059								
1812, 2 Over 1		$22	$28	$38	$65	$150	$250	$1,000	$2,200
1812		20	27	35	55	100	200	500	1,000
1813	1,241,903	22	27	35	55	100	185	500	1,000
1813, 50 C. Over UNI	*	22	27	40	70	140	300	700	2,100
1814, All kinds	1,039,075								
1814, 4 Over 3		22	28	45	80	150	350	800	2,100
1814		22	27	38	55	100	185	500	1,100

* Included in number above.

1817, 7 Over 3 — 1817, 7 Over 4 — 1817, "Punctuated" Date

	Mintage	G-4	VG-8	F-12	VF-20	EF-40	AU-50	MS-60	MS-63
1815, 5 Over 2	47,150	$500	$750	$900	$1,200	$2,200	$3,000	$5,500	$15,000
1817, All kinds	1,215,567								
1817, 7 Over 3		30	45	100	200	350	650	1,500	4,500
1817, 7 Over 4 (8 known)				80,000	110,000	150,000			
1817, Dated 181.7		22	27	37	45	85	175	475	1,000
1817		22	27	37	42	65	150	450	1,000

1818, 2nd 8 Over 7   **1819, 9 Over 8**   **1820, 20 Over 19**

	Mintage	G-4	VG-8	F-12	VF-20	EF-40	AU-50	MS-60	MS-63
1818, 2nd 8 Over 7 . . . .*		$22	$27	$32	$40	$65	$175	$500	$1,000
1818 1,960,322		22	27	32	40	65	150	450	925
1819, 9 Over 8 . . . .*		22	27	32	40	65	150	450	925
1819 2,208,000		20	27	32	40	65	150	450	925
1820, 20 Over 19 . . . .*		22	32	37	55	120	300	600	1,000
1820 751,122		20	27	32	40	60	150	475	950
1821 1,305,797		20	27	32	40	60	150	450	950
1822 1,559,573		20	27	32	40	60	150	475	1,000
1823 1,694,200		20	27	32	40	60	150	400	900

* Included in number below.

"Various Dates"
Probably 4 Over 2 Over 0.
     1824, 4 Over 1   **1828, Curl Base, Knob 2**   **1828, Square Base 2**

	Mintage	G-4	VG-8	F-12	VF-20	EF-40	AU-50	MS-60	MS-63
1824, All kinds 3,504,954									
1824, 4 Over Various Dates		$20	$25	$32	$40	$60	$150	$450	$850
1824, 4 Over 1		20	27	32	40	60	150	475	850
1824		20	25	32	40	60	150	500	875
1825 2,943,166		20	25	32	40	60	150	425	825
1826 4,004,180		20	25	32	40	60	150	425	825
1827, All kinds 5,493,400									
1827, 7 Over 6		22	32	37	45	75	150	525	900
1827		20	25	32	40	60	150	425	825
1828, All kinds 3,075,200									
1828, Curl Base No Knob 2		20	25	32	40	60	150	425	825
1828, Curl Base Knob 2		25	35	45	55	75	170	575	850
1828, Square Base 2		20	25	32	40	60	150	425	825
1829, 9 Over 7 . . . .*		20	27	35	45	75	190	450	1,000
1829 3,712,156		20	25	32	40	60	150	400	850
1830 4,764,800		20	25	32	40	60	150	400	850
1831 5,873,660		20	25	32	40	60	150	400	850
1832 4,797,000		20	25	32	40	60	150	400	850
1833 5,206,000		20	25	32	40	60	150	400	850
1834 6,412,004		20	25	32	40	60	150	400	850
1835 5,352,006		20	25	32	40	60	150	400	850
1836 6,545,000		20	25	32	40	60	150	400	850
1836, 50 Over 00 . . . .*		25	35	45	65	100	225	675	1,700

* Included in regular mintage.

CAPPED BUST, REEDED EDGE (1836–1839)

G-4 Good: LIBERTY barely discernible on headband.
VG-8 Very Good: Some letters in LIBERTY clear.
F-12 Fine: LIBERTY complete but faint.
VF-20 Very Fine: LIBERTY sharp. Shoulder clasp clear.
EF-40 Extremely Fine: LIBERTY sharp and strong. Hair details visible.
AU-50 About Uncirculated: Slight trace of wear on cap, cheek, and hair above forehead, and on eagle's claws, wing tops, and head.
MS-60 Uncirculated: No trace of wear. Light blemishes.
MS-63 Choice Uncirculated: Some distracting marks or blemishes in focal areas. Impaired luster possible.

Reverse 50 CENTS (1836–1837)

	Mintage	G-4	VG-8	F-12	VF-20	EF-40	AU-50	MS-60	MS-63
1836	. . . . .1,200+	$400	$500	$700	$900	$1,200	$2,000	$4,500	$8,000
1837	3,629,820	22	25	35	50	90	175	475	1,000

Reverse HALF DOL. (1838–1839)

On half dollars of 1838 and 1839, the mintmark appears on the obverse; on those thereafter, it is on the reverse below the eagle.

	Mintage	G-4	VG-8	F-12	VF-20	EF-40	AU-50	MS-60	MS-63
1838	3,546,000	$20	$25	$35	$50	$80	$150	$425	$1,000
1838O	20						100,000	150,000	
1839	1,392,976	20	25	35	50	75	150	525	1,000
1839O	116,000	65	100	135	185	325	600	1,500	2,750

LIBERTY SEATED (1839–1891)

G-4 Good: Scant rim. LIBERTY on shield worn off. Date and letters legible.
VG-8 Very Good: Rim fairly defined. Some letters in LIBERTY evident.
F-12 Fine: LIBERTY complete, but weak.
VF-20 Very Fine: LIBERTY mostly sharp.
EF-40 Extremely Fine: LIBERTY entirely sharp. Scroll edges and clasp distinct.
AU-50 About Uncirculated: Slight wear on Liberty's breast and knees; eagle's head, claws, and wing tops.
MS-60 Uncirculated: No trace of wear. Light blemishes.
MS-63 Choice Uncirculated: Some distracting blemishes in prime focal areas. Impaired luster possible.
PF-63 Choice Proof: Reflective surfaces with only a few blemishes in secondary focal places. No major flaws.

See next page for chart.   **117**

Variety 1 – No Motto Above Eagle (1839–1853)

No Drapery
From Elbow

Drapery
From Elbow
(Starting
1839)

1842, Small Date

	Mintage	G-4	VG-8	F-12	VF-20	EF-40	AU-50	MS-60	MS-63
1839, No Drapery From Elbow ....*		$18	$30	$50	$140	$325	$500	$2,600	$8,500
1839, Drapery 1,972,400		11	13	19	30	50	65	275	950
1840 1,435,008		11	14	21	35	60	70	275	650
18400 855,100		11	13	18	30	48	60	300	800
1841 310,000		13	15	22	65	110	140	500	800
18410 401,000		10	14	19	30	50	65	375	750
1842, Small Date 2,012,764		10	13	20	35	55	70	450	950
1842, Medium Date ....**		10	13	19	30	50	65	300	850
18420, Small Date 754,000		200	375	600	1,100	1,900	2,750	4,750	—
18420, Medium Date ....**		10	12	18	28	45	65	300	1,600
1843 3,844,000		10	12	18	28	45	65	300	425
18430 2,268,000		10	12	18	28	45	65	300	450
1844 1,766,000		10	12	18	28	45	65	300	425
18440 2,005,000		10	12	18	28	45	65	300	900
1845 589,000		11	13	20	32	50	90	380	1,200
18450 2,094,000		10	12	17	24	45	65	360	450
1846 2,210,000		10	12	17	24	45	65	300	500
1846, 6 Over Horizontal 6 ....**		40	75	120	175	300	500	1,100	4,000
18460 2,304,000		11	13	17	24	45	75	450	900
1847 1,156,000		10	12	17	24	45	65	300	425
18470 2,584,000		10	12	17	24	45	65	300	1,000
1848 580,000		14	18	28	40	75	180	420	600
18480 3,180,000		10	12	17	24	45	65	360	700
1849 1,252,000		10	12	17	24	45	65	340	700
18490 2,310,000		10	12	17	24	45	65	300	800
1850 227,000		90	100	175	190	300	350	725	1,600
18500 2,456,000		10	12	17	24	45	65	300	575
1851 200,750		60	100	175	250	260	275	700	1,400
18510 402,000		10	12	18	23	45	65	300	500
1852 77,130		125	180	280	360	400	550	800	1,100
18520 144,000		20	30	45	70	180	225	1,000	3,200
18530 (3 known)			100,000	150,000	250,000				

* Included in number below. **Included in number above.

Variety 2 – Arrows at Date, Rays Around Eagle (1853)

	Mintage	G-4	VG-8	F-12	VF-20	EF-40	AU-50	MS-60	MS-63
1853	3,532,708	$11	$14	$20	$60	$120	$300	$950	$1,500
1853O	1,328,000	12	16	22	65	130	340	1,400	2,000

Variety 3 – Arrows at Date, No Rays (1854–1855)

	Mintage	G-4	VG-8	F-12	VF-20	EF-40	AU-50	MS-60	MS-63
1854	2,982,000	$10	$12	$18	$30	$55	$85	$360	$650
1854O	5,240,000	10	12	18	30	55	85	360	650
1855, Over 1854	*	15	35	70	120	220	275	800	1,300
1855	759,500	10	12	18	30	55	85	360	650
1855O	3,688,000	10	12	18	30	55	85	360	650
1855S	129,950	150	185	300	600	1,400	2,600	6,750	—

* Included in number below.

Variety 1 Resumed (1856–1866; Weight Standard of 1853)

	Mintage	G-4	VG-8	F-12	VF-20	EF-40	AU-50	MS-60	MS-63	PF-63
1856	938,000	$10	$12	$18	$23	$40	$80	$220	$400	
1856O	2,658,000	10	12	20	24	40	80	220	400	
1856S	211,000	15	20	37	90	200	425	1,700	—	
1857	1,988,000	10	12	18	23	40	80	220	400	
1857O	818,000	10	12	20	24	40	80	240	650	
1857S	158,000	18	30	45	85	180	425	1,800	—	
1858 (300+)	4,225,700	10	11	18	28	40	80	220	400	$1,300
1858O	7,294,000	10	11	18	23	40	80	220	400	
1858S	476,000	12	14	22	30	55	120	525	1,500	
1859 (800)	747,200	10	11	18	23	45	85	225	450	800
1859O	2,834,000	10	11	18	23	45	85	225	450	
1859S	566,000	12	14	22	30	80	85	250	1,000	
1860 (1,000)	302,700	12	14	20	28	50	85	225	450	600
1860O	1,290,000	10	11	18	23	45	80	225	450	
1860S	472,000	12	14	22	25	45	80	350	1,000	
1861 (1,000)	2,887,400	10	11	18	23	45	80	225	400	600
1861O	2,532,633	10	11	18	23	45	80	225	400	
1861S	939,500	10	11	18	23	45	80	275	425	
1862 (550)	253,000	14	20	25	50	80	100	450	650	600
1862S	1,352,000	10	11	18	23	45	80	275	450	
1863 (460)	503,200	12	16	22	28	55	85	275	675	600
1863S	916,000	10	11	18	23	45	85	275	450	
1864 (470)	379,100	14	18	24	32	55	100	275	450	600
1864S	658,000	10	11	18	23	45	85	275	1,000	
1865 (500)	511,400	12	14	22	28	50	90	300	450	600
1865S	675,000	10	11	18	23	45	85	275	400	
1866S, No Motto	60,000	100	200	300	400	900	1,200	2,300	5,000	

Variety 4 – Motto Above Eagle (1866–1873, 1875–1891)

	Mintage	G-4	VG-8	F-12	VF-20	EF-40	AU-50	MS-60	MS-63	PF-63
1866 . . . .(725) . . .744,900		$9	$11	$17	$23	$45	$80	$220	$450	$450
1866S 994,000		9	11	17	23	45	90	320	800	
1867 . . . .(625) . . .449,300		11	15	25	35	65	95	275	500	450
1867S 1,196,000		9	10	17	22	45	80	300	650	
1868 . . . .(600) . . .417,600		13	15	23	30	70	120	325	475	450
1868S 1,160,000		9	11	17	23	40	90	325	600	
1869 . . . .(600) . . .795,300		9	11	17	23	40	90	275	450	450
1869S 656,000		9	11	17	23	42	90	350	850	
1870 . . . .(1,000) . .633,900		9	11	17	23	40	80	300	450	450
1870CC 54,617		300	475	900	2,100	6,000	12,000	—	—	
1870S 1,004,000		9	11	17	23	45	95	300	1,000	
1871 . . . .(960) .1,203,600		9	11	17	23	45	95	275	450	450
1871CC 153,950		65	100	170	300	900	1,500	6,500	22,000	
1871S 2,178,000		9	11	17	23	42	90	300	500	
1872 . . . .(950) . . .880,600		9	11	17	23	40	90	275	550	450
1872CC 257,000		30	45	90	180	450	900	2,200	15,000	
1872S 580,000		10	15	22	35	75	140	425	1,000	
1873 . . . .(600) . . .801,200		9	11	17	23	40	95	250	450	450
1873CC 122,500		60	100	150	275	650	1,900	4,500	27,000	

Variety 5 – Arrows at Date (1873–1874)

	Mintage	G-4	VG-8	F-12	VF-20	EF-40	AU-50	MS-60	MS-63	PF-63
1873 . . . .(550) .1,815,150		$13	$19	$25	$48	$130	$160	$500	$900	$1,100
1873CC 214,560		60	95	150	400	800	1,100	2,750	8,500	
1873S 228,000		20	30	45	95	180	300	950	2,750	
1874 . . . .(700) .2,359,600		13	19	22	48	130	160	500	900	1,100
1874CC 59,000		125	200	400	700	1,100	2,000	4,500	9,500	
1874S 394,000		16	25	40	90	150	250	875	1,600	

Variety 4 Resumed (1875–1891)

	Mintage	G-4	VG-8	F-12	VF-20	EF-40	AU-50	MS-60	MS-63	PF-63
1875 . . . .(700)	.6,026,800	$9	$10	$16	$22	$35	$75	$220	$300	$450
1875CC 1,008,000		9	12	25	35	60	100	275	500	
1875S 3,200,000		9	10	16	22	35	75	220	300	
1876 . . . .(1,150)	.8,418,000	9	10	16	22	35	75	220	300	450
1876CC 1,956,000		9	10	16	22	40	80	275	575	
1876S 4,528,000		9	10	16	22	35	75	220	300	
1877 . . . .(510)	.8,304,000	9	10	16	22	35	75	220	300	450
1877CC 1,420,000		9	10	16	22	40	85	260	500	
1877S 5,356,000		9	10	16	22	35	75	220	300	
1878 . . . .(800)	.1,377,600	9	10	16	22	35	75	220	300	450
1878CC 62,000		125	200	300	600	1,200	1,800	3,000	10,500	
1878S 12,000		6,500	12,000	15,000	18,000	19,000	23,000	26,000	50,000	
1879 . . . .(1,100) 4,800		90	110	130	170	200	280	425	500	450
1880 . . . .(1,355) 8,400		90	110	130	170	190	250	375	500	450
1881 . . . .(975) 10,000		90	110	130	170	190	250	375	500	450
1882 . . . .(1,100) 4,400		100	120	180	200	210	280	425	500	450
1883 . . . .(1,039) 8,000		90	110	130	170	190	245	375	500	450
1884 . . . .(875) 4,400		100	120	180	200	210	280	450	525	450
1885 . . . .(930) 5,200		100	120	180	200	210	260	475	550	450
1886 . . . .(886) 5,000		100	120	180	200	210	260	475	550	450
1887 . . . .(710) 5,000		125	150	180	200	220	270	485	575	450
1888 . . . .(832) 12,001		90	120	130	170	190	250	425	500	450
1889 . . . .(711) 12,000		90	110	130	170	190	250	425	500	450
1890 . . . .(590) 12,000		90	110	130	170	190	250	425	500	450
1891 . . . .(600) . . .200,000		20	25	40	50	65	95	275	370	450

BARBER OR LIBERTY HEAD (1892–1915)

Like the dime and quarter dollar, this type was designed by Charles E. Barber, whose initial B is on the truncation of the neck.

G-4 Good: Date and legends legible. LIBERTY worn off headband.

VG-8 Very Good: Some letters legible in LIBERTY.

F-12 Fine: LIBERTY nearly completely legible, but worn.

VF-20 Very Fine: All letters in LIBERTY evenly plain.

EF-40 Extremely Fine: LIBERTY bold, and its ribbon distinct.

AU-50 About Uncirculated: Slight trace of wear above forehead, leaf tips, and cheek, and on eagle's head, tail, and wing tips.

MS-60 Uncirculated: No trace of wear. Light blemishes.

MS-63 Choice Uncirculated: Some distracting contact marks or blemishes in prime focal areas. Impaired luster possible.

PF-63 Choice Proof: Reflective surfaces with only a few blemishes in secondary focal places. No major flaws.

Mintmark location on reverse, below eagle.

See next page for chart.

	Mintage	G-4	VG-8	F-12	VF-20	EF-40	AU-50	MS-60	MS-63	PF-63
1892 . . . .(1,245) . . .934,000		$11.00	$14	$30	$40	$125	$160	$220	$400	$425
1892O 390,000		115.00	150	190	210	250	275	460	850	
1892S 1,029,028		100.00	120	175	200	240	300	475	1,200	
1893 . . . .(792) . .1,826,000		8.00	12	28	40	100	150	300	700	425
1893O 1,389,000		10.00	20	32	65	160	200	310	750	
1893S 740,000		60.00	80	100	160	240	325	620	1,750	
1894 . . . .(972) . .1,148,000		10.00	20	32	60	130	170	270	500	425
1894O 2,138,000		7.50	10	30	50	130	160	260	500	
1894S 4,048,690		8.00	12	28	45	120	150	255	675	
1895 . . . .(880) . .1,834,338		7.50	12	28	40	110	150	260	500	425
1895O 1,766,000		8.00	12	28	50	110	165	275	675	
1895S 1,108,086		10.00	14	40	70	125	175	275	650	
1896 . . . .(762) . . .950,000		8.00	10	28	50	110	150	275	425	450
1896O 924,000		14.00	17	60	85	175	300	650	2,600	
1896S 1,140,948		35.00	45	70	110	185	240	600	1,600	
1897 . . . .(731) . .2,480,000		7.50	8	15	35	65	140	220	400	450
1897O 632,000		50.00	100	200	325	400	550	800	1,600	
1897S 933,900		50.00	75	125	210	350	450	675	1,600	
1898 . . . .(735) . .2,956,000		7.50	8	13	30	75	150	200	400	450
1898O 874,000		10.00	25	100	125	185	250	475	1,600	
1898S 2,358,550		8.00	12	22	50	100	150	400	1,700	
1899 . . . .(846) . .5,538,000		7.50	8	14	30	65	140	200	400	450
1899O 1,724,000		8.00	10	22	50	100	160	325	700	
1899S 1,686,411		8.00	10	22	45	100	150	300	1,000	
1900 . . . .(912) . .4,762,000		7.50	8	14	35	65	140	200	400	425
1900O 2,744,000		7.50	9	20	40	125	160	325	1,450	
1900S 2,560,322		7.50	9	18	40	100	140	275	1,100	
1901 . . . .(813) . .4,268,000		7.50	8	14	30	60	150	200	400	425
1901O 1,124,000		7.50	10	25	60	140	200	700	2,600	
1901S 847,044		13.50	23	70	150	285	450	900	3,100	
1902 . . . .(777) . .4,922,000		7.50	8	14	30	60	150	200	450	425
1902O 2,526,000		7.50	8	18	35	90	150	350	1,750	
1902S 1,460,670		7.50	9	20	45	110	165	350	1,000	
1903 . . . .(755) . .2,278,000		7.50	8	14	35	70	150	210	750	425
1903O 2,100,000		7.50	8	16	40	90	160	300	1,000	
1903S 1,920,772		7.50	8	16	40	95	170	300	950	
1904 . . . .(670) . .2,992,000		7.50	8	14	30	65	140	200	550	425
1904O 1,117,600		9.00	12	28	90	150	225	550	1,500	
1904S 553,038		15.00	27	110	225	450	700	3,000	8,000	
1905 . . . .(727) . . .662,000		9.00	12	30	50	110	140	230	700	425
1905O 505,000		10.00	15	40	80	140	175	350	850	
1905S 2,494,000		7.50	8	18	40	90	150	300	900	
1906 . . . .(675) . .2,638,000		7.50	8	14	36	75	120	200	375	425
1906D 4,028,000		7.50	8	15	36	75	120	200	375	
1906O 2,446,000		7.50	8	16	38	80	120	275	700	
1906S 1,740,154		7.50	8	18	40	90	120	275	525	
1907 . . . .(575) . .2,598,000		7.50	8	14	32	70	120	200	400	425
1907D 3,856,000		7.50	8	14	32	70	120	200	400	
1907O 3,946,600		7.50	8	14	32	70	140	220	400	
1907S 1,250,000		7.50	8	23	60	120	275	525	2,750	
1908 . . . .(545) . .1,354,000		7.50	8	14	30	70	120	200	400	425
1908D 3,280,000		7.50	8	14	30	65	120	200	400	
1908O 5,360,000		7.50	8	14	30	70	120	210	425	
1908S 1,644,828		7.50	8	20	50	110	170	350	1,200	
1909 . . . .(650) . .2,368,000		7.50	8	14	30	65	120	200	400	425

HALF DOLLARS

	Mintage	G-4	VG-8	F-12	VF-20	EF-40	AU-50	MS-60	MS-63	PF-63
19090	.925,400	$7.50	$8	$18	$45	$120	$200	$350	$850	
1909S	.1,764,000	7.50	8	14	32	90	140	260	550	
1910 . . . .(551) . . .	.418,000	8.00	11	28	55	130	150	290	500	$425
1910S	.1,948,000	7.50	8	14	35	85	130	250	850	
1911 . . . .(543) .	.1,406,000	7.50	8	14	28	65	120	180	400	425
1911D	.695,080	7.50	8	15	30	75	125	240	425	
1911S	.1,272,000	7.50	8	14	30	75	130	250	600	
1912 . . . .(700) .	.1,550,000	7.50	8	14	28	70	120	200	400	425
1912D	.2,300,800	7.50	8	14	28	70	120	200	400	
1912S	.1,370,000	7.50	8	14	30	75	130	240	475	
1913 . . . .(627) . .	.188,000	25.00	30	85	150	220	350	500	800	500
1913D	.534,000	7.50	8	16	35	90	120	225	425	
1913S	.604,000	7.50	10	20	40	100	140	275	550	
1914 . . . .(380) . . .	.124,230	60.00	70	135	220	290	425	600	900	700
1914S	.992,000	7.50	8	14	30	80	140	275	500	
1915 . . . .(450) . . .	.138,000	40.00	65	110	150	250	380	600	1,100	600
1915D	.1,170,400	7.50	8	12	28	60	130	200	400	
1915S	.1,604,000	7.50	8	12	28	60	130	200	400	

LIBERTY WALKING (1916–1947)

This type was designed by Adolph A. Weinman. The designer's monogram AAW appears under the tip of the wing feathers. On the 1916 coins and some of the 1917 coins, the mintmark is located on the obverse below the motto.

G-4 Good: Rims defined. Motto IN GOD WE TRUST legible.

VG-8 Very Good: Motto distinct. About half of skirt lines at left clear.

F-12 Fine: All skirt lines evident, but worn in spots. Clear details in sandal below motto.

VF-20 Very Fine: Skirt lines sharp, including leg area. Little wear on breast and right arm.

EF-40 Extremely Fine: All skirt lines bold.

AU-50 About Uncirculated: Slight trace of wear on Liberty's head, knee, and breast tips and on eagle's claws and head.

MS-60 Uncirculated: No trace of wear. Light blemishes.

MS-63 Choice Uncirculated: Some distracting contact marks or blemishes in prime focal areas. Impaired luster possible.

PF-63 Choice Proof: Reflective surfaces with only a few blemishes in secondary focal places. No major flaws.

PF-65 Gem Proof: Brilliant surfaces with no noticeable blemishes or flaws. A few scattered, barely noticeable marks or hairlines possible.

1916–1917

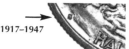

1917–1947

Mintmark Locations

Choice Uncirculated well-struck specimens are worth more than values listed.

	Mintage	G-4	VG-8	F-12	VF-20	EF-40	AU-50	MS-60	MS-63
1916	.608,000	$19	$25	$40	$90	$125	$150	$200	$250
1916D, Obverse Mintmark	.1,014,400	20	26	35	70	115	145	200	300
1916S, Obverse Mintmark	.508,000	50	65	100	225	325	400	650	1,200
1917	.12,292,000	6	6	7	12	20	35	75	120

Chart continued on next page.

	Mintage	G-4	VG-8	F-12	VF-20	EF-40	AU-50	MS-60	MS-63
1917D, Obverse Mintmark	765,400	$10.00	$15	$32	$70	$110	$150	$275	$650
1917D, Reverse Mintmark	1,940,000	6.50	9	25	60	140	250	450	950
1917S, Obverse Mintmark	952,000	15.00	21	60	165	375	700	1,300	2,500
1917S, Reverse Mintmark	5,554,000	6.00	7	8	20	38	85	175	1,000
1918	6,634,000	6.00	7	8	35	90	150	300	650
1918D	3,853,040	6.00	7	8	45	120	250	650	1,350
1918S	10,282,000	6.00	7	8	20	40	100	250	1,300
1919	962,000	10.00	15	35	150	275	400	650	1,800
1919D	1,165,000	9.00	15	40	160	350	850	2,500	8,500
1919S	1,552,000	9.00	14	35	140	400	900	1,600	5,500
1920	6,372,000	6.00	7	8	22	45	85	150	350
1920D	1,551,000	6.00	8	30	120	240	450	750	2,200
1920S	4,624,000	6.00	7	10	40	110	220	400	1,500
1921	246,000	95.00	120	175	500	900	1,500	2,500	5,000
1921D	208,000	175.00	200	300	600	1,000	1,900	2,750	7,000
1921S	548,000	25.00	35	110	450	2,500	4,400	7,000	16,000
1923S	2,178,000	6.00	6	12	55	185	400	1,000	1,800
1927S	2,392,000	6.00	6	8	25	70	200	600	1,200
1928S	1,940,000	6.00	6	9	35	75	220	600	1,300
1929D	1,001,200	6.00	6	8	15	45	140	225	400
1929S	1,902,000	6.00	6	8	15	50	140	225	500
1933S	1,786,000	6.00	6	8	9	30	140	320	650
1934	6,964,000	6.00	6	6	6	6	14	40	50
1934D	2,361,000	6.00	6	6	6	18	45	75	125
1934S	3,652,000	6.00	6	6	6	15	60	175	450
1935	9,162,000	6.00	6	6	6	6	12	25	40
1935D	3,003,800	6.00	6	6	6	18	30	75	125
1935S	3,854,000	6.00	6	6	6	18	60	125	235

	Mintage	G-4	VG-8	F-12	VF-20	EF-40	AU-50	MS-60	MS-63	PF-63	PF-65
1936 ...(3,901)	12,614,000	$6	$6	$6	$6	$6	$12	$27	$40	$950	$3,500
1936D	4,252,400	6	6	6	6	12	20	45	60		
1936S	3,884,000	6	6	6	6	12	22	75	90		
1937 ...(5,728)	9,522,000	6	6	6	6	6	12	22	35	300	800
1937D	1,676,000	6	6	6	6	18	50	120	150		
1937S	2,090,000	6	6	6	6	12	32	85	120		
1938 ...(8,152)	4,110,000	6	6	6	6	7	25	35	65	275	650
1938D	491,600	50	60	70	80	95	140	275	350		
1939 ...(8,808)	6,812,000	6	6	6	6	6	12	22	35	250	575
1939D	4,267,800	6	6	6	6	6	12	22	40		
1939S	2,552,000	6	6	6	6	10	35	70	90		

	Mintage	VG-8	F-12	VF-20	EF-40	AU-50	MS-60	MS-63	PF-63	PF-65
1940 ....(11,279)	9,156,000	$6	$6	$6	$6	$7	$15	$22	$225	$550
1940S	4,550,000	6	6	6	6	7	30	40		
1941 ....(15,412)	24,192,000	6	6	6	6	7	15	30	235	500
1941D	11,248,400	6	6	6	6	7	18	35		
1941S	8,098,000	6	6	6	6	20	32	55		
1942 ....(21,120)	47,818,000	6	6	6	6	7	15	25	235	500
1942D	10,973,800	6	6	6	6	7	18	35		
1942S	12,708,000	6	6	6	6	7	20	28		
1943	53,190,000	6	6	6	6	7	15	21		
1943D	11,346,000	6	6	6	6	7	22	32		
1943S	13,450,000	6	6	6	6	7	20	25		
1944	28,206,000	6	6	6	6	7	15	21		
1944D	9,769,000	6	6	6	6	7	18	25		

	Mintage	VG-8	F-12	VF-20	EF-40	AU-50	MS-60	MS-63
1944S	8,904,000	$6	$6	$6	$6	$7	$22	$28
1945	31,502,000	6	6	6	6	7	15	21
1945D	9,966,800	6	6	6	6	7	15	22
1945S	10,156,000	6	6	6	6	7	15	25
1946	12,118,000	6	6	6	6	7	15	21
1946D	2,151,000	6	6	6	6	7	15	21
1946S	3,724,000	6	6	6	6	7	15	21
1947	4,094,000	6	6	6	6	7	15	21
1947D	3,900,600	6	6	6	6	7	15	21

FRANKLIN (1948–1963)

The Benjamin Franklin half dollar and the Roosevelt dime were both designed by John R. Sinnock. His initials appear below the shoulder.

VF-20 Very Fine: At least half of the lower and upper incused lines on rim of Liberty Bell on reverse visible.

EF-40 Extremely Fine: Wear spots at top of end of Franklin's curls and hair at back of ears. Wear evident at top and on lettering of Liberty Bell.

MS-60 Uncirculated: No trace of wear. Light blemishes.

MS-63 Choice Uncirculated: Some distracting contact marks or blemishes in prime focal areas. Impaired luster possible.

MS-65 Gem Uncirculated: Only light, scattered contact marks that are not distracting. Strong luster, good eye appeal.

PF-63 Choice Proof: Reflective surfaces with only a few blemishes in secondary focal places. No major flaws.

PF-65 Gem Proof: Brilliant surfaces with no noticeable blemishes or flaws. A few scattered, barely noticeable marks or hairlines possible.

Mintmark Location

Choice, well-struck Uncirculated halves with full bell lines command higher prices.

	Mintage	VF-20	EF-40	MS-60	MS-63	MS-65	PF-63	PF-65
1948	3,006,814	$6	$6	$7	$10	$40		
1948D	4,028,600	6	6	7	8	65		
1949	5,614,000	6	6	15	20	70		
1949D	4,120,600	6	8	15	23	385		
1949S	3,744,000	6	9	25	35	60		
1950	(51,386) . . 7,742,123	6	6	12	16	50	$115	$200
1950D	8,031,600	6	6	9	15	225		
1951	(57,500) . 16,802,102	6	6	7	8	30	65	150
1951D	9,475,200	6	6	11	17	120		
1951S	13,696,000	6	6	9	15	50		
1952	(81,980) . 21,192,093	6	6	7	8	27	35	100
1952D	25,395,600	6	6	7	8	100		
1952S	5,526,000	6	6	15	20	55		
1953	(128,800) . 2,668,120	6	6	7	12	100	26	60
1953D	20,900,400	6	6	7	8	50		
1953S	4,148,000	6	6	9	15	30		

Chart continued on next page.

	Mintage	VF-20	EF-40	MS-60	MS-63	MS-65	PF-63	PF-65
1954 ....(233,300) ..13,188,202		$6	$6	$7	$7.00	$27	$18	$45
1954D 25,445,580		6	6	7	8.00	65		
1954S 4,993,400		6	6	7	8.50	25		
1955 ....(378,200) ...2,498,181		6	7	9	16.00	30	14	40
1956 ....(669,384) ...4,032,000		6	6	7	8.00	20	7	20
1957 ......(1,247,952) ...5,114,000		6	6	7	7.00	20	7	12
1957D 19,966,850		6	6	7	7.00	20		
1958 ....(875,652) ...4,042,000		6	6	7	7.00	25	7	15
1958D 23,962,412		6	6	7	7.00	20		
1959 ......(1,149,291) ...6,200,000		6	6	7	7.00	50	5	7
1959D 13,053,750		6	6	7	7.00	65		
1960 ......(1,691,602) ...6,024,000		6	6	7	7.00	65	5	7
1960D 18,215,812		6	6	7	7.00	100		
1961 ......(3,028,244) ...8,290,000		6	6	7	7.00	40	5	7
1961D 20,276,442		6	6	7	7.00	65		
1962 ......(3,218,019) ...9,714,000		6	6	7	7.00	65	5	7
1962D 35,473,281		6	6	7	7.00	65		
1963 ......(3,075,645) ..22,164,000		6	6	7	7.00	25	5	7
1963D 67,069,292		6	6	7	7.00	25		

KENNEDY (1964 TO DATE)

Gilroy Roberts, then chief engraver of the Mint, designed the obverse of this coin. His stylized initials are on the truncation of the forceful bust of President John F. Kennedy. The reverse, which uses the eagle from the Great Seal for the motif, is the work of assistant engraver Frank Gasparro.

Mintmark Location (1964)

Mintmark Location (1968 to Date)

Silver Coinage (1964)

	Mintage	MS-63	PF-63	PF-65
1964 ....(3,950,762) ...273,304,004		$7	$7.50	$8
1964D 156,205,446		7		

Silver Clad Coinage (1965–1970)

	Mintage	MS-63	PF-63	PF-65		Mintage	MS-63	PF-63	PF-65
1965 65,879,366		$3			1969D 129,881,800		$3		
1966 108,984,932		3			1969S ....(2,934,631)			$3.50	$4
1967 295,046,978		3			1970D 2,150,000		10		
1968D 246,951,930		3			1970S ....(2,632,810)			4.00	8
1968S ....(3,041,506)			$3.50	$4					

Clad Coinage and Silver Proofs (1971 to Date)

	Mintage	MS-63	PF-63	PF-65		Mintage	MS-63	PF-63	PF-65
1971	.155,164,000	$0.55			1973	.64,964,000	$0.55		
1971D	.302,097,424	0.55			1973D	.83,171,400	0.55		
1971S	.(3,220,733)		$1.50	$3	1973S	.(2,760,339)		$1.50	$2.50
1972	.153,180,000	0.60			1974	.201,596,000	0.55		
1972D	.141,890,000	0.60			1974D	.79,066,300	0.55		
1972S	.(3,260,996)		1.50	3	1974S	.(2,612,568)		1.50	3.00

Bicentennial Coinage Dated 1776–1976

	Mintage	MS-63	PF-63	PF-65
1776–1976, Clad	.234,308,000	$0.55		
1776–1976D, Clad	.287,565,248	0.55		
1776–1976S, Clad	.(7,059,099)		$0.75	$1.25
1776–1976S, Silver	.11,000,000	1.50		
1776–1976S, Silver	.(4,000,000)		2.00	3.50

Note: Mintage figures for 1976-S silver coins are approximate; many were melted in 1982.

Eagle Reverse Resumed (1977)

	Mintage	MS-63	PF-63	PF-65		Mintage	MS-63	PF-63	PF-65
1977	.43,598,000	$0.60			1983D	.32,472,244	$2.00		
1977D	.31,449,106	0.60			1983S	.(3,279,126)		$1.00	$1.75
1977S	.(3,251,152)		$1	$1.25	1984P	.26,029,000	0.75		
1978	.14,350,000	0.60			1984D	.26,262,158	0.75		
1978D	.13,765,799	1.00			1984S	.(3,065,110)		1.00	2.00
1978S	.(3,127,781)		1	1.50	1985P	.18,706,962	1.50		
1979	.68,312,000	0.55			1985D	.19,814,034	1.25		
1979D	.15,815,422	0.55			1985S	.(3,362,821)		1.00	1.75
1979S	.(3,677,175)				1986P	.13,107,633	2.50		
Filled S			1	1.25	1986D	.15,336,145	2.00		
Clear S			6	9.00	1986S	.(3,010,497)		3.00	4.50
1980P	.44,134,000	0.55			1987P (a)	.2,890,758	2.00		
1980D	.33,456,449	0.55			1987D (a)	.2,890,758	2.00		
1980S	.(3,554,806)		1	1.50	1987S	.(4,227,728)		1.00	1.75
1981P	.29,544,000	0.75			1988P	.13,626,000	1.50		
1981D	.27,839,533	0.55			1988D	.12,000,096	1.00		
1981S	.(4,063,083)		1	1.50	1988S	.(3,262,948)		2.00	2.50
1982P	.10,819,000	1.50			1989P	.24,542,000	1.00		
1982D	.13,140,102	1.50			1989D	.23,000,216	0.90		
1982S	.(3,857,479)		1	1.50	1989S	.(3,220,194)		1.50	3.00
1983P	.34,139,000	2.00			1990P	.22,278,000	1.00		

a. Not issued for circulation.

Chart continued on next page.

Mintage	MS-63	PF-63	PF-65
1990D 20,096,242	$1.10		
1990S . . . .(3,299,559)		$1.50	$2.00
1991P 14,874,000	0.75		
1991D 15,054,678	1.25		
1991S . . . .(2,867,787)		4.00	5.00
1992P 17,628,000	0.50		
1992D 17,000,106	1.00		
1992S . . . .(2,858,981)		3.00	3.50
1992S, Silver . . .(1,317,579)		7.00	7.50
1993P 15,510,000	0.50		
1993D 15,000,006	0.50		
1993S . . . .(2,633,439)		5.00	6.00
1993S, Silver . . . .(761,353)		10.00	16.00
1994P 23,718,000	0.50		
1994D 23,828,110	0.50		
1994S . . . .(2,484,594)		3.00	4.00
1994S, Silver . . . .(785,329)		12.00	17.00
1995P 26,496,000	0.50		
1995D 26,288,000	0.50		
1995S . . . .(2,117,496)		10.00	14.00
1995S, Silver . . . .(679,985)		35.00	45.00
1996P 24,442,000	0.50		
1996D 24,744,000	0.50		
1996S . . . .(1,750,244)		3.00	5.00
1996S, Silver . . . .(775,021)		15.00	20.00
1997P 20,882,000	0.50		
1997D 19,876,000	0.50		
1997S . . . .(2,055,000)		9.00	14.00
1997S, Silver . . . .(741,678)		20.00	30.00
1998P 15,646,000	0.50		
1998D 15,064,000	0.50		
1998S . . . .(2,086,507)		5.00	7.00
1998S, Silver . . . .(878,792)		9.00	12.00
1998S, Silver,			
Matte Finish . . . . . .(b)		100.00	125.00
1999P 8,900,000	0.55		
1999D 10,682,000	0.55		
1999S . . . .(2,543,401)		5.00	10.00
1999S, Silver . . . .(804,565)		9.00	15.00
2000P 22,600,000	0.60		

Mintage	MS-63	PF-63	PF-65
2000D 19,466,000	$0.60		
2000S . . . .(3,082,483)		$2.00	$3
2000S, Silver . . . .(965,421)		7.00	8
2001P (a) 21,200,000	4.00		
2001D 19,504,000	0.55		
2001S . . . .(2,294,909)		3.25	4
2001S, Silver . . . .(889,697)		8.00	9
2002P (a) 3,100,000	0.65		
2002D (a) 2,500,000	0.65		
2002S . . . .(2,319,766)		2.00	3
2002S, Silver . . . .(892,229)		8.00	9
2003P (a) 2,500,000	0.65		
2003D (a) 2,500,000	0.65		
2003S . . . .(2,172,684)		2.00	3
2003S, Silver . . .(1,125,755)		8.00	9
2004P (a) 2,900,000	0.65		
2004D (a) 2,900,000	0.65		
2004S . . . .(1,789,488)		3.00	5
2004S, Silver . . .(1,175,934)		8.00	9
2005P (a) 3,800,000	0.65		
2005D (a) 3,500,000	0.65		
2005S . . . .(2,275,000)		2.00	3
2005S, Silver . . .(1,069,679)		7.00	8
2006P (a) 2,400,000	0.65		
2006D (a) 2,000,000	0.65		
2006S . . . .(2,000,428)		2.00	3
2006S, Silver . . .(1,054,008)		7.00	8
2007P (a) *2,400,000*	0.65		
2007D (a) *2,400,000*	0.65		
2007S . . . .*(1,384,797)*		2.00	3
2007S, Silver . . . .*(875,050)*		7.00	8
2008P *1,700,000*	0.65		
2008D (a) *1,700,000*	0.65		
2008S . . . .*(1,377,424)*		2.00	3
2008S, Silver . . . .*(620,684)*		7.00	8
2009P	0.65		
2009D	0.65		
2009S		2.00	3
2009S, Silver		7.00	8

a. Not issued for circulation. b. Included in commemorative set (see page 219).

The silver dollar was authorized by Congress April 2, 1792. Its weight was specified at 416 grains and its fineness at .8924. The first issues appeared in 1794, and until 1804 all silver dollars had the value stamped on the edge: HUNDRED CENTS, ONE DOLLAR OR UNIT. After a lapse in coinage of the silver dollar during the period 1804 to 1835, coins were made with either plain (1836 only) or reeded edges and the value was placed on the reverse side.

The weight was changed by the law of January 18, 1837 to 412-1/2 grains, fineness .900. The coinage was discontinued by the Act of February 12, 1873 and reauthorized by the Act of February 28, 1878. The dollar was again discontinued after 1935, and since then copper-nickel and other base-metal pieces have been coined for circulation.

FLOWING HAIR (1794–1795)

AG-3 About Good: Clear enough to identify.
G-4 Good: Date and letters legible. Main devices outlined, but lacking in detail.
VG-8 Very Good: Major details discernible. Letters well formed but worn.
F-12 Fine: Hair ends distinguishable. Top hair lines visible, but otherwise worn smooth.
VF-20 Very Fine: Some detail visible in hair in center. Other details more bold.
EF-40 Extremely Fine: Hair well defined but with some wear.
AU-50 About Uncirculated: Slight trace of wear on tips of highest curls; breast feathers usually weak.
MS-60 Uncirculated: No trace of wear. Light blemishes.

	Mintage	AG-3	G-4	VG-8	F-12	VF-20	EF-40	AU-50	MS-60
1794	1,758	$15,000	$27,000	$40,000	$50,000	$90,000	$150,000	$210,000	—
1795	160,295	425	800	1,000	2,000	3,000	8,000	12,000	$27,500

DRAPED BUST (1795–1804)
Small Eagle Reverse (1795–1798)

AG-3 About Good: Clear enough to identify.
G-4 Good: Bust outlined, no detail. Date legible, some leaves evident.
VG-8 Very Good: Drapery worn except deepest folds. Hair lines smooth.
F-12 Fine: All drapery lines distinguishable. Some detail visible in hair lines near cheek and neck.
VF-20 Very Fine: Left side of drapery worn smooth.
EF-40 Extremely Fine: Drapery distinctly visible. Hair well outlined and detailed.
AU-50 About Uncirculated: Slight trace of wear on the bust shoulder and hair to left of forehead, as well as on eagle's breast and top edges of wings.
MS-60 Uncirculated: No trace of wear. Light blemishes.

Entry continues on next page.   **129**

	Mintage	AG-3	G-4	VG-8	F-12	VF-20	EF-40	AU-50	MS-60
1795, Bust Type	42,738	$375	$650	$900	$1,500	$2,500	$5,500	$8,500	$22,000
1796	79,920	375	650	900	1,500	2,500	5,500	8,500	22,000
1797	7,776	375	650	900	1,500	2,500	5,500	8,500	22,000
1798	327,536	375	650	900	1,500	2,500	5,500	9,000	22,000

Heraldic Eagle Reverse (1798–1804)

G-4 Good: Letters and date legible. E PLURIBUS UNUM illegible.

VG-8 Very Good: Motto partially legible. Only deepest drapery details visible. All other lines smooth.

F-12 Fine: All drapery lines distinguishable. Some detail visible in hair lines near cheek and neck.

VF-20 Very Fine: Left side of drapery worn smooth.

EF-40 Extremely Fine: Drapery distinct. Hair well detailed.

AU-50 About Uncirculated: Slight trace of wear on the bust shoulder and hair to left of forehead, as well as on eagle's breast and top edges of wings.

MS-60 Uncirculated: No trace of wear. Light blemishes.

	Mintage	G-4	VG-8	F-12	VF-20	EF-40	AU-50	MS-60
1798, Heraldic Eagle	*	$450	$550	$750	$1,300	$2,500	$5,000	$11,000
1799	423,515	450	550	750	1,300	2,500	5,000	11,000
1800	220,920	450	550	750	1,300	2,500	5,000	11,000
1801	54,454	450	550	750	1,300	2,500	5,000	11,000
1802	41,650	450	550	750	1,300	2,500	5,000	11,000
1803	85,634	450	550	750	1,300	2,500	5,000	12,000
1804, Variety 1, O Above Cloud					*Proof:* $3,500,000			
1804, Variety 2, O Above Space Between Clouds					*Proof:* $2,500,000			

* Included in number above.

GOBRECHT DOLLARS (1836–1839)

Silver dollars of 1836, 1838, and 1839 were mostly made as patterns and restrikes, but some were made in quantities for general circulation.

	VF-20	EF-40	AU-50	PF-60
1836, C. GOBRECHT F. on base. Reverse eagle flying upward amid stars. Plain edge. Although scarce, this is the most common variety and was issued for circulation as regular coinage.	$5,500	$8,500	$11,000	$13,500
1838, Similar obverse, designer's name omitted, stars added around border. Reverse eagle flying left in plain field. Reeded edge.	9,000	13,500	16,000	19,000
1839, Obverse as above. Reverse eagle in plain field. Reeded edge. Issued for circulation as regular coinage.	8,500	12,000	14,000	16,000

LIBERTY SEATED (1840–1873)

In 1840, silver dollars were again issued for general circulation. The seated figure of Liberty device was adopted for the obverse, and a heraldic eagle for the reverse.

VG-8 Very Good: Any three letters of LIBERTY at least two-thirds complete.

F-12 Fine: All seven letters of LIBERTY visible, though weak.

VF-20 Very Fine: LIBERTY strong, but slight wear visible on its ribbon.

EF-40 Extremely Fine: Horizontal lines of shield complete. Eagle's eye plain.

AU-50 About Uncirculated: Traces of light wear on only the high points of the design. Half of mint luster present.

MS-60 Uncirculated: No trace of wear. Light marks or blemishes.

PF-60 Proof: Several contact marks, hairlines, or light rubs possible on surface. Luster possibly dull and eye appeal lacking.

PF-63 Choice Proof: Reflective surfaces with only a few blemishes in secondary focal places. No major flaws.

No Motto (1840–1865)

Location of mintmark, when present, is on reverse, below eagle.

See next page for chart.

	Mintage	VG-8	F-12	VF-20	EF-40	AU-50	MS-60	PF-60	PF-63
1840 61,005		$140	$160	$190	$340	$485	$1,700	$8,250	$20,000
1841 173,000		110	130	170	275	400	1,100	8,500	21,000
1842 184,618		110	130	170	275	400	925	8,500	20,000
1843 165,100		110	130	170	275	400	950	8,500	20,000
1844 20,000		115	170	210	310	600	1,600	7,000	20,000
1845 24,500		120	170	210	340	680	4,500	8,500	20,000
1846 110,600		110	130	170	275	400	975	6,500	17,000
18460 59,000		140	180	215	300	550	2,700		
1847 140,750		110	130	170	275	365	900	8,750	16,500
1848 15,000		200	275	375	500	875	2,000	8,750	20,000
1849 62,600		110	130	170	275	350	1,100	9,750	26,000
1850 7,500		300	350	550	850	1,300	3,000	8,750	17,500
18500 40,000		140	225	400	825	1,700	7,100		
1851 1,300		3,000	4,750	6,500	8,750	14,000	17,000	16,000	21,500
1852 1,100		2,750	4,750	6,500	8,750	14,000	17,000	17,500	23,000
1853 46,110		135	185	235	360	775	1,500	13,000	23,000
1854 33,140		825	1,300	1,600	2,500	3,800	5,000	7,750	13,000
1855 26,000		550	875	1,250	2,000	3,100	5,250	7,750	14,000
1856 63,500		200	290	375	775	1,400	2,800	3,800	9,750
1857 94,000		200	290	350	750	1,000	1,800	3,100	5,000
1858 . . . .(300+)		1,900	2,250	2,800	3,500	4,500		5,500	8,000
1859 . . . . .(800) 255,700		145	215	270	345	500	1,400	1,300	2,800
18590 360,000		110	130	170	275	400	720		
1859S 20,000		185	280	370	1,100	2,500	8,500		
1860 . . . .(1,330) 217,600		120	175	230	325	450	775	1,100	2,300
18600 515,000		110	130	170	275	375	675		
1861 . . . .(1,000) 77,500		325	450	575	700	1,350	1,850	1,100	2,300
1862 . . . . .(550) 11,540		290	385	490	675	1,250	1,850	1,100	2,400
1863 . . . . .(460) 27,200		210	250	270	375	800	1,700	1,100	2,400
1864 . . . . .(470) 30,700		125	175	290	375	800	2,000	1,100	2,400
1865 . . . . .(500) 46,500		125	175	270	350	775	1,700	1,100	2,400

With Motto (1866–1873)

Motto IN GOD WE TRUST on Reverse (1866–1873)

	Mintage	VG-8	F-12	VF-20	EF-40	AU-50	MS-60	PF-60	PF-63
1866 . . . . . .(725) 48,900		$135	$175	$250	$350	$600	$1,100	$850	$2,000
1867 . . . . . .(625) 46,900		135	175	235	300	550	1,100	850	2,000
1868 . . . . . .(600) 162,100		115	150	220	260	525	1,000	850	2,000
1869 . . . . . .(600) 423,700		115	150	185	250	450	975	850	2,000

	Mintage	VG-8	F-12	VF-20	EF-40	AU-50	MS-60	PF-60	PF-63
1870 ....(1,000) ...415,000		$115	$150	$185	$250	$375	$875	$850	$2,000
1870CC 11,758		260	380	600	900	2,200	7,000		
1870S			100,000	200,000	300,000	500,000	700,000		
1871 ......(960) ...1,073,800		115	150	175	250	375	775	850	2,000
1871CC 1,376		1,400	2,200	3,000	6,000	14,000	37,000		
1872 ......(950) ...1,105,500		120	155	185	260	400	775	850	2,000
1872CC 3,150		750	1,200	1,800	3,000	7,000	15,000		
1872S 9,000		200	275	375	900	1,700	5,000		
1873 ......(600) 293,000		125	175	190	300	475	975	850	2,000
1873CC 2,300		2,750	4,000	6,500	10,000	17,500	50,000		

TRADE DOLLARS (1873–1885)

This trade dollar was issued for circulation in the Orient to compete with dollar-size coins of other countries. It weighed 420 grains compared to 412-1/2 grains, the weight of the regular silver dollar.

VG-8 Very Good: About half of mottoes IN GOD WE TRUST (on Liberty's pedestal) and E PLURIBUS UNUM (on obverse ribbon) visible. Rim on both sides well defined.

F-12 Fine: Mottoes and liberty legible but worn.

EF-40 Extremely Fine: Mottoes and liberty sharp. Only slight wear on rims.

AU-50 About Uncirculated: Slight trace of wear on Liberty's left breast and left knee and on hair above ear, as well as on eagle's head, knee, and wing tips.

MS-60 Uncirculated: No trace of wear. Light blemishes.

MS-63 Choice Uncirculated: Some distracting contact marks or blemishes in prime focal areas. Impaired luster possible.

PF-63 Choice Proof: Reflective surfaces with only a few blemishes in secondary focal places. No major flaws.

1875-S, S Over CC

	Mintage	VG-8	F-12	EF-40	AU-50	MS-60	MS-63	PF-63
1873 ....(865) 396,635		$55	$65	$85	$150	$400	$1,850	$1,600
1873CC 124,500		100	150	320	800	2,500	1,300	
1873S 703,000		55	65	90	175	500	1,100	
1874 ....(700) ...987,100		55	65	85	150	275	850	1,600
1874CC 1,373,200		100	150	250	300	700	3,800	
1874S 2,549,000		55	65	85	150	275	850	
1875 ....(700) 218,200		80	180	295	500	1,000	1,700	1,600
1875CC 1,573,700		80	180	285	450	900	1,500	
1875S 4,487,000		55	65	85	150	275	850	
1875S, S Over CC ....*		125	200	450	700	1,500	6,000	
1876 ....(1,150) 455,000		55	65	85	150	275	850	1,600
1876CC 509,000		80	125	225	600	1,700	13,000	

* Included in number above.

Chart continued on next page.

	Mintage	VG-8	F-12	EF-40	AU-50	MS-60	MS-63	PF-63
1876S	...5,227,000	$55	$65	$85	$150	$275	$850	
1877	(510)...3,039,200	55	65	85	150	275	850	$1,600
1877CC	...534,000	100	150	300	375	700	3,500	
1877S	...9,519,000	55	65	85	150	275	850	
1878	(900)			600				1,600
1878CC **(a)**	...97,000	250	375	1,100	2,000	6,500	13,000	
1878S	...4,162,000	55	65	85	150	275	850	
1879	(1,541)			600				1,600
1880	(1,987)			600				1,600
1881	(960)			600				1,700
1882	(1,097)			600				1,700
1883	(979)			600				1,700
1884 **(b)**	(10)			600				300,000
1885 **(b)**	(5)			600				900,000

a. 44,148 trade dollars were melted on July 19, 1878. Many of these may have been 1878-CC. **b.** The trade dollars of 1884 and 1885 were unknown to collectors until 1908. None are listed in the Mint director's report, and numismatists believe that they are not a part of the regular Mint issue.

MORGAN (1878–1921)

George T. Morgan, formerly a pupil of William Wyon's at the Royal Mint in London, designed the new dollar. His initial M is found at the truncation of the neck, at the last tress. It also appears on the reverse on the left-hand loop of the ribbon.

Sharply struck prooflike coins have a highly reflective surface and usually command substantial premiums.

VF-20 Very Fine: Two thirds of hair lines from top of forehead to ear visible. Ear well defined. Feathers on eagle's breast worn.

EF-40 Extremely Fine: All hair lines strong and ear bold. Eagle's feathers all plain but with slight wear on breast and wing tips.

AU-50 About Uncirculated: Slight trace of wear on the bust shoulder and hair left of forehead, and on eagle's breast and top edges of wings.

MS-60 Uncirculated: No trace of wear. Full mint luster present, but may be noticeably marred by scuff marks or bag abrasions.

MS-63 Choice Uncirculated: No trace of wear; full mint luster; few noticeable surface marks.

MS-64 Uncirculated: A few scattered contact marks. Good eye appeal and attractive luster.

MS-65 Gem Uncirculated: Only light, scattered contact marks that are not distracting. Strong luster, good eye appeal.

8 Tail Feathers, 1878, Philadelphia Only

Mintmark location on reverse, below wreath.

SILVER AND RELATED DOLLARS

Most Proof Morgan dollars, where indicated in mintage records (quantity shown in parentheses), are valued approximately as follows:
Proof-60 – $600; Proof-63 – $1,200; Proof-65 – $3,000.

Most Uncirculated silver dollars have scratches or nicks because of handling of mint bags. Choice sharply struck coins with full brilliance and without blemishes are worth more than listed values.

	Mintage	VF-20	EF-40	AU-50	MS-60	MS-63	MS-65
1878, 8 Feathers . . . .(500) 749,500		$16	$18	$21	$70	$90	$750
1878, 7 Feathers . . . .(250) . . .9,759,300		13	15	16	35	50	750
1878, 7/8 Clear Dbl Feathers . . . .*		16	20	26	70	130	1,475
1878CC 2,212,000		52	65	70	120	200	1,000
1878S 9,774,000		13	15	16	26	40	165
1879 . . . .(1,100) . .14,806,000		13	15	16	16	30	500
1879CC, CC Over CC 756,000		75	250	425	1,550	3,200	13,000
1879O 2,887,000		13	15	16	36	95	1,600
1879S 9,110,000		13	15	16	23	26	90
1880 . . . .(1,355) . .12,600,000		13	15	16	23	26	375
1880CC, All kinds .591,000		100	130	170	300	350	700
1880O 5,305,000		13	15	16	32	185	9,500
1880S 8,900,000		13	15	16	22	27	95
1881 . . . .(984) . . .9,163,000		13	15	16	22	27	430
1881CC 296,000		145	185	200	220	280	475
1881O 5,708,000		13	14	15	22	27	730
1881S 12,760,000		13	14	15	22	26	95
1882 . . . .(1,100) . .11,100,000		13	14	15	22	26	170
1882CC 1,133,000		55	65	70	100	130	250
1882O 6,090,000		13	14	15	22	26	425
1882S 9,250,000		13	14	15	22	26	95
1883 . . . .(1,039) . .12,290,000		13	14	15	22	26	95
1883CC 1,204,000		60	70	80	100	130	235
1883O 8,725,000		13	14	15	22	26	95
1883S 6,250,000		15	16	70	300	1,300	10,000
1884 . . . .(875) . .14,070,000		13	14	15	22	26	135
1884CC 1,136,000		70	80	90	115	135	230
1884O 9,730,000		13	14	15	22	26	95
1884S 3,200,000		16	22	240	2,500	14,000	97,500
1885 . . . .(930) . .17,787,000		13	14	15	22	26	95
1885CC 228,000		250	275	290	310	350	775
1885O 9,185,000		13	14	15	22	26	95
1885S 1,497,000		15	20	50	90	135	800
1886 . . . .(886) . .19,963,000		13	14	14	22	26	95
1886O 10,710,000		15	16	50	325	2,200	97,000
1886S 750,000		30	40	60	140	235	1,650
1887 . . . .(710) . .20,290,000		13	14	15	22	26	95
1887O 11,550,000		13	14	15	23	65	1,200
1887S 1,771,000		13	15	20	60	125	1,500
1888 . . . .(833) . .19,183,000		13	14	15	22	26	100
1888O 12,150,000		13	14	15	22	26	210
1888S 657,000		80	95	110	150	210	1,600
1889 . . . .(811) . .21,726,000		13	14	15	22	26	95
1889CC 350,000		775	1,850	3,750	11,000	17,000	155,000
1889O 11,875,000		13	15	22	75	200	2,200

* Included in number above.

Chart continued on next page.

135

	Mintage	VF-20	EF-40	AU-50	MS-60	MS-63	MS-65
1889S	700,000	$25	$35	$50	$120	$225	$900
1890 (590)	16,802,000	13	14	15	22	26	950
1890CC	2,309,041	60	80	95	180	450	3,000
1890O	10,701,000	13	14	15	30	55	700
1890S	8,230,373	13	14	15	30	55	450
1891 (650)	8,693,556	13	14	15	30	90	2,700
1891CC	1,618,000	60	75	100	200	450	2,300
1891O	7,954,529	13	15	25	75	180	3,350
1891S	5,296,000	13	14	15	23	70	600
1892 (1,245)	1,036,000	13	15	40	85	210	1,750
1892CC	1,352,000	125	220	300	750	1,200	4,600
1892O	2,744,000	13	15	35	85	165	2,300
1892S	1,200,000	50	140	1,000	16,500	33,000	100,000
1893 (792)	378,000	100	130	175	325	700	3,500
1893CC	677,000	225	800	975	1,800	3,600	27,000
1893O	300,000	150	275	460	1,100	3,750	110,000
1893S	100,000	3,500	4,800	13,000	45,000	80,000	265,000
1894 (972)	110,000	850	1,100	1,300	2,500	3,500	17,000
1894O	1,723,000	27	50	130	325	2,100	23,000
1894S	1,260,000	40	67	185	310	600	3,000
1895 (880)			15,000 (a)	18,000 (a)	23,000 (a)	32,000 (a)	42,000 (a)
1895O	450,000	220	350	800	8,500	24,000	120,000
1895S	400,000	175	325	775	1,900	3,000	11,000
1896 (762)	9,976,000	13	14	15	22	26	95
1896O	4,900,000	13	15	90	550	4,000	90,000
1896S	5,000,000	30	95	375	675	1,500	8,600
1897 (731)	2,822,000	13	14	15	22	28	125
1897O	4,004,000	13	15	60	360	2,750	26,000
1897S	5,825,000	13	14	15	30	55	300
1898 (735)	5,884,000	13	14	15	22	26	126
1898O	4,440,000	13	14	15	22	26	95
1898S	4,102,000	15	20	45	135	225	1,000
1899 (846)	330,000	90	120	150	200	225	500
1899O	12,290,000	13	14	15	22	26	95
1899S	2,562,000	15	23	60	170	260	900
1900 (912)	8,830,000	13	14	15	22	16	95
1900O	12,590,000	13	14	15	22	16	100
1900S	3,540,000	15	25	45	150	225	750
1901 (813)	6,962,000	26	55	250	1,100	8,500	115,000
1901O	13,320,000	13	14	15	22	26	100
1901S	2,284,000	16	25	75	250	370	1,900
1902 (777)	7,994,000	13	14	15	25	55	225
1902O	8,636,000	13	14	15	22	26	95
1902S	1,530,000	70	100	135	200	325	1,400
1903 (755)	4,652,000	25	32	36	45	50	130
1903O	4,450,000	200	210	225	240	260	425
1903S	1,241,000	90	185	900	2,000	3,250	5,250
1904 (650)	2,788,000	13	14	20	45	150	1,900

a. Values are for Proofs.

	Mintage	VF-20	EF-40	AU-50	MS-60	MS-63	MS-65
19040	3,720,000	$13	$14	$15	$22	$26	$95
1904S	2,304,000	35	120	320	675	1,600	4,000
1921	44,690,000	13	13	14	15	16	90
1921D	20,345,000	13	14	14	17	32	175
1921S	21,695,000	13	14	14	16	32	610

PEACE (1921–1935)

Anthony De Francisci, a medalist, designed this dollar. His monogram is located in the field of the coin under the neck of Liberty.

VF-20 Very Fine: Hair over eye well worn. Some strands over ear well defined. Some eagle feathers on top and outside edge of right wing visible.

EF-40 Extremely Fine: Hair lines over brow and ear are strong, though slightly worn. Outside wing feathers at right and those at top visible but faint.

AU-50 About Uncirculated: Slight trace of wear. Most luster present, although marred by contact marks.

MS-60 Uncirculated: No trace of wear. Full mint luster, but possibly noticeably marred by stains, surface marks, or bag abrasions.

MS-63 Choice Uncirculated: Some distracting contact marks or blemishes in prime focal areas. Impaired luster possible.

MS-64 Uncirculated: A few scattered contact marks. Good eye appeal and attractive luster.

MS-65 Gem Uncirculated: Only light, scattered, non-distracting contact marks. Strong luster, good eye appeal.

PF-65 Choice Proof: Satin surfaces, no noticeable blemishes or flaws.

Mintmark location on reverse, below ONE.

Most Uncirculated silver dollars have scratches or nicks because of handling of mint bags. Choice sharply struck coins with full brilliance and without blemishes are worth more than listed values.

	Mintage	VF-20	EF-40	AU-50	MS-60	MS-63	MS-65	PF-65
1921	1,006,473	$50	$60	$75	$125	$240	$1,400	$22,000
1922	51,737,000	13	13	14	15	20	80	30,000
1922D	15,063,000	13	14	14	15	25	200	
1922S	17,475,000	13	14	14	15	33	1,200	
1923	30,800,000	13	13	14	15	19	82	
1923D	6,811,000	13	14	15	18	65	550	
1923S	19,020,000	13	14	14	16	40	3,250	
1924	11,811,000	13	13	14	15	19	85	
1924S	1,728,000	13	14	30	100	235	5,000	
1925	10,198,000	13	13	14	15	19	85	
1925S	1,610,000	13	14	16	33	90	12,000	
1926	1,939,000	13	14	14	18	40	175	

Chart continued on next page.

	Mintage	VF-20	EF-40	AU-50	MS-60	MS-63	
1926D	2,348,700	$13	$14	$16	$31	$85	
1926S	6,980,000	13	14	14	20	47	
1927	848,000	13	15	23	37	85	
1927D	1,268,900	13	15	45	80	200	
1927S	866,000	13	15	40	75	200	
1928	360,649	215	245	275	300	375	
1928S	1,632,000	13	15	26	85	325	
1934	954,057	13	14	20	60	100	
1934D	1,569,500	13	14	20	70	185	
1934S	1,011,000	33	80	295	1,000	2,200	5,0...
1935	1,576,000	13	14	15	45	65	335
1935S	1,964,000	13	14	50	125	235	700

EISENHOWER (1971–1978)
Eagle Reverse (1971–1974)

Honoring both President Dwight D. Eisenhower and the first landing of man on the moon, this design is the work of Chief Engraver Frank Gasparro, whose initials are on the truncation and below the eagle. The reverse is an adaptation of the official Apollo 11 insignia.

Mintmark location is above date.

	Mintage	EF-40	MS-63	PF-63	PF-65
1971, Copper-Nickel Clad	47,799,000	$1.05	$1.75		
1971D, Copper-Nickel Clad	68,587,424	1.05	1.25		
1971S, Silver Clad	(4,265,234) . . . 6,868,530		6.00	$6.50	$7.00
1972, Copper-Nickel Clad	75,890,000	1.05	1.25		
1972D, Copper-Nickel Clad	92,548,511	1.05	1.25		
1972S, Silver Clad	(1,811,631) . . . 2,193,056		5.75	6.00	6.50
1973, Copper-Nickel Clad **(a)**	2,000,056	1.50	5.50		
1973D, Copper-Nickel Clad **(a)**	2,000,000	1.50	5.50		
1973S, Copper-Nickel Clad	(2,760,339)			3.00	7.00
1973S, Silver Clad	(1,013,646) . . . 1,883,140		6.00	10.00	18.00
1974, Copper-Nickel Clad	27,366,000	1.05	2.00		
1974D, Copper-Nickel Clad	45,517,000	1.05	2.00		
1974S, Copper-Nickel Clad	(2,612,568)			2.50	3.50
1974S, Silver Clad	(1,306,579) . . . 1,900,156		6.00	6.50	7.00

a. 1,769,258 of each sold only in sets and not released for circulation. Unissued coins destroyed at mint.

Bicentennial Coinage Dated 1776–1976

Obverse

Reverse Variety 2   Reverse Variety 1

Variety 1: Design in low relief, bold lettering on reverse.
Variety 2: Sharp design, delicate lettering on reverse.

	Mintage	EF-40	MS-63	PF-63	PF-65
1776–1976, Copper-Nickel Clad, Variety 1	4,019,000	$1.10	$3.00		
1776–1976, Copper-Nickel Clad, Variety 2	113,318,000	1.10	1.50		
1776–1976D, Copper-Nickel Clad, Variety 1	21,048,710	1.10	1.50		
1776–1976D, Copper-Nickel Clad, Variety 2	82,179,564	1.10	1.50		
1776–1976S, Copper-Nickel Clad, Variety 1	(2,845,450)			$2.50	$5.50
1776–1976S, Copper-Nickel Clad, Variety 2	(4,149,730)			2.50	3.50
1776–1976S, Silver Clad, Variety 1	11,000,000		6.00		
1776–1976S, Silver Clad, Variety 1	(4,000,000)			6.00	10.00

Eagle Reverse Resumed (1977–1978)

	Mintage	EF-40	MS-63	PF-63	PF-65
1977, Copper-Nickel Clad	12,596,000	$1.05	$2.00		
1977D, Copper-Nickel Clad	32,983,006	1.05	1.50		
1977S, Copper-Nickel Clad	(3,251,152)			$2.50	$4.00
1978, Copper-Nickel Clad	25,702,000	1.05	1.25		
1978D, Copper-Nickel Clad	33,012,890	1.05	1.50		
1978S, Copper-Nickel Clad	(3,127,781)			2.50	4.75

SUSAN B. ANTHONY (1979–1999)

Clear S   Filled S

	Mintage	MS-63
1979P, Narrow Rim	360,222,000	$1.00
1979P, Wide Rim	*	8.50
1979D	288,015,744	1.00

* Included in number above.

Chart continued on next page.

	Mintage	MS-63	PF-63	PF-65
1979S	109,576,000	$1.00		
1979S, Proof, Filled S	(3,677,175)		$2.50	$5
1979S, Proof, Clear S	*		35.00	60
1980P	27,610,000	1.00		
1980D	41,628,708	1.00		
1980S	20,422,000	1.00		
1980S, Proof	(3,554,806)		2.50	5
1981P	3,000,000	2.00		
1981D	3,250,000	2.00		
1981S	3,492,000	2.00		
1981S, Proof, First S	(4,063,083)		2.50	4
1981S, Proof, Clear S	*		90.00	125
1999P	29,592,000	1.25		
1999P, Proof	(75,000)		10.00	15
1999D	11,776,000	1.25		

* Included in number above.

SACAGAWEA (2000 TO DATE)

The design of this coin was selected in national competition from among 120 submissions that were considered by a panel appointed by Treasury Secretary Robert Rubin. The adopted motif depicts Sacagawea, a young Native American Shoshone, as rendered by artist Glenna Goodacre. On her back she carries Jean Baptiste, her infant son. The reverse shows an eagle in flight, designed by Mint engraver Thomas D. Rogers Sr.

The composition exemplifies the spirit of Liberty, Peace, and Freedom shown by Sacagawea in her conduct as interpreter and guide to explorers Meriwether Lewis and William Clark during their famed journey westward from the great northern plains to the Pacific.

These coins have a distinctive golden color and a plain edge to distinguish them from other denominations or coins of a similar size. The change in composition and appearance was mandated under the United States Dollar Coin Act of 1997.

Several distinctive finishes can be identified on the Sacagawea dollars as a result of the mint attempting to adjust the dies, blanks, strikes, or finishing to produce coins with minimal spotting and a better surface color. One group of 5,000 pieces dated 2000, with a special finish were presented to sculptor Glenna Goodacre in payment for the obverse design. Unexplained error coins made from mismatched dies (a state quarter obverse combined with a Sacagawea dollar reverse) are extremely rare.

	Mintage	MS-63	PF-63	PF-65
2000P	767,140,000	$1		
2000D	518,916,000	1		
2000S	(4,047,904)		$3	$6

	Mintage	MS-63	PF-63	PF-65
2001P	62,468,000	$1.00		
2001D	70,939,500	1.00		
2001S	(3,183,740)		$20	$40
2002P	3,865,610	1.10		
2002D	3,732,000	1.10		
2002S	(3,211,995)		8	15
2003P	3,080,000	1.20		
2003D	3,080,000	1.20		
2003S	(3,298,439)		4	8
2004P	2,660,000	1.10		
2004D	2,660,000	1.10		
2004S	(2,965,422)		4	8
2005P	2,520,000	1.10		
2005D	2,520,000	1.10		

	Mintage	MS-63	PF-63	PF-65
2005S	(3,344,679)		$3	$5
2006P	4,900,000	$1.10		
2006D	2,800,000	1.10		
2006S	(3,054,436)		3	5
2007P (a)	3,640,000	1.10		
2007D (a)	3,920,000	1.10		
2007S	(2,259,847)		3	5
2008P (a)	1,820,000	1.10		
2008D (a)	1,820,000	1.10		
2008S	(1,998,108)		3	5
2009P		1.10		
2009D		1.10		
2009S			3	5

a. Not issued for circulation.

PRESIDENTIAL DOLLARS (2006–2016)

Four different coins, each bearing the image of a former U.S. president, are issued each year in the order that the presidents served. The size and composition of these coins is the same as that of the Sacagawea dollars that are also made each year. A companion series of $10 gold bullion coins (listed in the Bullion section) honors the spouse of each president.

Presidential Dollars Reverse

Date, Mintmark, and Mottos Incused on Edge

	Mintage	MS-65	PF-65
2007P, Washington	176,680,000	$1	$3
2007D, Washington	163,680,000	1	3
2007S, Washington	(3,165,183)	1	3
2007P, J. Adams	112,420,000	1	3
2007D, J. Adams	112,140,000	1	3
2007S, J. Adams	(3,362,237)	1	3

	Mintage	MS-65	PF-65
2007P, Jefferson	100,800,000	$1	$3
2007D, Jefferson	102,810,000	1	3
2007S, Jefferson	(3,362,237)	1	3
2007P, Madison		1	3
2007D, Madison		1	3
2007S, Madison	(3,362,237)	1	3

	Mintage	MS-65	PF-65		Mintage	MS-65	PF-65
2008P, Monroe	$1	$3		2008P, Jackson	$1	$3
2008D, Monroe	1	3		2008D, Jackson	1	3
2008S, Monroe	1	3		2008S, Jackson	1	3
2008P, J.Q. Adams	1	3		2008P, Van Buren	1	3
2008D, J.Q. Adams	1	3		2008D, Van Buren	1	3
2008S, J.Q. Adams	1	3		2008S, Van Buren	1	3

Note: Errors have been reported in the Presidential dollar series, including coins minted without edge lettering. Depending on their rarity, dealers may pay a premium for such errors.

	Mintage	MS-65	PF-65		Mintage	MS-65	PF-65
2009P, Harrison	$1	$3		2009P, Polk	$1	$3
2009D, Harrison	1	3		2009D, Polk	1	3
2009S, Harrison	1	3		2009S, Polk	1	3
2009P, Tyler	1	3		2009P, Taylor	1	3
2009D, Tyler	1	3		2009D, Taylor	1	3
2009S, Tyler	1	3		2009S, Taylor	1	3

Coinage of the gold dollar was authorized by the Act of March 3, 1849. The weight was 25.8 grains, fineness .900. The first type, struck until 1854, is known as the Liberty Head type.

In 1854, the piece was made larger in diameter and thinner. The design was changed to a feather headdress on a female, generally referred to as the Indian Princess Head type. In 1856 the type was changed slightly by enlarging the size of the head.

LIBERTY HEAD (1849–1854)

VF-20 Very Fine: LIBERTY on headband complete and legible. Knobs on coronet defined.
EF-40 Extremely Fine: Slight wear on Liberty's hair. Knobs on coronet sharp.
AU-50 About Uncirculated: Trace of wear on headband. Nearly full luster.
AU-55 Choice About Uncirculated: Evidence of friction on design high points.
MS-60 Uncirculated: No trace of wear. Light marks and blemishes.
MS-63 Choice Uncirculated: Some distracting contact marks or blemishes in prime focal areas. Impaired luster possible.

	Mintage	VF-20	EF-40	AU-50	AU-55	MS-60	MS-63
1849	688,567	$100	$150	$175	$200	$295	$1,300
1849, No L on Truncation	*	100	150	175	200	325	1,500
1849C	11,634	700	1,000	1,450	2,000	4,600	10,000
1849D	21,588	900	1,200	1,500	2,300	3,900	6,000
1849O	21,500	120	180	235	385	600	2,000
1850	481,953	100	150	160	175	275	800
1850C	6,966	725	1,000	1,700	3,400	6,000	17,000
1850D	8,382	900	1,150	2,100	3,600	7,200	12,000
1850O	14,000	195	260	550	1,150	2,100	3,750
1851	3,317,671	100	150	160	175	210	800
1851C	41,267	800	975	1,250	1,600	1,900	4,750
1851D	9,882	850	1,150	1,500	1,800	3,700	9,000
1851O	290,000	130	165	180	240	500	1,500
1852	2,045,351	100	150	160	175	210	800
1852C	9,434	750	1,000	1,250	1,500	2,750	7,200
1852D	6,360	950	1,250	1,500	1,850	5,000	1,900
1852O	140,000	120	190	250	475	850	3,900
1853	4,076,051	100	150	160	175	210	800
1853C	11,515	750	900	1,500	1,900	3,800	8,500
1853D	6,583	900	1,200	1,900	3,200	6,000	17,000
1853O	290,000	125	165	170	240	450	1,600
1854	855,502	100	150	160	175	210	800
1854D	2,935	950	1,400	3,000	4,000	7,000	20,000
1854S	14,632	210	320	460	850	1,700	3,400

* Included in number above.

INDIAN PRINCESS HEAD,
SMALL HEAD (1854–1856)

VF-20 Very Fine: Feather-curl tips on headdress outlined but details worn.

EF-40 Extremely Fine: Slight wear on tips of feather curls on headdress.

AU-50 About Uncirculated: Trace of wear on feathers, nearly full luster.

AU-55 Choice About Uncirculated: Evidence of friction on design high points. Most of original mint luster present.

MS-60 Uncirculated: No trace of wear. Light marks and blemishes.

MS-63 Choice Uncirculated: Some distracting contact marks or blemishes in prime focal areas. Impaired luster possible.

PF-63 Choice Proof: Reflective surfaces with only a few blemishes in secondary focal areas. No major flaws.

	Mintage	VF-20	EF-40	AU-50	AU-55	MS-60	MS-63	PF-63
1854	783,943	$225	$340	$415	$850	$1,800	$7,500	—
1855	758,269	225	340	415	850	1,800	7,500	—
1855C	9,803	875	2,250	3,750	6,750	17,500		
1855D	1,811	3,200	6,750	16,500	21,000	37,000	67,500	
1855O	55,000	325	440	985	1,850	4,700	16,000	
1856S	24,600	575	950	1,350	2,100	5,200	25,000	

INDIAN PRINCESS HEAD,
LARGE HEAD (1856–1889)

VF-20 Very Fine: Slight detail in curled feathers in headdress. Details worn smooth at eyebrow, hair below headdress, and behind ear and bottom curl.

EF-40 Extremely Fine: Slight wear above and to right of eye and on top of curled feathers.

AU-50 About Uncirculated: Trace of wear on feathers, nearly full luster.

AU-55 Choice About Uncirculated: Evidence of friction on design high points. Most of original mint luster present.

MS-60 Uncirculated: No trace of wear. Light marks and blemishes.

MS-63 Choice Uncirculated: Some distracting contact marks or blemishes in prime focal areas. Impaired luster possible.

PF-63 Choice Proof: Reflective surfaces with only a few blemishes in secondary focal places. No major flaws.

	Mintage	VF-20	EF-40	AU-50	AU-55	MS-60	MS-63	PF-63
1856	1,762,936	$115	$165	$175	$200	$220	$750	$16,000
1856D	1,460	2,600	4,100	5,500	8,600	22,000	40,000	
1857	774,789	115	160	170	195	215	725	8,500
1857C	13,280	725	925	2,300	3,200	8,200	21,000	
1857D	3,533	775	1,150	2,750	3,650	7,700	25,000	
1857S	10,000	375	425	850	1,150	4,200	14,500	
1858	117,995	115	160	170	195	215	725	4,900
1858D	3,477	950	1,250	2,150	3,000	6,000	16,500	

GOLD DOLLARS

	Mintage	VF-20	EF-40	AU-50	AU-55	MS-60	MS-63	PF-63
1858S	10,000	$275	$340	$870	$1,050	$3,950	$12,000	
1859	.....(80) 168,244	115	160	170	195	215	725	$3,500
1859C	5,235	750	1,000	2,200	4,000	8,000	22,000	
1859D	4,952	750	850	1,900	3,150	7,250	16,000	
1859S	15,000	175	375	800	1,350	3,750	11,000	
1860	.....(154) 36,514	115	160	170	195	275	750	3,500
1860D	1,566	1,850	3,750	4,750	6,500	12,000	38,000	
1860S	13,000	220	350	470	750	1,800	3,800	
1861	.....(349) 527,150	100	160	170	195	225	750	3,750
1861D	1,250	5,000	7,500	14,000	16,000	23,500	45,000	
1862	.....(35) ...1,361,355	100	160	170	195	220	750	4,350
1863	.....(50) 6,200	335	650	1,250	1,500	2,950	5,100	4,000
1864	.....(50) 5,900	275	325	560	650	750	1,950	5,750
1865	.....(25) 3,725	275	350	575	650	1,100	2,200	4,000
1866	.....(30) 7,100	275	350	500	575	750	1,400	4,250
1867	.....(50) 5,200	325	375	500	575	850	1,450	4,250
1868	.....(25) 10,500	175	275	325	375	750	1,400	4,750
1869	.....(25) 5,900	225	300	475	550	850	1,400	4,750
1870	.....(35) 6,300	225	300	360	425	750	1,400	4,750
1870S	3,000	375	575	875	1,200	1,800	5,250	
1871	.....(30) 3,900	225	275	310	400	600	1,400	3,750
1872	.....(30) 3,500	225	275	310	425	600	1,400	5,500
1873, Close 3	.....(25) 1,800	275	550	700	800	1,200	2,800	10,500
1873, Open 3	123,300	100	160	170	190	220	750	
1874	.....(20) 198,800	100	160	170	190	220	750	5,750
1875	.....(20) 400	1,400	2,800	3,500	3,750	5,250	8,000	10,500
1876	.....(45) 3,200	180	210	300	365	500	750	3,900
1877	.....(20) 3,900	160	210	300	365	500	750	4,700
1878	.....(20) 3,000	160	210	300	365	500	750	3,900
1879	.....(30) 3,000	120	180	210	250	360	750	4,100
1880	.....(36) 1,600	120	175	180	215	325	750	3,700
1881	.....(87) 7,620	120	175	180	215	325	750	3,700
1882	.....(125) 5,000	120	165	180	215	325	750	3,500
1883	.....(207) 10,800	120	165	180	215	325	750	3,500
1884	.....(1,006) 5,230	120	165	180	215	325	750	3,500
1885	.....(1,105) 11,156	120	165	180	215	325	750	3,500
1886	.....(1,016) 5,000	120	165	180	215	325	750	3,500
1887	.....(1,043) 7,500	120	165	180	215	325	750	3,500
1888	.....(1,079) 15,501	120	165	180	215	325	750	3,500
1889	.....(1,779) 28,950	120	165	180	215	325	750	3,500

Although authorized by the Act of April 2, 1792, coinage of quarter eagles ($2.50 gold coins) was not begun until 1796.

CAPPED BUST TO RIGHT (1796–1807)

F-12 Fine: Hair worn smooth on high spots. E PLURIBUS UNUM on ribbon weak but legible.
VF-20 Very Fine: Some wear on high spots.
EF-40 Extremely Fine: Only slight wear on Liberty's hair and cheek.
AU-50 About Uncirculated: Trace of wear on cap, hair, cheek, and drapery.
AU-55 Choice About Uncirculated: Evidence of friction on design high points. Some original mint luster.
MS-60 Uncirculated: No trace of wear. Light blemishes.

	No Stars on Obverse (1796)		Stars on Obverse (1796–1807)			

	Mintage	F-12	VF-20	EF-40	AU-50	AU-55	MS-60
1796, No Stars on Obverse	963	$22,000	$29,000	$55,000	$70,000	$80,000	$140,000
1796, Stars on Obverse	432	18,000	27,000	46,000	60,000	70,000	125,000
1797	427	11,000	13,000	21,000	38,000	42,000	85,000
1798	1,094	3,500	5,500	7,200	15,000	22,000	45,000
1802, 2 Over 1	3,035	3,500	5,500	6,200	8,500	12,000	18,000
1804, 13-Star Reverse	*	19,000	24,000	60,000	90,000	115,000	185,000
1804, 14-Star Reverse	3,327	3,250	5,000	6,500	9,000	10,500	17,000
1805	1,781	3,250	5,000	6,500	8,000	10,500	17,000
1806, 6/4, 8 Stars Left, 5 Right	1,136	3,500	5,250	6,750	8,500	12,000	18,000
1806, 6/5, 7 Stars Left, 6 Right	480	4,500	6,500	9,000	15,000	22,000	55,000
1807	6,812	3,250	4,800	5,750	8,500	10,500	16,000

* Included in number below.

CAPPED BUST TO LEFT, LARGE SIZE (1808)

F-12 Fine: E PLURIBUS UNUM on reverse, and LIBERTY on headband, legible but weak.
VF-20 Very Fine: Motto and LIBERTY clear.
EF-40 Extremely Fine: All details of hair plain.
AU-50 About Uncirculated: Trace of wear above eye, on top of cap, and on cheek and hair.
AU-55 Choice About Uncirculated: Evidence of friction on design high points. Some original mint luster present.
MS-60 Uncirculated: No trace of wear. Light blemishes.

	Mintage	F-12	VF-20	EF-40	AU-50	AU-55	MS-60
1808	2,710	$18,000	$24,000	$31,000	$60,000	$73,000	$110,000

CAPPED HEAD TO LEFT (1821–1834)

Those dated 1829 to 1834 are smaller in diameter than the 1821 to 1827 pieces.

	Mintage	F-12	VF-20	EF-40	AU-50	AU-55	MS-60
1821	6,448	$3,500	$4,750	$6,000	$7,500	$8,500	$17,500
1824, 4 Over 1	2,600	3,500	4,750	6,000	7,500	8,500	15,000
1825	4,434	3,500	4,750	6,000	7,500	8,500	13,000
1826, 6 Over 6	760	4,000	5,500	6,250	8,000	12,000	25,000
1827	2,800	3,750	5,250	6,000	7,500	8,500	15,000
1829	3,403	3,500	4,250	5,000	6,500	8,000	10,000
1830	4,540	3,500	4,250	5,000	6,500	8,000	10,000
1831	4,520	3,500	4,250	5,000	6,500	8,000	10,000
1832	4,400	3,500	4,250	5,000	6,500	8,000	11,000
1833	4,160	3,500	4,250	5,250	6,750	8,000	12,000
1834, With Motto	4,000	5,000	7,500	11,000	15,000	19,000	27,000

CLASSIC HEAD, NO MOTTO ON REVERSE (1834–1839)

In 1834, the quarter eagle was redesigned. A ribbon binding the hair, bearing the word LIBERTY, replaces the Liberty cap. The motto was omitted from the reverse.

F-12 Fine: LIBERTY on headband legible and complete. Curl under ear outlined but no detail.
VF-20 Very Fine: LIBERTY plain; detail in hair curl.
EF-40 Extremely Fine: Small amount of wear on top of hair and below L in LIBERTY. Wear evident on wing.
AU-50 About Uncirculated: Trace of wear on coronet and hair above ear.
AU-55 Choice About Uncirculated: Evidence of friction on design high points. Some of original mint luster present.
MS-60 Uncirculated: No trace of wear. Light blemishes.
MS-63 Choice Uncirculated: Some distracting contact marks or blemishes in prime focal areas. Impaired luster possible.

Mintmark location.

	Mintage	F-12	VF-20	EF-40	AU-50	AU-55	MS-60	MS-63
1834, No Motto	112,234	$185	$300	$425	$750	$900	$2,200	$5,000
1835	131,402	185	300	425	750	900	2,200	5,500
1836	547,986	185	300	425	750	900	2,200	5,250
1837	45,080	200	300	425	750	900	2,700	9,500
1838	47,030	200	300	425	750	900	2,200	5,500
1838C	7,880	800	1,100	2,000	5,000	6,750	17,500	30,000
1839	27,021	215	350	600	1,350	2,000	3,800	15,000
1839C	18,140	800	1,200	1,700	3,000	5,000	14,500	32,000
1839D	13,674	800	1,200	2,300	4,500	6,750	17,000	35,000
18390	9,369	325	425	750	1,400	1,900	4,500	17,000

LIBERTY HEAD (1840–1907)

Mintmark location.

4 Plain 4

4 Crosslet 4

	Mintage	VF-20	EF-40	AU-50	AU-55	MS-60	MS-63
1840	18,859	$150	$650	$2,000	$2,350	$4,750	$9,000
1840C	12,822	850	1,200	3,100	4,300	9,000	20,000
1840D	3,532	2,000	5,000	7,000	13,000	23,000	
18400	33,580	185	550	1,300	2,300	7,000	18,500

Chart continued on next page. 147

	Mintage	VF-20	EF-40	AU-50	AU-55	MS-60	MS-63
1841	(unknown)	$36,000	$70,000	$80,000	$85,000	$110,000	
1841C	10,281	850	1,200	2,000	4,800	10,000	$32,500
1841D	4,164	1,000	2,700	7,000	9,000	17,500	38,000
1842	2,823	700	1,850	4,750	7,000	15,000	37,500
1842C	6,729	1,000	2,300	5,250	7,000	18,000	35,000
1842D	4,643	1,250	2,750	8,250	12,500	25,000	40,000
1842O	19,800	250	700	1,500	3,000	7,500	20,000
1843	100,546	135	210	300	650	1,750	3,500
1843C	26,064	850	1,200	2,100	3,000	6,500	14,000
1843D	36,209	900	1,300	2,100	5,500	7,000	20,000
1843O	364,002	140	180	265	550	1,500	6,000
1844	6,784	275	650	1,450	3,250	5,500	16,500
1844C	11,622	900	1,500	4,500	7,000	13,000	33,000
1844D	17,332	1,000	1,400	2,000	3,500	5,100	18,000
1845	91,051	190	230	275	375	875	3,500
1845D	19,460	1,000	1,400	2,600	5,000	10,000	26,000
1845O	4,000	725	1,650	4,500	5,250	14,000	37,500
1846	21,598	200	375	650	1,500	4,000	17,500
1846C	4,808	975	1,850	6,500	8,500	13,000	27,000
1846D	19,303	1,000	1,400	2,000	3,500	8,000	20,000
1846O	62,000	220	300	800	1,500	4,750	14,500
1847	29,814	170	275	625	850	2,650	6,500
1847C	23,226	850	1,200	1,800	2,500	4,800	11,000
1847D	15,784	975	1,425	2,000	3,200	7,500	18,500
1847O	124,000	165	275	750	1,250	3,000	13,500
1848	6,500	375	650	1,350	2,250	4,500	12,000

CAL. Gold Quarter Eagle (1848)

In 1848, about 230 ounces of gold were sent to Secretary of War William L. Marcy by Colonel R.B. Mason, military governor of California. The gold was turned over to the Mint and made into quarter eagles. The distinguishing mark "CAL." was punched above the eagle on the reverse side, while the coins were in the die.

CAL. Above Eagle on Reverse (1848)

	Mintage	VF-20	EF-40	AU-50	AU-55	MS-60	MS-63
1848, CAL. Above Eagle	1,389	$11,000	$22,000	$26,000	$32,500	$45,000	$57,000
1848C	16,788	850	1,250	2,350	3,000	8,500	23,000
1848D	13,771	1,000	1,450	2,250	3,000	7,000	22,000
1849	23,294	200	340	625	900	1,500	5,000
1849C	10,220	800	1,200	3,500	3,500	14,000	35,000
1849D	10,945	900	1,200	2,750	4,000	9,000	
1850	252,923	135	165	275	375	800	2,900
1850C	9,148	800	1,100	2,650	5,000	10,000	27,000
1850D	12,148	900	1,100	2,450	4,750	9,000	32,000

	Mintage	VF-20	EF-40	AU-50	AU-55	MS-60	MS-63	PF-63
1850O	84,000	$160	$350	$900	$1,350	$3,500	$10,000	
1851	1,372,748	135	155	175	190	240	900	
1851C	14,923	850	1,200	3,500	4,500	9,250	27,500	
1851D	11,264	1,000	1,500	3,000	4,750	9,000	23,500	
1851O	148,000	140	160	650	1,250	3,000	9,500	
1852	1,159,681	135	155	175	190	250	900	
1852C	9,772	850	1,300	3,350	5,000	11,000	25,000	
1852D	4,078	1,000	1,950	5,500	6,250	12,500	30,000	
1852O	140,000	140	230	700	1,200	3,750	9,000	
1853	1,404,668	135	155	175	195	275	900	
1853D	3,178	1,200	2,250	3,700	5,000	12,000	35,000	
1854	596,258	130	155	175	195	275	1,175	
1854C	7,295	850	1,550	3,900	5,250	10,000	30,000	
1854D	1,760	2,100	4,000	8,500	12,500	20,000	55,000	
1854O	153,000	135	165	325	550	1,200	6,000	
1854S	246	80,000	150,000	225,000				
1855	235,480	135	155	175	195	280	1,250	
1855C	3,677	1,100	2,000	4,500	6,000	17,000	33,000	
1855D	1,123	2,500	5,750	13,500	20,000	38,000	62,500	
1856	384,240	135	155	175	200	300	1,100	$35,000
1856C	7,913	900	1,750	3,000	5,000	10,000	20,000	
1856D	874	5,000	9,000	19,000	25,000	55,000	95,000	
1856O	21,100	155	525	925	2,400	4,000	23,500	
1856S	72,120	150	275	675	1,200	3,350	8,000	
1857	214,130	135	155	175	210	300	1,300	30,000
1857D	2,364	1,000	1,950	2,950	4,750	9,750	22,000	
1857O	34,000	150	275	750	1,250	3,250	9,500	
1857S	69,200	150	260	650	1,500	4,000	9,500	
1858	47,377	135	185	265	350	800	2,500	21,000
1858C	9,056	850	1,200	2,250	2,600	7,000	25,000	
1859 (80)	39,364	135	190	300	400	925	2,400	14,000
1859D	2,244	1,250	2,250	3,600	5,000	14,500	50,000	
1859S	15,200	235	700	1,900	2,600	5,000	13,000	
1860 (112)	22,563	135	190	350	400	850	1,800	13,500
1860C	7,469	850	1,400	2,800	6,000	16,500	28,000	
1860S	35,600	165	500	850	1,200	3,000	8,000	
1861 (90)	1,283,788	135	155	180	195	250	800	14,500
1861S	24,000	260	675	2,250	3,100	5,800	13,000	
1862, 2 Over 1	*	650	1,300	2,600	3,200	6,250		
1862 (35)	98,508	150	235	375	450	925	2,850	12,500
1862S	8,000	650	1,600	3,300	4,750	13,500	28,500	
1863, Proof only (30)								36,000
1863S	10,800	360	1,100	2,400	4,000	10,500	20,000	
1864 (50)	2,824	4,250	8,500	17,500	20,000	30,000		9,000
1865 (25)	1,520	3,600	5,500	14,500	16,000	28,000	34,000	11,500
1865S	23,376	160	475	1,100	1,500	3,350	7,500	
1866 (30)	3,080	950	2,650	4,250	5,500	9,000	19,000	8,000
1866S	38,960	210	475	1,100	1,650	4,750	15,500	
1867 (50)	3,200	275	600	875	1,250	3,000	6,000	8,000
1867S	28,000	180	475	900	1,500	3,100	9,000	
1868 (25)	3,600	170	300	500	650	1,175	5,500	9,000

* Included in number below.

Chart continued on next page.

QUARTER EAGLES

	Mintage	VF-20	EF-40	AU-50	AU-55	MS-60	MS-63	PF-63
1868S	.34,000	$140	$225	$825	$1,000	$3,000	$9,000	
1869	(25) 4,320	180	250	550	900	2,400	5,500	$6,500
1869S	.29,500	165	360	625	1,250	3,200	6,750	
1870	(35) 4,520	175	325	575	950	2,850	6,000	6,750
1870S	.16,000	140	325	600	1,250	3,200	10,500	
1871	(30) 5,320	180	250	450	625	1,750	3,000	6,750
1871S	.22,000	140	210	415	575	1,725	3,600	
1872	(30) 3,000	280	600	825	1,750	3,600	9,000	5,750
1872S	.18,000	140	280	700	1,200	3,450	8,500	
1873	(25) ...178,000	135	155	185	200	300	800	5,500
1873S	.27,000	160	280	675	800	2,100	6,250	
1874	(20) 3,920	185	280	550	725	1,650	4,500	7,500
1875	(20) 400	3,000	4,000	7,000	8,500	15,000	24,000	17,000
1875S	.11,600	135	225	600	900	3,350	6,750	
1876	(45) 4,176	215	500	700	1,250	2,600	4,600	5,500
1876S	.5,000	175	400	725	1,500	2,600	7,000	
1877	(20) 1,632	280	600	825	1,150	2,350	7,000	6,000
1877S	.35,400	135	150	180	210	475	1,800	
1878	(20) ...286,240	125	150	180	200	300	800	8,750
1878S	.178,000	125	150	180	200	260	1,500	
1879	(30) ...88,960	120	150	175	190	260	800	6,250
1879S	.43,500	150	210	375	725	1,600	3,800	
1880	(36) 2,960	160	260	475	625	1,000	2,800	6,250
1881	(51) 640	1,500	2,400	3,500	4,200	6,500	12,000	6,000
1882	(67) 4,000	150	225	310	390	525	2,000	4,500
1883	(82) 1,920	150	300	750	975	1,500	4,000	4,500
1884	(73) 1,950	150	300	450	600	1,200	2,250	4,500
1885	(87) 800	475	1,300	1,800	2,000	3,500	6,000	4,750
1886	(88) 4,000	150	200	325	375	850	1,800	4,750
1887	(122) 6,160	140	190	260	300	525	1,800	4,350
1888	(97) ...16,001	135	170	210	220	240	800	4,350
1889	(48) ...17,600	135	160	200	210	250	800	5,250
1890	(93) 8,720	140	175	220	240	375	850	4,500
1891	(80) ...10,960	120	155	180	200	310	850	4,250
1892	(105) 2,440	140	180	250	290	575	1,950	4,250
1893	(106) ...30,000	120	150	170	190	220	800	4,250
1894	(122) 4,000	125	170	240	260	600	1,250	4,250
1895	(119) 6,000	120	160	210	225	300	850	4,250
1896	(132) ...19,070	120	150	175	190	220	800	4,250
1897	(136) ...29,768	120	150	175	190	220	800	4,100
1898	(165) ...24,000	120	150	175	190	220	800	4,250
1899	(150) ...27,200	120	150	175	190	220	800	4,100
1900	(205) ...67,000	120	160	200	210	220	800	4,100
1901	(223) ...91,100	120	150	175	190	220	800	4,100
1902	(193) ...133,540	120	150	175	190	220	800	4,100
1903	(197) ...201,060	120	150	175	190	220	800	4,100
1904	(170) ...160,790	120	150	175	190	220	800	4,100
1905	(144) ...217,800	120	150	175	190	220	800	4,100
1906	(160) ...176,330	120	150	175	190	220	800	4,100
1907	(154) ...336,294	120	150	175	190	220	800	4,100

INDIAN HEAD (1908–1929)

Bela Lyon Pratt designed this coin and the similar $5 gold piece. The design is incuse.

VF-20 Very Fine: Hair-cord knot distinct. Feathers at top of head clear. Cheekbone worn.
EF-40 Extremely Fine: Cheekbone, war bonnet, and headband feathers slightly worn.
AU-50 About Uncirculated: Trace of wear on cheekbone and headdress.
MS-60 Uncirculated: No trace of wear. Light blemishes.
MS-63 Choice Uncirculated: Some distracting contact marks or blemishes in prime focal areas. Impaired luster possible.
MS-64 Uncirculated: A few scattered contact marks visible. Good eye appeal and attractive luster.
Matte PF-63 Choice Proof: Few blemishes in secondary focal areas. No major flaws. Matte surfaces.

Mintmark location is on reverse, to left of arrows.

	Mintage	VF-20	EF-40	AU-50	MS-60	MS-63	MS-64	MATTE PF-63
1908 . . . .(236) 564,821		$125	$150	$160	$240	$1,200	$1,600	$5,500
1909 . . . .(139) 441,760		125	150	160	250	1,600	2,100	5,500
1910 . . . .(682) 492,000		125	150	160	250	1,500	2,100	5,500
1911 . . . .(191) 704,000		125	150	160	250	1,200	1,800	5,500
1911D 55,680		1,800	3,200	3,500	7,500	18,500	25,000	
1912 . . . .(197) 616,000		125	150	160	250	1,700	2,700	5,500
1913 . . . .(165) 722,000		125	150	160	250	1,100	1,900	5,750
1914 . . . .(117) 240,000		130	165	180	400	3,500	6,500	5,750
1914D 448,000		125	150	160	250	1,700	4,000	
1915 . . . .(100) 606,000		125	150	160	250	1,000	1,750	6,000
1925D 578,000		125	150	160	240	800	1,200	
1926 446,000		125	150	160	240	800	1,200	
1927 388,000		125	150	160	240	800	1,200	
1928 416,000		125	150	160	240	800	1,200	
1929 532,000		125	150	160	240	800	1,200	

THREE-DOLLAR GOLD PIECES

The three-dollar gold piece was authorized by the Act of February 21, 1853. Coinage was struck beginning in 1854. It was never popular and saw very little circulation.

VF-20 Very Fine: Eyebrow, hair about forehead and ear, and bottom curl all worn smooth. Faint details visible on curled feather-ends of headdress.

EF-40 Extremely Fine: Light wear above and to right of eye, and on top of curled feathers.

AU-50 About Uncirculated: Trace of wear on top of curled feathers and in hair above and to right of eye.

AU-55 Choice About Uncirculated: Evidence of friction on design high points. Much of original mint luster present.

MS-60 Uncirculated: No trace of wear. Light blemishes.

MS-63 Choice Uncirculated: Some distracting contact marks or blemishes in prime focal areas. Impaired luster possible.

Mintmark location is on reverse, below wreath.

PF-63 Choice Proof: Reflective surfaces with only a few blemishes in secondary focal places. No major flaws.

	Mintage	VF-20	EF-40	AU-50	AU-55	MS-60	MS-63	PF-63
1854	138,618	$625	$900	$1,250	$1,700	$2,200	$5,250	$50,000
1854D	1,120	7,500	14,000	25,000	37,000	60,000		
1854O	24,000	850	1,600	2,700	6,500	15,000	25,000	
1855	50,555	575	850	1,100	1,400	2,100	6,000	28,000
1855S	6,600	900	1,800	4,750	7,000	18,000	67,000	
1856	26,010	650	950	1,200	1,700	2,200	6,250	17,000
1856S	34,500	700	1,100	2,000	4,000	8,500	18,000	
1857	20,891	650	950	1,200	1,800	2,250	7,500	15,000
1857S	14,000	750	1,600	4,000	5,500	14,000		
1858	2,133	800	1,300	1,900	3,400	6,000	14,000	16,500
1859	(80) 15,558	675	875	1,200	1,500	2,100	6,000	12,000
1860	(119) 7,036	675	875	1,200	1,600	2,300	6,000	8,000
1860S	7,000	700	1,500	4,500	7,000	15,000	35,500	
1861	(113) 5,959	675	875	1,400	1,600	3,000	7,000	12,000
1862	(35) 5,750	675	875	1,400	1,600	3,000	7,000	9,000
1863	(39) 5,000	675	875	1,400	1,600	3,000	7,000	10,000
1864	(50) 2,630	675	975	1,500	1,700	3,200	7,000	10,000
1865	(25) 1,140	950	1,900	3,800	4,800	7,000	13,000	15,000
1866	(30) 4,000	675	875	1,300	1,700	3,000	7,500	10,000
1867	(50) 2,600	675	875	1,300	1,700	3,000	7,500	10,000
1868	(25) 4,850	675	875	1,300	1,700	2,500	7,000	10,000
1869	(25) 2,500	675	875	1,300	1,700	3,000	8,000	10,000
1870	(35) 3,500	675	950	1,400	1,800	3,100	8,000	10,000
1870S *(unique)*		—						
1871	(30) 1,300	700	950	1,300	1,700	3,200	7,250	10,000
1872	(30) 2,000	700	950	1,300	1,700	3,200	7,250	10,000
1873, Open 3 (Original)	(25)	3,400	5,000	14,000	18,000			19,000
1873, Close 3		2,500	4,000	7,000	11,000	22,000	32,000	20,000
1874	(20) 41,800	650	900	1,100	1,600	2,100	5,000	13,000
1875, Proof only	(20)			36,000	50,000			75,000
1876, Proof only	(45)			12,000	16,000			25,000
1877	(20) 1,468	1,200	2,700	5,500	7,500	14,000	28,000	15,000
1878	(20) 82,304	600	850	1,200	1,600	2,100	5,000	13,000
1879	(30) 3,000	625	900	1,300	1,750	2,200	5,250	11,000
1880	(36) 1,000	650	1,400	1,700	1,825	2,500	5,250	11,000
1881	(54) 500	1,100	2,100	3,600	4,200	5,500	11,000	11,000
1882	(76) 1,500	675	900	1,300	1,600	2,500	5,250	8,500
1883	(89) 900	700	1,100	1,675	2,000	2,700	5,250	8,500
1884	(106) 1,000	700	1,300	1,750	2,000	2,700	5,250	8,500
1885	(109) 801	700	1,300	1,800	2,200	3,500	9,000	9,000
1886	(142) 1,000	700	1,100	1,750	2,000	3,200	6,250	8,500
1887	(160) 6,000	600	850	1,300	1,600	2,500	5,000	8,500
1888	(291) 5,000	600	850	1,200	1,600	2,200	5,000	8,500
1889	(129) 2,300	600	850	1,200	1,600	2,200	5,000	8,500

STELLA (1879–1880)

These pattern coins were first suggested by the Hon. John A. Kasson, then U.S. envoy extraordinary and minister plenipotentiary to Austria-Hungary. It was through the efforts of Dr. W.W. Hubbell, who patented the alloy goloid (used in making another pattern piece, the goloid metric dollar) that we have these beautiful and interesting coins.

The $4 Stella—so called because of the five-pointed star on the reverse—was envisioned by Kasson as America's answer to various foreign gold coins popular in the international market. The British sovereign, Italy's 20 lire, and the 20 pesetas of Spain were three such coins: each smaller than a U.S. $5 gold piece, they were used widely in international trade.

The Stella was one of many proposals made to Congress for an international trade coin, and one of only several that made it to pattern coin form (others include the 1868 $5 and 1874 Bickford $10).

Odds were stacked against the Stella from the start. The denomination of four U.S. dollars didn't match any of the coin's European counterparts, and at any rate the U.S. double eagle ($20 coin)—already used in international commerce—was a more convenient medium of exchange. The Stella was never minted in quantities for circulation.

There are two distinct types in both years of issue. Charles E. Barber designed the Flowing Hair type, and George T. Morgan the Coiled Hair. They were struck as patterns in gold, aluminum, copper, and white metal. Only those struck in gold are listed.

Flowing Hair   Coiled Hair

	Mintage	EF-40	AU-50	PF-60	PF-63	PF-65
1879, Flowing Hair	(425+)	$36,000	$47,000	$65,000	$100,000	$140,000
1879, Coiled Hair *(12 known)*		75,000	95,000	125,000	200,000	375,000
1880, Flowing Hair *(17 known)*		65,000	70,000	80,000	135,000	250,000
1880, Coiled Hair *(18 known)*		140,000	170,000	225,000	375,000	700,000

The half eagle ($5 gold coin) was the first gold coin struck for the United States. It was authorized to be coined by the Act of April 2, 1792. The first type weighed 135 grains, of .91667 fineness. The weight was changed by the Act of June 28, 1834, to 129 grains, of .899225 fineness. Fineness became .900 by the Act of January 18, 1837.

CAPPED BUST TO RIGHT (1795–1807)

F-12 Fine: Liberty's hair worn smooth but with distinct outline. For heraldic type, E PLURIBUS UNUM faint but legible.
VF-20 Very Fine: Slight to noticeable wear on high spots such as hair, turban, and eagle's head and wings.
EF-40 Extremely Fine: Slight wear on hair and highest part of cheek.
AU-50 About Uncirculated: Trace of wear on cap, hair, cheek, and drapery.
MS-60 Uncirculated: No trace of wear. Light blemishes.
MS-63 Choice Uncirculated: Some distracting marks or blemishes in focal areas. Impaired luster possible.

Small Eagle (1795–1798)

1795
Obverse

1795
Reverse

1796, 6 Over 5

1797, 15 Stars

1797, 16 Stars

	Mintage	F-12	VF-20	EF-40	AU-50	AU-55	MS-60	MS-63
1795, Small Eagle 8,707		$8,500	$12,000	$15,000	$21,000	$25,000	$40,000	$110,000
1796, 6 Over 5 6,196		9,000	15,000	20,000	25,000	30,000	55,000	140,000
1797, 15 Stars 3,609		10,000	15,000	24,000	50,000	65,000	100,000	
1797, 16 Stars 3,609		10,000	15,000	22,000	45,000	55,000	90,000	
1798, Small Eagle *(7 known)*	65,000	120,000	150,000	250,000	400,000	—		

Heraldic Eagle (1795–1807)

	Mintage	F-12	VF-20	EF-40	AU-50	AU-55	MS-60	MS-63
1795, Heraldic Eagle . . . .*		$7,000	$10,000	$16,000	$30,000	$36,000	$55,000	$115,000
1797, 7 Over 5 . . . .*		7,000	10,000	16,500	35,000	42,500	100,000	
1798, Large 8, 13-Star Reverse . . .24,867		1,700	2,300	3,200	6,500	8,000	13,000	
1798, Large 8, 14-Star Reverse . . . .**		2,000	2,700	4,500	10,000	16,000	24,000	
1799 7,451		1,800	2,400	3,000	5,500	6,000	13,000	37,000
1800 37,628		1,750	2,200	2,600	4,700	5,200	8,000	16,000

* Included in number below. ** Included in number above.

	Mintage	F-12	VF-20	EF-40	AU-50	AU-55	MS-60	MS-63
1802, 2 Over 1	53,176	$1,750	$2,200	$2,600	$4,500	$5,000	$7,000	$14,000
1803, 3 Over 2	33,506	1,750	2,200	2,600	4,500	5,000	7,000	14,000
1804	30,475	1,750	2,200	2,600	4,500	5,000	7,000	14,000
1805	33,183	1,750	2,200	2,600	4,500	5,000	7,000	14,000
1806	64,093	1,750	2,200	2,600	4,500	5,000	7,000	14,000
1807	32,488	1,750	2,200	2,600	4,500	5,000	7,000	14,000

CAPPED BUST TO LEFT (1807–1812)

F-12 Fine: LIBERTY on cap legible but partly weak.
VF-20 Very Fine: Headband edges slightly worn. LIBERTY bold.
EF-40 Extremely Fine: Slight wear on highest portions of hair; 80% of major curls plain.
AU-50 About Uncirculated: Trace of wear above eye and on top of cap, cheek, and hair.
AU-55 Choice About Uncirculated: Evidence of friction on design high points. Some mint luster present.
MS-60 Uncirculated: No trace of wear. Light blemishes.
MS-63 Choice Uncirculated: Some distracting contact marks or blemishes in prime focal areas. Impaired luster possible.

	Mintage	F-12	VF-20	EF-40	AU-50	AU-55	MS-60	MS-63
1807	51,605	$1,500	$1,700	$2,500	$4,000	$5,000	$6,000	$12,000
1808, All kinds	55,578							
1808, 8 Over 7		1,700	2,500	3,000	5,000	6,000	8,000	18,000
1808		1,500	1,700	2,500	3,500	5,000	6,000	12,000
1809, 9 Over 8	33,875	1,500	1,700	2,500	3,500	5,000	6,000	12,000
1810	100,287	1,500	1,700	2,500	3,500	5,000	6,000	12,000
1811	99,581	1,500	1,700	2,500	3,500	5,000	6,000	12,000
1812	58,087	1,500	1,700	2,500	3,500	5,000	6,000	12,000

CAPPED HEAD TO LEFT (1813–1834)
Large Diameter (1813–1829)

	Mintage	F-12	VF-20	EF-40	AU-50	AU-55	MS-60	MS-63
1813	95,428	$1,500	$1,900	$2,500	$3,500	$4,000	$6,000	$11,000
1814, 4 Over 3	15,454	1,750	2,000	2,750	4,000	4,750	7,000	19,000
1815	635	25,000	35,000	55,000	90,000	125,000	190,000	300,000
1818	48,588	1,800	2,000	2,500	4,000	4,750	6,500	20,000
1819	51,723	7,500	12,500	17,500	25,000	30,000	40,000	70,000
1820	263,806	1,800	2,000	2,500	4,000	4,750	7,500	17,000
1821	34,641	8,000	12,000	16,000	22,000	35,000	60,000	110,000
1822 (3 known)	17,796			3,000,000				
1823	14,485	1,800	2,500	3,500	5,000	6,500	13,000	22,500
1824	17,340	3,500	7,500	10,500	15,000	17,500	25,000	50,000
1825, 5 Over Partial 4	29,060	3,500	5,500	8,000	12,500	15,000	25,000	50,000
1825, 5 Over 4 (2 known)	*			225,000				
1826	18,069	2,700	5,000	6,500	10,000	12,500	17,500	35,000
1827	24,913	4,500	6,500	8,500	12,500	15,000	25,000	45,000
1828, 8 Over 7 (5 known)	*	10,000	15,000	27,500	40,000	50,000	100,000	250,000
1828	28,029	4,000	8,000	12,500	20,000	25,000	45,000	75,000
1829, Large Date	57,442	10,000	18,000	25,000	40,000	45,000	80,000	150,000

* Included in number above.

Reduced Diameter (1829–1834)

	Mintage	F-12	VF-20	EF-40	AU-50	AU-55	MS-60	MS-63
1829, Small Date ....*		$25,000	$35,000	$60,000	$80,000	$100,000	$150,000	$200,000
1830 126,351		9,500	12,500	13,500	15,500	17,500	25,000	45,000
1831 140,594		9,500	12,500	13,500	15,500	17,500	25,000	45,000
1832, Curved-Base 2,								
12 Stars *(5 known)* 157,487		29,000	50,000	150,000	200,000			
1832, Sq-Base 2, 13 Stars ....**		9,500	12,500	13,500	15,500	18,000	30,000	45,000
1833 193,630		9,500	12,500	13,500	15,500	17,500	25,000	45,000
1834 50,141		9,500	12,500	13,500	15,500	17,500	27,500	47,500

* Included in mintage for 1829, Large Date (previous page). ** Included in number above.

CLASSIC HEAD (1834–1838)

	Mintage	F-12	VF-20	EF-40	AU-50	AU-55	MS-60	MS-63
1834 657,460		$300	$400	$500	$900	$1,100	$2,500	$6,000
1835 371,534		300	400	500	900	1,100	2,500	6,000
1836 553,147		300	400	500	900	1,100	2,500	6,000
1837 207,121		300	400	525	900	1,100	2,600	9,500
1838 286,588		300	400	525	950	1,200	2,600	8,000
1838C 17,179		800	1,500	3,200	7,500	9,500	21,000	55,000
1838D 20,583		750	1,400	3,000	6,000	8,500	17,000	27,000

LIBERTY HEAD (1839–1908)
Variety 1 – No Motto Above Eagle (1839–1866)

VF-20 Very Fine: LIBERTY on coronet bold. Major lines show in curls on neck.

EF-40 Extremely Fine: Details clear in curls on neck. Slight wear on top and lower part of coronet and on hair.

AU-50 About Uncirculated: Trace of wear on coronet and hair above eye.

AU-55 Choice About Uncirculated: Evidence of friction on design high points. Some original mint luster.

MS-60 Uncirculated: No trace of wear. Light blemishes.

MS-63 Choice Uncirculated: Some distracting contact

Mintmark: 1839, above date;
1840–1908, below eagle.

marks or blemishes in prime focal areas. Impaired luster possible.

PF-63 Choice Proof: Attractive reflective surfaces with only a few blemishes in secondary focal places. No major flaws.

1842, Large Date

Large Letters

Small Letters

	Mintage	VF-20	EF-40	AU-50	AU-55	MS-60	MS-63	PF-63
1839	118,143	$285	$325	$750	$1,250	$2,500	$14,000	
1839C	17,205	1,200	1,600	4,000	6,000	12,500	32,000	
1839D	18,939	1,000	1,500	3,650	5,500	13,000		
1840	137,382	260	275	875	1,375	2,600	7,500	
1840C	18,992	1,000	1,750	4,750	8,000	17,500	47,500	
1840D	22,896	1,000	1,450	4,750	5,250	10,500	33,500	
1840O	40,120	275	575	1,275	2,250	7,000	17,500	
1841	15,833	275	625	1,250	1,550	3,550	7,750	$47,500
1841C	21,467	950	1,300	2,150	4,000	11,500	32,500	
1841D	29,392	1,000	1,300	2,250	4,000	10,000	19,000	
1842, Small Letters	27,578	240	750	2,200	3,750	9,500	16,750	57,500
1842, Large Letters	*	475	1,400	2,000	3,250	7,750	17,500	
1842C, Small Date	27,432	7,250	16,500	30,000	40,000	77,500		
1842C, Large Date	*	950	1,400	2,350	4,750	12,000	27,500	
1842D, Small Date	59,608	1,000	1,350	2,200	3,750	10,500	25,000	
1842D, Large Date	*	1,675	4,250	10,000	14,000	34,000		
1842O	16,400	700	2,100	6,750	8,000	16,000	30,000	
1843	611,205	250	280	295	375	900	6,000	
1843C	44,277	950	1,300	2,650	3,750	8,000	24,000	
1843D	98,452	1,000	1,300	2,250	3,750	8,000	18,000	
1843O, Small Letters	19,075	375	1,000	1,650	3,250	13,500	28,000	
1843O, Large Letters	82,000	250	775	1,375	3,000	8,500	20,000	
1844	340,330	250	265	270	350	1,000	5,000	
1844C	23,631	950	2,100	4,500	6,000	15,500	30,000	
1845D	90,629	1,000	1,300	2,000	3,000	7,000	18,000	
1844O	364,600	250	265	410	1,000	3,000	10,000	
1845	417,099	235	250	260	325	1,450	6,500	
1845D	90,629	1,000	1,300	2,000	3,000	7,000	18,000	
1845O	41,000	275	475	1,900	3,000	7,500	17,000	
1846, Large Date	395,942	235	250	275	700	1,900	11,000	
1846, Small Date	*	235	250	260	425	1,750	9,500	
1846C	12,995	1,000	2,000	4,500	5,000	14,000	45,000	
1846D	80,294	1,000	1,450	2,500	3,250	9,000	16,500	
1846O	58,000	265	675	2,200	3,250	7,000	15,000	
1847	915,981	235	250	260	325	1,000	5,000	
1847C	84,151	950	1,350	2,400	3,000	8,000	18,000	
1847D	64,405	1,000	1,350	2,200	3,250	7,250	13,500	
1847O	12,000	1,300	5,000	6,750	9,000	18,000	26,500	
1848	260,775	235	250	290	400	1,000	7,500	
1848C	64,472	950	1,350	2,500	3,750	12,000	30,000	
1848D	47,465	1,000	1,350	2,200	3,750	10,000	19,000	
1849	133,070	235	250	500	800	1,900	9,500	
1849C	64,823	950	1,350	2,100	4,000	9,500	20,000	
1849D	39,036	1,000	1,350	2,300	3,500	9,500	22,000	
1850	64,491	250	425	750	850	2,600	9,000	

* Included in number above.

Chart continued on next page.

	Mintage	VF-20	EF-40	AU-50	AU-55	MS-60	MS-63	PF-63
1850C	63,591	$950	$1,350	$2,100	$2,500	$8,500	$17,000	
1850D	43,984	1,000	1,300	2,800	5,500	22,000		
1851	377,505	235	250	270	500	2,000	7,250	
1851C	49,176	950	1,300	2,250	4,000	8,000	25,000	
1851D	62,710	1,000	1,300	2,200	4,250	7,000	16,000	
1851O	41,000	400	1,000	2,750	4,000	6,500	13,000	
1852	573,901	235	250	270	300	850	5,000	
1852C	72,574	950	1,350	2,000	2,400	5,000	15,000	
1852D	91,584	1,000	1,350	2,100	3,500	7,500	16,000	
1853	305,770	235	250	270	375	1,000	6,000	
1853C	65,571	950	1,350	2,200	3,100	6,000	17,000	
1853D	89,678	1,000	1,350	2,200	3,200	7,250	15,000	
1854	160,675	235	250	360	800	1,450	6,000	
1854C	39,283	950	1,350	2,700	3,500	7,000	25,000	
1854D	56,413	1,000	1,350	2,200	3,500	7,500	18,000	
1854O	46,000	250	370	975	1,650	5,750	14,500	
1854S (3 known)	268	—	—	500,000	—			
1855	117,098	235	250	270	400	1,250	6,000	
1855C	39,788	950	1,400	2,300	3,500	10,000	25,000	
1855D	22,432	1,000	1,350	2,250	3,500	11,000	28,000	
1855O	11,100	425	1,500	3,250	4,500	14,500		
1855S	61,000	275	650	1,550	3,750	9,000		
1856	197,990	235	250	270	400	1,500	8,000	—
1856C	28,457	950	1,300	2,300	4,100	14,500		
1856D	19,786	1,000	1,300	2,600	3,750	7,750	25,000	
1856O	10,000	450	850	3,250	4,500	8,750		
1856S	105,100	235	425	875	1,750	4,750	20,000	
1857	98,188	235	250	275	400	1,100	5,500	—
1857C	31,360	950	1,300	2,250	3,500	6,000	18,000	
1857D	17,046	1,000	1,300	2,500	3,500	9,250	30,000	
1857O	13,000	450	975	3,250	4,250	8,000	35,000	
1857S	87,000	235	375	800	2,000	6,750	13,500	
1858	15,136	235	375	500	950	2,750	6,500	—
1858C	38,856	950	1,350	2,200	3,250	7,250	27,000	
1858D	15,362	1,000	1,350	2,200	3,750	8,000	27,500	
1858S	18,600	475	1,600	3,850	7,000	18,000		
1859	(80) 16,734	235	425	575	1,200	5,000	8,000	$28,000
1859C	31,847	950	1,350	2,650	3,750	10,500	30,000	
1859D	10,366	1,000	1,350	2,250	4,250	10,000	28,000	
1859S	13,220	875	2,500	3,750	5,750	18,000		
1860	(62) 19,763	235	400	775	950	2,600	10,000	22,000
1860C	14,813	950	1,500	2,300	4,000	9,250	20,000	
1860D	14,635	1,000	1,450	2,500	5,000	12,000	36,000	
1860S	21,200	750	1,200	3,000	5,000	17,000		
1861	(66) 688,084	235	250	275	375	850	3,000	21,000
1861C	6,879	1,400	2,800	5,500	8,000	17,000	68,000	
1861D	1,597	3,500	6,000	13,000	19,000	38,000	95,000	
1861S	18,000	600	3,000	4,000	5,500	22,500		
1862	(35) 4,430	350	1,000	2,000	2,750	10,000	25,000	21,000
1862S	9,500	2,000	4,500	10,000	16,000	40,000		
1863	(30) 2,442	750	2,500	4,000	5,500	15,000		21,000
1863S	17,000	850	2,500	6,500	8,000	18,000		
1864	(50) 4,170	400	1,250	2,750	3,500	8,000		21,000
1864S	3,888	3,500	9,000	12,000	25,000	40,000		
1865	(25) 1,270	750	1,500	5,500	6,750	10,000		21,000
1865S	27,612	650	1,500	2,500	3,500	10,000	15,000	
1866S	9,000	1,000	2,200	6,500	9,000	22,500		

Variety 2 – Motto Above Eagle (1866–1908)

VF-20 Very Fine: Half of hair lines above coronet missing. Hair curls under ear evident, but worn. Motto and its ribbon sharp.
EF-40 Extremely Fine: Small amount of wear on top of hair and below L in LIBERTY. Wear evident on wing tips and neck of eagle.
AU-50 About Uncirculated: Trace of wear on tip of coronet and hair above eye.
AU-55 Choice About Uncirculated: Evidence of friction on design high points. Some original mint luster present.
MS-60 Uncirculated: No trace of wear. Light blemishes.
MS-63 Choice Uncirculated: Some distracting contact marks or blemishes in prime focal areas. Impaired luster possible.
PF-63 Choice Proof: Reflective surfaces with only a few blemishes in secondary focal places. No major flaws.

	Mintage	VF-20	EF-40	AU-50	AU-55	MS-60	MS-63	PF-63
1866 . . . .(30) 6,700		$400	$900	$2,000	$2,500	$8,000		$13,000
1866S 34,920		500	1,500	4,500	5,500	14,000		
1867 . . . .(50) 6,870		270	900	2,000	2,500	6,500		11,000
1867S 29,000		750	1,550	4,500	6,000	16,000		
1868 . . . .(25) 5,700		400	650	1,500	2,000	6,000		13,000
1868S 52,000		270	1,000	1,900	2,500	10,000		
1869 . . . .(25) 1,760		500	1,250	1,700	2,200	9,000		13,000
1869S 31,000		300	1,000	1,700	2,500	15,000		
1870 . . . .(35) 4,000		400	1,200	1,200	1,800	8,500		13,000
1870CC 7,675		3,000	9,000	17,500	22,000	60,000		
1870S 17,000		450	1,500	4,500	6,000	18,000		
1871 . . . .(30) 3,200		500	850	1,850	2,500	8,000		12,000
1871CC 20,770		750	2,250	8,000	12,000	30,000	$60,000	
1871S 25,000		260	500	1,500	2,000	8,000		
1872 . . . .(30) 1,660		450	1,000	1,500	2,000	7,500	11,000	12,000
1872CC 16,980		850	3,200	13,000	18,000	38,000		
1872S 36,400		250	350	1,500	1,850	7,500		
1873 . . . .(25) 112,505		235	250	260	275	450	2,200	12,000
1873CC 7,416		1,500	8,000	16,000	23,000	37,500		
1873S 31,000		250	750	1,850	2,150	11,000		
1874 . . . .(20) 3,488		300	850	1,250	1,500	6,500	12,500	12,000
1874CC 21,198		500	1,200	6,000	7,500	25,000		
1874S 16,000		300	1,200	2,500	3,000	12,000		
1875 . . . .(20) 200		22,000	30,000	40,000	55,000			45,000
1875CC 11,828		900	2,500	7,500	11,000	30,000		
1875S 9,000		300	1,100	2,800	4,200	12,000		
1876 . . . .(45) 1,432		675	1,300	2,000	3,000	6,500	13,000	10,000
1876CC 6,887		800	3,500	8,500	10,500	25,000		
1876S 4,000		850	1,800	5,000	6,000	14,000		
1877 . . . .(20) 1,132		500	1,500	2,000	2,750	7,000	15,000	14,000
1877CC 8,680		600	2,000	6,500	8,500	27,500		
1877S 26,700		235	300	700	800	4,000	10,000	
1878 . . . .(20) 131,720		225	230	240	250	270	1,000	15,000
1878CC 9,054		1,700	5,200	13,000	17,000	40,000		
1878S 144,700		225	230	245	250	300	2,000	
1879 . . . .(30) 301,920		225	230	240	250	270	1,000	12,000
1879CC 17,281		300	950	2,250	3,500	14,000		
1879S 426,200		225	230	240	250	400	1,500	
1880 . . . .(36) . .3,166,400		225	230	235	240	245	650	10,000
1880CC 51,017		275	500	1,000	2,000	6,500		
1880S 1,348,900		225	230	235	240	245	650	

Chart continued on next page.

	Mintage	VF-20	EF-40	AU-50	AU-55	MS-60	MS-63	PF-63
1881 ....(42)...5,708,802		$225	$230	$235	$240	$245	$650	$9,500
1881CC 13,886		350	850	4,000	5,500	15,000	37,500	
1881S 969,000		225	230	235	240	245	650	
1882 ....(48)...2,514,520		225	230	235	240	245	650	9,500
1882CC 82,817		300	425	550	750	5,200	25,000	
1882S 969,000		225	230	235	240	245	650	
1883 ....(61)....233,400		225	230	235	240	245	800	9,500
1883CC 12,598		350	750	2,000	3,200	13,000		
1883S 83,200		225	230	250	260	450	1,500	
1884 ....(48)....191,030		225	230	235	250	400	1,480	9,500
1884CC 16,402		400	700	1,800	3,200	12,500		
1884S 177,000		225	230	235	240	260	1,260	
1885 ....(66)....601,440		225	230	235	240	245	650	9,500
1885S 1,211,500		225	230	235	240	245	650	
1886 ....(72)....388,360		225	230	235	240	245	700	9,200
1886S 3,268,000		225	230	235	240	245	650	
1887, Proof only ......(87).........								32,500
1887S 1,912,000		225	230	235	240	245	650	
1888 ....(95)...18,201		225	230	235	240	250	900	7,500
1888S 293,900		225	230	240	260	750	2,400	
1889 ....(45).....7,520		225	240	300	325	750	1,300	8,500
1890 ....(88).....4,240		225	270	350	525	1,300	4,000	8,500
1890CC 53,800		225	240	330	375	800	4,500	
1891 ....(53).....61,360		225	230	240	275	280	1,000	8,500
1891CC 208,000		225	240	340	360	550	2,100	
1892 ....(92)....753,480		225	230	235	240	245	650	8,500
1892CC 82,968		225	240	375	450	1,000	3,750	
18920 10,000		300	600	820	900	2,000	7,000	
1892S 298,400		225	230	250	270	300	2,000	
1893 ....(77)...1,528,120		225	230	235	240	245	650	8,500
1893CC 60,000		260	260	410	560	900	4,000	
18930 110,000		235	250	300	360	600	3,800	
1893S 224,000		225	230	235	240	245	700	
1894 ....(75)....957,880		225	230	235	240	245	650	8,500
18940 16,600		225	275	325	400	820	3,250	
1894S 55,900		250	290	335	410	1,800	6,400	
1895 ....(81)...1,345,855		225	230	235	240	245	650	7,200
1895S 112,000		230	235	250	330	2,000	3,750	
1896 ....(103)....58,960		225	230	235	240	245	700	7,200
1896S 155,400		230	240	260	325	685	3,600	
1897 ....(83)....867,800		225	230	235	240	245	650	7,200
1897S 354,000		225	230	235	300	550	3,300	
1898 ....(75)....633,420		225	230	235	240	245	650	7,200
1898S 1,397,400		225	230	235	250	250	700	
1899 ....(99)...1,710,630		225	230	235	240	245	650	7,200
1899S 1,545,000		225	230	235	240	250	650	
1900 ....(230)...1,405,500		225	230	235	240	245	650	7,200
1900S 329,000		225	230	235	240	245	650	
1901 ....(140)....615,900		225	230	235	240	245	650	7,200
1901S, 1 Over 0 3,648,000		225	230	235	240	285	650	
1901S ....*		225	230	235	240	245	650	
1902 ....(162)....172,400		225	230	235	240	245	650	7,200
1902S 939,000		225	230	235	240	245	650	
1903 ....(154)....226,870		225	230	235	240	245	650	7,200
1903S 1,855,000		225	230	235	240	245	650	

* Included in number above.

	Mintage	VF-20	EF-40	AU-50	AU-55	MS-60	MS-63	PF-63
1904 . . . .(136) 392,000		$225	$230	$235	$240	$245	$650	$7,200
1904S .97,000		225	230	235	300	500	2,500	
1905 . . . .(108) 302,200		225	230	235	240	245	650	7,200
1905S 880,700		225	230	235	275	360	950	
1906 . . . .(85) 348,735		225	230	235	240	245	650	7,200
1906D 320,000		225	230	235	240	245	650	
1906S 598,000		225	230	235	240	245	700	
1907 . . . .(92) 626,100		225	230	235	240	245	650	7,200
1907D 888,000		225	230	235	240	245	650	
1908 421,874		225	230	235	240	245	650	

INDIAN HEAD (1908–1929)

This type conforms in design to the quarter eagle of the same date. The incuse designs and lettering make the Indian Head a unique series, along with the quarter eagle, in United States coinage.

VF-20 Very Fine: Noticeable wear on large middle feathers and tip of eagle's wing.
EF-40 Extremely Fine: Cheekbone, war bonnet, and head-band feathers slightly worn. Feathers on eagle's upper wing show considerable wear.
AU-50 About Uncirculated: Trace of wear on cheekbone and headdress.
AU-55 Choice About Uncirculated: Evidence of friction on design high points. Much of original mint luster present.
MS-60 Uncirculated: No trace of wear. Light blemishes.
MS-63 Choice Uncirculated: Some distracting contact marks or blemishes in prime focal areas. Impaired luster possible.

Mintmark Location

Matte PF-63 Choice Proof: Matte surfaces with few blemishes in secondary focal places. No major flaws.

Scarcer coins with well-struck mintmarks command higher prices.

	Mintage	VF-20	EF-40	AU-50	AU-55	MS-60	MS-63	MATTE PF-63
1908 . . . .(167) 577,845		$235	$245	$255	$260	$300	$1,600	$7,000
1908D 148,000		235	245	255	260	300	1,600	
1908S 82,000		245	275	300	340	800	2,000	
1909 . . . .(78) 627,060		235	245	255	260	300	1,600	7,500
1909D 3,423,560		235	245	255	260	300	1,600	
1909O 34,200		1,600	1,850	3,200	4,750	14,000	40,000	
1909S 297,200		245	260	280	300	850	7,500	
1910 . . . .(250) 604,000		235	245	255	260	300	1,600	7,500
1910D 193,600		235	245	255	260	300	1,850	
1910S 770,200		245	260	280	290	650	3,800	
1911 . . . .(139) 915,000		235	245	255	260	300	1,600	7,200
1911D 72,500		300	350	400	700	2,500	24,000	
1911S 1,416,000		245	260	280	300	400	2,700	
1912 . . . .(144) 790,000		235	245	255	260	300	1,600	7,200
1912S 392,000		245	270	300	350	1,000	8,500	
1913 . . . .(99) 915,901		235	245	255	260	300	1,600	7,200
1913S 408,000		245	260	280	325	900	8,500	
1914 . . . .(125) 247,000		235	245	255	260	300	1,600	7,200
1914D 247,000		235	245	255	260	300	2,000	
1914S 263,000		245	270	300	315	850	8,500	
1915 . . . .(75) 588,000		235	245	255	260	300	1,600	9,000
1915S 164,000		245	270	325	420	1,350	10,000	
1916S 240,000		245	270	320	420	450	2,300	
1929 662,000		4,500	6,000	6,500	8,000	9,000	13,000	

Coinage authority including specified weights and fineness of the eagle conforms to that of the half eagle. The small eagle reverse was used until 1797, when the large, heraldic eagle replaced it.

CAPPED BUST TO RIGHT (1795–1804)

F-12 Fine: Details on turban and head obliterated.

VF-20 Very Fine: Hair lines in curls on neck and details under turban and over forehead worn but distinguishable.

EF-40 Extremely Fine: Definite wear on hair to left of eye and strand of hair across and around turban, as well as on eagle's wing tips.

AU-50 About Uncirculated: Trace of wear on cap, hair, cheek, and drapery

AU-55 Choice About Uncirculated: Evidence of friction on design high points. Most of original mint luster present.

MS-60 Uncirculated: No trace of wear. Light blemishes.

MS-63 Choice Uncirculated: Some distracting contact marks or blemishes in prime focal areas. Impaired luster possible.

Small Eagle (1795–1797)

	Mintage	F-12	VF-20	EF-40	AU-50	AU-55	MS-60	MS-63
1795	5,583	$12,500	$14,000	$20,000	$28,000	$37,500	$60,000	$160,000
1796	4,146	12,500	16,000	22,000	30,000	36,000	65,000	180,000
1797, Small Eagle	3,615	17,000	22,000	27,000	55,000	65,000	135,000	

Heraldic Eagle (1797–1804)

	Mintage	F-12	VF-20	EF-40	AU-50	AU-55	MS-60	MS-63
1797, Large Eagle	10,940	$6,000	$7,000	$10,000	$16,500	$20,000	$25,000	$55,000
1798, 8/7, 9 Stars Left, 4 Rt	900	8,000	10,000	19,000	26,000	36,000	65,000	170,000
1798, 8/7, 7 Stars Left, 6 Rt	842	17,000	25,000	45,000	90,000	100,000	150,000	
1799	37,449	4,500	6,000	7,000	10,000	12,000	17,000	27,000
1800	5,999	4,500	6,000	7,000	10,000	13,000	20,000	43,000
1801	44,344	4,500	6,000	7,000	10,000	13,000	16,000	26,000
1803	15,017	4,500	6,000	7,000	11,000	14,000	17,000	37,000
1804	3,757	9,000	11,000	16,000	20,000	30,000	50,000	140,000

LIBERTY HEAD, NO MOTTO ABOVE EAGLE (1838–1866)

In 1838 the weight and diameter of the eagle were reduced and the obverse and reverse were redesigned. Liberty now faced left and the word LIBERTY was placed on the coronet.

VF-20 Very Fine: Hair lines above coronet partly worn. Curls under ear worn but defined.

EF-40 Extremely Fine: Small amount of wear on top of hair and below L in LIBERTY. Wear evident on wing tips and neck of eagle.

AU-50 About Uncirculated: Trace of wear on tip of coronet and hair above eye.

AU-55 Choice About Uncirculated: Evidence of friction on design high points. Some of original mint luster present.

Mintmark is on reverse, below eagle.

MS-60 Uncirculated: No trace of wear. Light blemishes.

MS-63 Choice Uncirculated: Some distracting contact marks or blemishes in prime focal areas. Impaired luster possible.

PF-63 Choice Proof: Attractive reflective surfaces with only a few blemishes in secondary focal places. No major flaws.

	Mintage	VF-20	EF-40	AU-50	AU-55	MS-60	MS-63	PF-63
1838	7,200	$560	$1,575	$3,400	$4,800	$22,000	$55,000	
1839, Large Letters	25,801	560	1,075	3,000	4,000	20,000	36,000	
1839, Small Letters	12,447	775	1,950	4,000	5,200	22,000	64,000	
1840	47,338	470	480	800	1,000	6,800		
1841	63,131	450	460	640	800	5,000	18,000	
1841O	2,500	1,200	2,700	7,200	9,600	21,000		
1842	81,507	450	455	700	1,000	6,800	13,000	
1842O	27,400	450	455	1,400	2,000	11,700	23,000	
1843	75,462	450	455	800	1,200	8,000		
1843O	175,162	450	455	620	1,000	7,200		
1844	6,361	580	1,640	3,200	4,000	11,000	20,000	
1844O	118,700	460	475	1,040	1,240	9,800		
1845	26,153	450	465	1,260	1,500	9,000		
1845O	47,500	450	460	1,120	1,700	10,000	30,000	
1846	20,095	450	600	3,200	4,200	15,000		
1846O	81,780	455	470	2,000	2,520	9,000	27,000	
1847	862,258	450	455	460	465	2,100	16,500	
1847O	571,500	450	455	460	465	3,750	14,000	
1848	145,484	450	455	500	600	3,420	18,000	$135,000
1848O	35,850	450	750	2,000	2,480	9,400	20,000	
1849	653,618	450	455	460	465	2,400	9,200	
1849O	23,900	500	1,200	3,000	3,980	15,800		
1850	291,451	450	455	460	465	2,650	12,600	
1850O	57,500	450	500	1,960	2,420	11,300		
1851	176,328	450	455	460	465	3,000	18,000	
1851O	263,000	450	460	560	680	4,160	16,000	
1852	263,106	450	455	460	475	3,000	18,000	
1852O	18,000	500	620	2,280	4,000	13,000		
1853, 3 Over 2	201,253	450	500	1,100	1,400	10,400		
1853	*	450	455	460	470	2,600	12,000	
1853O	51,000	450	470	600	985	9,100		
1854	54,250	450	455	460	560	4,000	13,000	
1854O	52,500	450	460	960	1,160	6,260	25,000	
1854S	123,826	450	455	495	680	7,160	28,000	
1855	121,701	450	455	460	500	2,660	12,300	—
1855O	18,000	450	800	3,000	4,100	15,000		

* Included in number above.

Chart continued on next page.

	Mintage	VF-20	EF-40	AU-50	AU-55	MS-60	MS-63	PF-63
1855S	9,000	$900	$1,360	$4,000	$5,500	$22,400		
1856	60,490	450	455	460	600	2,650	$8,000	—
1856O	14,500	475	850	2,300	3,000	11,000		
1856S	68,000	450	460	640	1,300	6,500	14,000	
1857	16,606	450	600	1,160	1,800	9,000		—
1857O	5,500	600	1,140	1,975	2,380	13,800		
1857S	26,000	450	500	1,260	1,340	7,725	10,800	
1858	2,521	3,000	4,500	7,000	9,000	23,000		—
1858O	20,000	450	500	1,000	1,500	6,500	15,000	
1858S	11,800	900	1,875	2,700	6,000	19,800		
1859	(80) 16,013	450	455	700	1,300	5,000	8,000	$39,000
1859O	2,300	3,000	4,500	9,000	12,000	33,000		
1859S	7,000	1,200	3,000	7,500	9,000	30,000		
1860	(50) 15,055	450	460	900	1,400	4,750	11,300	28,000
1860O	11,100	450	800	1,400	1,800	8,800		
1860S	5,000	1,500	3,200	9,200	12,000	28,000		
1861	(69) 113,164	450	455	460	465	2,100	8,000	26,000
1861S	15,500	900	2,000	3,480	6,000	22,000		
1862	(35) 10,960	450	650	1,325	1,500	7,600		26,000
1862S	12,500	1,000	2,000	3,000	5,000	24,000		
1863	(30) 1,218	2,500	5,000	10,000	12,000	33,000	60,000	28,000
1863S	10,000	900	2,060	5,000	7,000	15,600		
1864	(50) 3,530	1,200	2,200	4,420	5,280	10,000		28,000
1864S	2,500	3,000	6,590	15,800	17,800	36,000		
1865	(25) 3,980	1,100	1,900	4,500	5,000	25,000	35,000	28,000
1865S	16,700	2,000	5,125	9,600	11,400	31,000		
1866S	8,500	1,100	2,300	7,500	9,000	30,000		

LIBERTY HEAD, MOTTO ABOVE EAGLE (1866–1907)

VF-20 Very Fine: Half of hair lines over coronet visible. Curls under ear worn but defined. IN GOD WE TRUST and its ribbon sharp.

EF-40 Extremely Fine: Small amount of wear on top of hair and below L in LIBERTY. Wear evident on wing tips and neck of eagle.

AU-50 About Uncirculated: Trace of wear on hair above eye and on coronet.

AU-55 Choice About Uncirculated: Evidence of friction on design high points. Some of original mint luster present.

Mintmark is on reverse, below eagle.

MS-60 Uncirculated: No trace of wear. Light blemishes.

MS-63 Choice Uncirculated: Some distracting marks or blemishes in focal areas. Impaired luster possible.

PF-63 Choice Proof: Reflective surfaces with only a few blemishes in secondary focal areas. No major flaws.

	Mintage	VF-20	EF-40	AU-50	AU-55	MS-60	MS-63	PF-63
1866	(30) 3,750	$500	$1,020	$2,720	$3,260	$14,500		$21,500
1866S	11,500	900	2,000	4,000	5,000	20,000		
1867	(50) 3,090	1,000	1,475	2,920	3,600	18,000		22,500
1867S	9,000	1,500	3,490	5,100	6,200	29,750		
1868	(25) 10,630	450	500	1,000	1,500	10,000		23,800
1868S	13,500	900	1,275	2,200	3,450	17,000		
1869	(25) 1,830	1,000	1,600	3,000	7,000	20,000		21,500
1869S	6,430	900	1,500	3,500	7,000	16,000		
1870	(35) 3,990	600	700	1,250	1,600	10,000		21,500
1870CC	5,908	6,000	16,000	30,000	50,000	70,000	$112,000	
1870S	8,000	600	1,500	3,800	7,500	18,000		
1871	(30) 1,790	900	1,700	2,485	5,000	12,750		22,800
1871CC	8,085	1,300	3,200	9,500	11,260	42,900	54,000	

EAGLES

	Mintage	VF-20	EF-40	AU-50	AU-55	MS-60	MS-63	PF-63
1871S	.16,500	$625	$1,000	$3,425	$4,040	$18,800		
1872	(30) .1,620	1,500	2,100	6,000	7,250	10,200	$23,000	$21,500
1872CC	.4,600	1,400	5,000	14,000	16,900	43,000	54,000	
1872S	.17,300	450	550	1,060	2,000	12,000		
1873	(25) .800	3,000	6,500	10,000	12,000	32,000		25,000
1873CC	.4,543	2,200	6,400	14,500	20,000	45,000	54,000	
1873S	.12,000	600	1,000	2,700	3,500	20,000		
1874	(20) .53,140	450	455	460	465	1,200	5,000	23,800
1874CC	.16,767	575	1,500	4,800	5,800	32,000	53,000	
1874S	.10,000	750	2,100	4,000	5,600	30,000		
1875	(20) .100	27,000	32,000	42,000				80,000
1875CC	.7,715	2,200	5,500	14,000	16,750	47,000	63,000	
1876	(45) .687	1,900	4,000	7,600	8,900	38,000		19,000
1876CC	.4,696	2,000	4,200	11,200	13,000	38,000	50,000	
1876S	.5,000	850	1,000	3,225	3,800	27,600		
1877	(20) .797	1,500	3,000	4,500	5,300	18,000		19,000
1877CC	.3,332	1,500	3,000	8,000	9,860	34,000		
1877S	.17,000	450	550	1,200	1,380	16,600		
1878	(20) .73,780	450	455	460	465	575	3,400	19,000
1878CC	.3,244	2,000	5,500	11,200	14,500	34,000		
1878S	.26,100	450	455	965	1,125	8,500	20,000	
1879	(30) .384,740	450	455	460	465	485	2,680	16,600
1879CC	.1,762	3,500	7,500	14,000	16,600	47,000		
1879O	.1,500	1,200	2,750	5,125	6,200	21,750		
1879S	.224,000	450	455	460	465	675	3,960	
1880	(36) .1,644,840	450	455	460	465	485	2,000	15,200
1880CC	.11,190	450	500	925	1,085	8,920		
1880O	.9,200	450	470	820	975	5,100		
1880S	.506,250	450	455	460	465	485		
1881	(40) .3,877,220	450	455	460	465	485	900	15,200
1881CC	.24,015	450	455	580	685	3,900	14,400	
1881O	.8,350	450	460	675	800	4,700		
1881S	.970,000	450	455	460	465	485	2,400	
1882	(40) .2,324,440	450	455	460	465	485	800	13,300
1882CC	.6,764	450	640	1,800	2,500	10,000	20,000	
1882O	.10,820	450	460	725	1,200	3,900	11,000	
1882S	.132,000	450	455	460	465	485	1,800	
1883	(40) .208,700	450	455	460	465	485	1,650	13,300
1883CC	.12,000	450	550	1,320	1,460	8,900	27,000	
1883O	.800	1,600	4,750	7,000	11,000	25,000		
1883S	.38,000	450	455	460	465	650	7,200	
1884	(45) .76,860	450	455	460	465	485	2,500	13,300
1884CC	.9,925	500	600	1,350	2,000	7,860	25,000	
1884S	.124,250	450	455	460	465	485	3,000	
1885	(65) .253,462	450	455	460	465	485	2,650	11,400
1885S	.228,000	450	455	460	465	485	2,000	
1886	(60) .236,100	450	455	460	465	485	2,200	10,900
1886S	.826,000	450	455	460	465	485	950	
1887	(80) .53,600	450	455	460	465	485	2,600	10,900
1887S	.817,000	450	455	460	465	485	1,800	
1888	(75) .132,921	450	455	460	465	485	2,600	10,500
1888O	.21,335	450	455	460	465	485	3,000	
1888S	.648,700	450	455	460	465	485	2,000	
1889	(45) .4,440	450	455	500	800	1,600	3,800	10,500
1889S	.425,400	450	455	460	465	485	950	
1890	(63) .57,980	450	455	460	465	500	3,200	8,500
1890CC	.17,500	450	455	460	600	1,250	9,000	
1891	(48) .91,820	450	455	460	465	485	2,650	8,500

	Mintage	VF-20	EF-40	AU-50	AU-55	MS-60	MS-63	PF-63
1891CC	.103,732	$450	$455	$460	$475	$550	$3,160	
1892	(72) 797,480	450	455	460	465	485	950	$8,500
1892CC	.40,000	450	455	460	600	2,200	5,860	
1892O	.28,688	450	455	460	465	500	3,600	
1892S	.115,500	450	455	460	465	500	2,600	
1893	(55) ..1,840,840	450	455	460	465	485	820	8,500
1893CC	.14,000	475	575	975	1,650	4,200	13,000	
1893O	.17,000	450	455	460	465	500	3,600	
1893S	.141,350	450	455	460	465	485	3,200	
1894	(43) ..2,470,735	450	455	460	465	485	800	8,500
1894O	.107,500	450	455	460	465	620	3,500	
1894S	.25,000	450	455	520	700	2,200	8,000	
1895	(56) ...567,770	450	455	460	465	485	850	8,500
1895O	.98,000	450	455	460	465	485	3,000	
1895S	.49,000	450	455	465	480	1,450	6,000	
1896	(78) 76,270	450	455	460	465	485	1,450	8,500
1896S	.123,750	450	455	475	490	1,425	7,500	
1897	(69) ..1,000,090	450	455	460	465	485	800	8,500
1897O	.42,500	450	455	460	465	565	2,750	
1897S	.234,750	450	455	460	465	575	2,800	
1898	(67) ...812,130	450	455	460	465	485	900	8,300
1898S	.473,600	450	455	460	465	485	2,800	
1899	(86) ..1,262,219	450	455	460	465	485	840	8,300
1899O	.37,047	450	455	460	465	490	3,200	
1899S	.841,000	450	455	460	465	485	1,750	
1900	(120) ...293,840	450	455	460	465	485	840	8,300
1900S	.81,000	450	455	460	465	580	3,200	
1901	(85) ..1,718,740	450	455	460	465	485	800	8,300
1901O	.72,041	450	455	460	465	485	2,000	
1901S	.2,812,750	450	455	460	465	485	800	
1902	(113) 82,400	450	455	460	465	485	1,000	8,300
1902S	.469,500	450	455	460	465	485	800	
1903	(96) 125,830	450	455	460	465	485	800	8,300
1903O	.112,771	450	455	460	465	490	2,000	
1903S	.538,000	450	455	460	465	485	875	
1904	(108) 161,930	450	455	460	465	485	800	8,300
1904O	.108,950	450	455	460	465	485	2,100	
1905	(86) 200,992	450	455	460	465	485	865	8,300
1905S	.369,250	450	455	460	465	700	3,200	
1906	(77) 165,420	450	455	460	465	485	1,100	8,300
1906D	.981,000	450	455	460	465	485	850	
1906O	.86,895	450	455	460	465	485	2,400	
1906S	.457,000	450	455	460	465	490	2,600	
1907	(74) ...1,203,899	450	455	460	465	485	800	8,300
1907D	.1,030,000	450	455	460	465	485	1,100	
1907S	.210,500	450	455	460	465	500	2,750	

INDIAN HEAD (1907–1933)

VF-20 Very Fine: Bonnet feathers worn near band. Wear visible on high points of hair.

EF-40 Extremely Fine: Slight wear on cheekbone and headdress feathers. Slight wear visible on eagle's eye and left wing.

AU-50 About Uncirculated: Trace of wear on hair above eye and on forehead.

AU-55 Choice About Uncirculated: Evidence of friction on design high points. Much of original mint luster present.

MS-60 Uncirculated: No trace of wear. Light blemishes.

MS-63 Choice Uncirculated: Some distracting contact marks or blemishes in prime focal areas. Impaired luster possible.

Matte PF-63 Choice Proof: Matte surfaces with few blemishes in secondary focal places. No major flaws.

No Motto
Mintmark is above left tip of branch on 1908-D No Motto.

With Motto
IN GOD WE TRUST
Mintmark is at left of arrow points.

Gem Uncirculated (MS-65) coins are rare and worth substantial premiums.

	Mintage	VF-20	EF-40	AU-50	AU-55	MS-60	MS-63
1907, Wire Rim, Periods	.500	$8,500	$9,500	$11,000	$12,500	$15,000	$20,000
1907, Rounded Rim, Periods Before and After *E*PLURIBUS*UNUM*	.50	16,000	20,000	25,000	30,000	35,000	60,000
1907, No Periods	.239,406	500	530	540	550	600	1,850
1908, No Motto	.33,500	500	520	530	550	610	2,850
1908D, No Motto	.210,000	500	520	530	560	620	4,250

Variety 2 – Motto on Reverse (1908–1933)

	Mintage	VF-20	EF-40	AU-50	AU-55	MS-60	MS-63	MATTE PF-63
1908 ....(116)	.341,370	$500	$520	$530	$550	$575	$1,400	$10,000
1908D	.836,500	500	520	530	550	600	4,600	
1908S	.59,850	500	525	535	570	1,600	5,800	
1909 ....(74)	.184,789	500	520	530	550	575	1,600	10,000
1909D	.121,540	500	520	530	550	585	2,700	
1909S	.292,350	500	520	530	550	590	2,800	
1910 ....(204)	.318,500	500	520	530	550	575	1,100	10,000
1910D	.2,356,640	500	520	530	550	575	1,100	
1910S	.811,000	500	520	530	550	590	4,000	
1911 ....(95)	.505,500	500	520	530	550	575	1,000	10,000
1911D	.30,100	525	550	620	820	2,850	12,000	
1911S	.51,000	500	560	550	575	760	4,800	
1912 ....(83)	.405,000	500	520	530	550	575	1,100	10,000
1912S	.300,000	500	520	530	550	610	3,700	
1913 ....(71)	.442,000	500	520	530	550	575	1,000	10,000
1913S	.66,000	525	540	620	820	2,600	18,000	
1914 ....(50)	.151,000	500	520	530	550	575	1,400	10,000
1914D	.343,500	500	520	530	550	575	1,400	
1914S	.208,000	500	520	530	550	575	3,600	
1915 ....(75)	.351,000	500	520	530	550	575	1,200	10,000
1915S	.59,000	525	540	620	820	2,100	8,500	
1916S	.138,500	500	520	530	550	590	3,200	
1920S	.126,500	5,000	6,500	7,000	9,000	18,000	55,000	
1926	.1,014,000	500	520	530	550	575	1,000	
1930S	.96,000	4,200	5,000	6,000	7,500	10,000	20,000	
1932	.4,463,000	500	520	530	550	575	1,000	
1933	.312,500	40,000	50,000	60,000	100,000	140,000	185,000	

This largest denomination of all regular United States issues was authorized to be coined by the Act of March 3, 1849. The coin's weight was set at 516 grains, and its fineness at .900. A single $20 gold pattern of 1849 resides in the Smithsonian.

LIBERTY HEAD (1849–1907)

VF-20 Very Fine: LIBERTY on crown bold; prongs on crown defined; lower half worn flat. Hair worn about ear.
EF-40 Extremely Fine: Trace of wear on rounded prongs of crown and down hair curls. Minor bagmarks.
AU-50 About Uncirculated: Trace of wear on hair over eye and on coronet.
AU-55 Choice About Uncirculated: Evidence of friction on design high points. Some of original mint luster present.
MS-60 Uncirculated: No trace of wear. Light blemishes.
MS-63 Choice Uncirculated: Some distracting marks or blemishes in focal areas. Impaired luster possible.
PF-63 Choice Proof: Reflective surfaces with only a few blemishes in secondary focal areas. No major flaws.

Without Motto on Reverse (1849–1866)

Mintmark is below eagle.

	Mintage	VF-20	EF-40	AU-50	AU-55	MS-60	MS-63	PF-63
1850	1,170,261	$920	$950	$1,525	$2,000	$5,500	$30,000	
18500	141,000	950	1,500	5,000	10,000	25,000		
1851	2,087,155	900	910	920	950	2,100	12,500	
18510	315,000	920	950	1,500	5,000	15,000	42,000	
1852	2,053,026	900	910	925	940	2,100	8,600	
18520	190,000	925	1,000	2,100	4,000	14,000	32,000	
1853	1,261,326	900	910	920	950	2,700	14,000	
18530	71,000	920	950	1,800	4,000	17,000		
1854	757,899	900	910	920	975	3,600	16,000	
18540	3,250	50,000	110,000	200,000	260,000	460,000		
1854S	141,468	910	930	950	1,500	3,200	9,000	
1855	364,666	910	930	950	1,400	6,000		
18550	8,000	1,900	5,000	15,000	22,000	60,000		
1855S	879,675	900	910	920	1,300	4,250	11,000	
1856	329,878	900	910	920	1,500	5,200	14,000	
18560	2,250	50,000	90,000	200,000	250,000	350,000	450,000	
1856S	1,189,750	900	910	920	1,000	3,000	7,400	
1857	439,375	900	910	920	950	2,000	16,100	
18570	30,000	950	1,500	3,500	7,500	18,000	80,000	
1857S	970,500	900	910	920	1,000	2,600	4,500	
1858	211,714	900	910	920	1,500	2,900	22,000	
18580	35,250	900	1,300	4,000	9,000	18,000		
1858S	846,710	900	910	920	1,500	5,600	18,000	
1859	(80) 43,597	900	1,160	2,300	3,500	18,000		$55,000
18590	9,100	2,500	4,750	15,000	20,000	60,000		
1859S	636,445	900	910	920	1,500	3,000		
1860	(59) 577,670	900	910	920	930	2,260	12,000	45,000
18600	6,600	1,750	3,600	13,000	22,000	70,000		
1860S	544,950	900	910	1,000	2,000	4,000	12,300	

Chart continued on next page.

	Mintage	VF-20	EF-40	AU-50	AU-55	MS-60	MS-63	PF-63
1861 . . . .(66) . . .2,976,453		$900	$910	$920	$930	$1,600	$6,000	$45,000
1861O 17,741		1,400	2,600	14,000	20,000	52,000		
1861S 768,000		900	910	1,100	2,000	6,500	35,000	
1862 . . . .(35) . . .92,133		900	1,000	2,500	4,000	10,000	20,600	38,000
1862S 854,173		900	910	1,000	2,000	6,200		
1863 . . . .(30) . . .142,790		900	910	1,500	4,000	11,000	22,000	
1863S 966,570		900	910	1,000	1,500	4,500	19,000	
1864 . . . .(50) . . .204,235		900	910	1,200	2,500	8,000	16,000	38,000
1864S 793,660		910	910	1,000	1,600	3,800	20,000	
1865 . . . .(25) . . .351,175		900	910	920	1,000	3,600	10,000	38,000
1865S 1,042,500		900	910	920	1,000	2,000	4,000	
1866S 12,000		1,900	6,000	20,000	40,000	110,000		

Motto Above Eagle
Value TWENTY D. (1866–1876)

	Mintage	VF-20	EF-40	AU-50	AU-55	MS-60	MS-63	PF-63
1866 . . . .(30) 698,745		$900	$910	$950	$1,200	$3,500	$18,000	$30,000
1866S 842,250		900	910	950	3,000	9,500		
1867 . . . .(50) . . .251,015		900	910	920	930	1,600	12,400	30,000
1867S 920,750		900	910	950	1,500	9,000		
1868 . . . .(25) . . .98,575		900	910	1,000	1,600	6,500	20,000	30,000
1868S 837,500		900	910	920	1,200	6,000		
1869 . . . .(25) . . .175,130		900	910	920	1,100	3,750	12,750	30,000
1869S 686,750		900	910	920	1,000	4,500	20,000	
1870 . . . .(35) . . .155,150		900	910	975	1,500	6,000		30,000
1870CC 3,789		100,000	150,000	225,000	300,000	600,000		
1870S 982,000		900	910	920	950	3,000	16,500	
1871 . . . .(30) . . .80,120		900	910	920	1,000	3,100	14,000	28,000
1871CC 17,387		3,100	6,000	13,000	19,000	32,000		
1871S 928,000		900	910	920	950	2,600	13,600	
1872 . . . .(30) . . .251,850		900	910	920	930	1,700	16,000	28,000
1872CC 26,900		1,200	1,500	3,500	7,000	18,000		
1872S 780,000		900	910	920	930	1,800	15,200	
1873 . . . .(25) . .1,709,800		900	910	920	930	1,000	7,250	28,000
1873CC 22,410		1,250	2,200	3,600	7,000	22,000	66,000	
1873S 1,040,600		900	910	920	930	1,200	12,000	
1874 . . . .(20) . . .366,780		900	910	920	930	1,200	12,300	30,000
1874CC 115,085		900	910	1,400	1,900	5,000		
1874S 1,214,000		900	910	920	930	1,000	15,000	
1875 . . . .(20) . . .295,720		900	910	920	930	1,000	6,800	55,000
1875CC 111,151		900	910	920	1,100	1,500	11,000	
1875S 1,230,000		900	910	920	930	1,000	10,000	
1876 . . . .(45) . . .583,860		900	910	920	930	1,000	7,300	29,000
1876CC 138,441		900	910	920	1,200	2,700	21,000	
1876S 1,597,000		900	910	920	930	1,000	7,500	

DOUBLE EAGLES

Value TWENTY DOLLARS (1877–1907)

	Mintage	VF-20	EF-40	AU-50	AU-55	MS-60	MS-63	PF-63
1877 . . . .(20) 397,650		$900	$910	$920	$930	$950	$6,000	$20,000
1877CC 42,565		900	950	1,500	2,500	11,000		
1877S 1,735,000		900	910	920	930	950	7,750	
1878 . . . .(20) 543,625		900	910	920	930	950	4,500	23,500
1878CC 13,180		1,100	1,800	2,800	5,500	17,000		
1878S 1,739,000		900	910	920	930	950	13,750	
1879 . . . .(30) 207,600		900	910	920	930	950	7,950	26,000
1879CC 10,708		1,300	2,100	3,500	6,000	20,000		
18790 .2,325		4,000	5,000	15,000	20,000	50,000	75,000	
1879S 1,223,800		900	910	920	930	950		
1880 . . . .(36) 51,420		900	910	920	930	1,600	10,400	21,000
1880S 836,000		900	910	920	930	950	9,400	
1881 . . . .(61) 2,199		3,000	4,500	9,000	12,000	32,000		23,500
1881S 727,000		900	910	920	930	950	11,000	
1882 . . . .(59) 571		4,500	13,000	19,000	25,000	55,000	90,000	23,500
1882CC 39,140		900	910	1,060	1,400	4,250		
1882S 1,125,000		900	910	920	930	950	8,500	
1883, Proof only . . . . . .(92)								40,000
1883CC 59,962		900	910	1,000	1,200	2,600	13,000	
1883S 1,189,000		900	910	920	930	950	5,500	
1884, Proof only . . . . . .(71)								38,000
1884CC 81,139		900	910	920	975	1,600	13,000	
1884S 916,000		900	910	920	930	950	3,750	
1885 . . . .(77) 751		3,700	4,750	6,200	7,060	21,000	35,000	21,000
1885CC 9,450		1,175	1,680	3,000	3,260	6,100	30,000	
1885S 683,500		900	910	920	930	950	4,200	
1886 . . . .(106) 1,000		6,000	9,500	18,000	22,000	32,000	62,000	21,000
1887, Proof only . . . . .(121)								38,000
1887S 283,000		900	910	920	930	950	8,900	
1888 . . . .(105) 226,161		900	910	920	930	950	2,975	16,500
1888S 859,600		900	910	920	930	950	2,750	
1889 . . . .(41) 44,070		900	910	920	930	950	6,860	16,500
1889CC 30,945		900	910	1,150	1,220	2,000	9,800	
1889S 774,700		900	910	920	930	950	4,000	
1890 . . . .(55) 75,940		900	910	920	930	950	4,200	16,500
1890CC 91,209		900	910	920	930	1,350	18,000	
1890S 802,750		900	910	920	930	950	5,000	
1891 . . . .(52) 1,390		1,800	2,800	4,900	9,000	35,000		16,000
1891CC 5,000		2,100	4,500	5,500	6,500	12,000	28,000	
1891S 1,288,125		900	910	920	930	950	2,000	
1892 . . . .(93) 4,430		950	1,000	1,500	1,600	4,000	14,000	16,000

Chart continued on next page.

171

	Mintage	VF-20	EF-40	AU-50	AU-55	MS-60	MS-63	PF-63
1892CC 27,265		$980	$990	$1,100	$1,200	$2,500	$13,500	
1892S 930,150		900	910	920	930	950	2,000	
1893 . . . .(59) 344,280		900	910	920	930	950	1,500	$16,000
1893CC 18,402		1,000	1,100	1,200	1,300	2,500	13,000	
1893S 996,175		900	910	920	930	950	2,150	
1894 . . . .(50) . . .1,368,940		900	910	920	930	950	1,100	16,000
1894S 1,048,550		900	910	920	930	950	1,500	
1895 . . . .(51) . . .1,114,605		900	910	920	930	950	1,000	16,000
1895S 1,143,500		900	910	920	930	950	1,400	
1896 . . . .(128) 792,535		900	910	920	930	950	1,100	16,000
1896S 1,403,925		900	910	920	930	950	1,300	
1897 . . . .(86) . . .1,383,175		900	910	920	930	950	1,000	16,000
1897S 1,470,250		900	910	920	930	950	1,000	
1898 . . . .(75) 170,395		900	910	920	930	975	3,000	16,000
1898S 2,575,175		900	910	920	930	950	1,000	
1899 . . . .(84) . . .1,669,300		900	910	920	930	950	1,000	16,000
1899S 2,010,300		900	910	920	930	950	1,100	
1900 . . . .(124) . . .1,874,460		900	910	920	930	950	1,000	16,000
1900S 2,459,500		900	910	920	930	950	1,150	
1901 . . . .(96) 111,430		900	910	920	930	950	1,000	16,000
1901S 1,596,000		900	910	920	930	950	2,400	
1902 . . . .(114) 31,140		900	910	920	930	970	6,500	16,000
1902S 1,753,625		900	910	920	930	950	2,100	
1903 . . . .(158) 287,270		900	910	920	930	950	1,000	16,000
1903S 954,000		900	910	920	930	950	1,120	
1904 . . . .(98) . . .6,256,699		900	910	920	930	950	1,000	16,000
1904S 5,134,175		900	910	920	930	950	1,000	
1905 . . . .(92) 58,919		900	910	920	930	970	7,000	16,000
1905S 1,813,000		900	910	920	930	970	2,100	
1906 . . . .(94) 69,596		900	910	920	930	950	4,000	16,000
1906D 620,250		900	910	920	930	950	1,200	
1906S 2,065,750		900	910	920	930	950	1,250	
1907 . . . .(78) . . .1,451,786		900	910	920	930	950	1,000	16,000
1907D 842,250		900	910	920	930	950	1,300	
1907S 2,165,800		900	910	920	930	950	1,200	

SAINT-GAUDENS (1907–1933)

The $20 gold piece designed by Augustus Saint-Gaudens is considered by many to be the most beautiful United States coin. The first coins issued were 11,250 high-relief pieces struck for general circulation. The relief is much higher than that of later issues and the date 1907 is in Roman numerals. A few of the Proof coins were made using the lettered-edge collar from the Ultra High Relief version. These can be distinguished by a pronounced bottom left serif on the N in UNUM, and other minor differences. Flat-relief double eagles were issued later in 1907 with Arabic numerals, and continued through 1933.

The field of the rare, Ultra High Relief experimental pieces is extremely concave and connects directly with the edge without any border, giving it a sharp knifelike appearance. Liberty's skirt shows two folds on the side of her right leg; the Capitol building in the background at left is very small; the sun, on the reverse side, has 14 rays, as opposed to the regular high-relief coins, which have only 13 rays extending from the sun. High-relief Proofs are trial or experimental pieces.

VF-20 Very Fine: Minor wear on Liberty's legs and toes. Eagle's left wing and breast feathers worn.
EF-40 Extremely Fine: Drapery lines on chest visible. Wear on left breast, knee, and below. Eagle's feathers on breast and right wing bold.
AU-50 About Uncirculated: Trace of wear on nose, breast, and knee. Wear visible on eagle's wings.
AU-55 Choice About Uncirculated: Evidence of friction on design high points. Most of mint luster remains.
MS-60 Uncirculated: No trace of wear. Light marks or blemishes.
MS-63 Select Uncirculated: Some distracting contact marks or blemishes in prime focal areas. Impaired luster possible.
Matte PF-63 Choice Proof: Matte surfaces with only a few blemishes in secondary focal places. No major flaws.

Ultra High Relief Pattern, MCMVII (1907)

	PF-67
1907, Ultra High Relief, Plain Edge *(unique)*	—
1907, Ultra High Relief, Lettered Edge	—

Without Motto IN GOD WE TRUST (1907–1908)
High Relief, MCMVII (1907)

	Mintage	VF-20	EF-40	AU-50	AU-55	MS-60	MS-63	PF
1907, High Relief, Roman Numerals (MCMVII), Wire Rim	12,367	$6,000	$7,000	$8,000	$8,500	$10,000	$18,000	—

Arabic Numerals, No Motto (1907–1908)

Mintmark is on obverse, above date.

No Motto

Motto IN GOD WE TRUST (1908–1933)

	Mintage	VF-20	EF-40	AU-50	AU-55	MS-60	MS-63	MATTE PF-63
1907	361,667	$910	$920	$930	$940	$960	$975	
1908	4,271,551	910	920	930	940	960	975	
1908D	663,750	910	920	930	940	960	975	
1908, With Motto (101)	156,359	910	920	930	940	960	1,200	$16,000
1908D, With Motto	349,500	910	920	930	940	960	1,000	
1908S, With Motto	22,000	1,000	1,400	1,900	2,750	5,200	12,500	

Chart continued on next page. 173

1909, 9 Over 8

	Mintage	VF-20	EF-40	AU-50	AU-55	MS-60	MS-63	MATTE PF-63
1909, 9 Over 8 . . . .*		$910	$920	$930	$940	$960	$4,500	
1909 . . . .(67) 161,282	910	920	930	940	960	2,200	$16,000
1909D 52,500	910	920	930	940	1,200	5,500	
1909S 2,774,925	910	920	930	940	960	975	
1910 . . . .(167) 482,000	910	920	930	940	960	975	16,000
1910D 429,000	910	920	930	940	960	975	
1910S 2,128,250	910	920	930	940	960	975	
1911 . . . .(100) 197,250	910	920	930	940	975	1,400	16,000
1911D 846,500	910	920	930	940	960	975	
1911S 775,750	910	920	930	940	960	975	
1912 . . . .(74) 149,750	910	920	930	940	960	1,100	16,000
1913 . . . .(58) 168,780	910	920	930	940	960	2,000	16,000
1913D 393,500	910	920	930	940	960	975	
1913S 34,000	910	920	930	940	1,000	2,600	
1914 . . . .(70) 95,250	910	920	930	940	960	1,400	16,000
1914D 453,000	910	920	930	940	960	975	
1914S 1,498,000	910	920	930	940	960	975	
1915 . . . .(50) 152,000	910	920	930	940	960	1,500	16,500
1915S 567,500	910	920	930	940	960	975	
1916S 796,000	910	920	930	940	960	975	
1920 228,250	910	920	930	940	960	975	
1920S 558,000	9,000	11,000	13,000	15,000	28,000	57,500	
1921 528,500	12,000	13,000	17,000	21,000	40,000	125,000	
1922 1,375,500	910	920	930	940	960	975	
1922S 2,658,000	910	920	930	940	1,200	2,500	
1923 566,000	910	920	930	940	960	975	
1923D 1,702,250	910	920	930	940	960	975	
1924 4,323,500	910	920	930	940	960	975	
1924D 3,049,500	920	1,000	1,100	1,200	1,600	5,500	
1924S 2,927,500	920	1,000	1,100	1,200	1,600	5,500	
1925 2,831,750	910	920	930	940	960	975	
1925D 2,938,500	1,000	1,200	1,500	1,800	2,500	6,250	
1925S 3,776,500	1,000	1,200	1,500	1,800	5,000	15,000	
1926 816,750	910	920	930	940	960	975	
1926D 481,000	2,000	3,500	4,000	4,500	8,000	20,000	
1926S 2,041,500	925	1,100	1,400	1,400	1,600	3,200	
1927 2,946,750	910	920	930	940	960	975	
1927D 180,000		250,000	325,000	380,000	550,000	750,000	
1927S 3,107,000	3,000	4,500	5,000	5,500	10,000	40,000	
1928 8,816,000	910	920	930	940	960	975	
1929 1,779,750	4,000	6,200	7,000	8,000	10,000	22,000	
1930S 74,000	9,000	15,000	16,000	18,000	22,000	60,000	
1931 2,938,250	5,000	9,000	9,200	9,500	15,000	35,000	
1931D 106,500	5,200	9,000	9,200	12,000	20,000	45,000	
1932 1,101,750	5,000	10,000	11,000	14,000	17,000	40,000	
1933 445,500	*None placed in circulation.*						

* Included in number below.

Collecting United States commemorative coins is like gathering snapshots for an album of important events, places, and people in the nation's history. Because they represent so many different aspects of America—from wars and Olympic games to presidents, state parks, and historical landmarks—every collector can assemble a set with its own special significance.

All U.S. commemorative coins are issued as legal tender, though in most cases the precious metal of the coins surpasses their face values. The weight and fineness for commemoratives follow those of standard-issue gold, silver, and clad coins.

CLASSIC SILVER AND GOLD COMMEMORATIVES

(1892–1893) World's Columbian Exposition Half Dollar

	Distribution	AU-50	MS-60	MS-63	MS-65
1892, Columbian Exposition	950,000	$10	$16	$40	$350
1893, Same type	1,550,405	10	16	38	400

(1893) World's Columbian Exposition, Isabella Quarter

	Distribution	AU-50	MS-60	MS-63	MS-65
1893, Columbian Exposition, Chicago	24,214	$350	$400	$500	$1,900

(1900) Lafayette Dollar

	Distribution	AU-50	MS-60	MS-63	MS-65
1900, Lafayette dollar	36,026	$325	$600	$1,200	$5,750

(1903) Louisiana Purchase Exposition

	Distribution	AU-50	MS-60	MS-63	MS-65
1903, Louisiana Purchase / Thomas Jefferson 17,500		$360	$425	$600	$1,600
1903, Louisiana Purchase / William McKinley 17,500		360	425	600	1,600

(1904–1905) Lewis and Clark Exposition

	Distribution	AU-50	MS-60	MS-63	MS-65
1904, Lewis and Clark Exposition 10,025		$550	$750	$1,300	$6,500
1905, Lewis and Clark Exposition 10,041		700	850	1,800	10,500

(1915) Panama-Pacific Exposition

	Distribution	AU-50	MS-60	MS-63	MS-65
1915S, Panama-Pacific Exposition half dollar 27,134		$300	$335	$475	$1,550
1915S, Panama-Pacific Exposition, $1 15,000		375	420	600	1,250
1915S, Panama-Pacific Exposition, $2.50 6,749		1,000	1,200	2,100	4,750
1915S, Panama-Pacific Exposition, $50 Round 483		35,000	40,000	50,000	95,000

(1915) Panama-Pacific Exposition

	Distribution	AU-50	MS-60	MS-63	MS-65
1915S, Panama-Pacific, $50 Octagonal	645	$30,000	$35,000	$45,000	$85,000

(1916–1917) McKinley Memorial

	Distribution	AU-50	MS-60	MS-63	MS-65
1916, McKinley Memorial	*15,000*	$350	$425	$475	$1,200
1917, McKinley Memorial	5,000	450	500	800	2,000

(1918) Illinois Centennial

	Distribution	AU-50	MS-60	MS-63	MS-65
1918, Illinois Centennial	100,058	$80	$90	$110	$270

(1920) Maine Centennial

	Distribution	AU-50	MS-60	MS-63	MS-65
1920, Maine Centennial	50,028	$70	$90	$110	$300

(1920–1921) Pilgrim Tercentenary

With 1921 in Field
on Obverse

	Distribution	AU-50	MS-60	MS-63	MS-65
1920, Pilgrim Tercentenary 152,112		$45	$60	$75	$225
1921, Same, With Date Added in Field 20,053		90	110	120	300

(1921) Missouri Centennial

With 2★4 in Field

	Distribution	AU-50	MS-60	MS-63	MS-65
1921, Missouri Centennial, "2★4" in Field 10,000		$350	$450	$600	$2,600
1921, Missouri Centennial, Plain 10,428		210	360	475	2,000

(1921) Alabama Centennial

Without 2X2 in Field

	Distribution	AU-50	MS-60	MS-63	MS-65
1921, Alabama Centennial, Plain 49,038		$100	$130	$150	$900
1921, Alabama Centennial, With "2X2" in Field of Obverse 15,014		160	185	300	950

(1922) Grant Memorial

	Distribution	AU-50	MS-60	MS-63	MS-65
1922, Grant Memorial, With Star half dollar* 4,256		$550	$725	$1,000	$4,100
1922, Same type, No Star in Obv Field half dollar 67,405		65	80	90	450
1922, Grant Memorial, With Star* gold dollar 5,016		900	1,000	1,200	2,300
1922, Grant Memorial, No Star gold dollar .5,016		900	1,000	1,200	2,300

* Fake stars usually have a flattened spot on the reverse.

(1923) Monroe Doctrine Centennial

	Distribution	AU-50	MS-60	MS-63	MS-65
1923S, Monroe Doctrine Centennial 274,077		$30	$40	$82	$1,350

(1924) Huguenot-Walloon Tercentenary

	Distribution	AU-50	MS-60	MS-63	MS-65
1924, Huguenot-Walloon Tercentenary 142,080		$75	$80	$100	$250

(1925) Lexington-Concord Sesquicentennial

	Distribution	AU-50	MS-60	MS-63	MS-65
1925, Lexington-Concord Sesquicentennial 162,013		$50	$67	$85	$375

(1925) Stone Mountain Memorial

	Distribution	AU-50	MS-60	MS-63	MS-65
1925, Stone Mountain Memorial 1,314,709		$30	$45	$50	$130

(1925) California Diamond Jubilee

	Distribution	AU-50	MS-60	MS-63	MS-65
1925S, California Diamond Jubilee 86,394		$100	$125	$250	$675

(1925) Fort Vancouver Centennial

	Distribution	AU-50	MS-60	MS-63	MS-65
1925, Fort Vancouver Centennial 14,994		$180	$225	$250	$760

COMMEMORATIVES

**(1926) Sesquicentennial
of American Independence**

	Distribution	AU-50	MS-60	MS-63	MS-65
1926, Sesquicentennial of American Independence half dollar	141,120	$50	$70	$100	$1,900
1926, Sesquicentennial of American Independence gold dollar	46,019	235	340	465	2,500

(1926–1939) Oregon Trail Memorial

	Distribution	AU-50	MS-60	MS-65
1926, Oregon Trail Memorial	47,955	$75	$95	$175
1926S, Same type, S mint	83,055	75	95	175
1928, Oregon Trail Memorial (same as 1926)	6,028	95	110	200
1933D, Oregon Trail Memorial	5,008	195	210	330
1934D, Oregon Trail Memorial	7,006	95	110	210
1936, Oregon Trail Memorial	10,006	85	100	175
1936S, Same type, S mint	5,006	85	100	200
1937D, Oregon Trail Memorial	12,008	85	100	175
1938, Oregon Trail Memorial (same as 1926)	6,006			
1938D, Same type, D mint	6,005	*Set:*	250	450
1938S, Same type, S mint	6,006			
1939, Oregon Trail Memorial (same as 1926)	3,004			
1939D, Same type, D mint	3,004	*Set:*	800	1,100
1939S, Same type, S mint	3,005			
Oregon Trail Memorial, single type coin		75	95	175

(1927) Vermont Sesquicentennial

	Distribution	AU-50	MS-60	MS-63	MS-65
1927, Vermont Sesquicentennial (Battle of Bennington)	28,142	$140	$160	$175	$530

(1928) Hawaiian Sesquicentennial

	Distribution	AU-50	MS-60	MS-63	MS-65
1928, Hawaiian Sesquicentennial	10,008	$1,200	$1,450	$1,800	$4,000
1928, Hawaiian Sesquicentennial, Sandblast Proof Presentation Piece	(50)			6,500	14,500

(1934) Maryland Tercentenary

	Distribution	AU-50	MS-60	MS-63	MS-65
1934, Maryland Tercentenary	25,015	$85	$95	$100	$200

(1934–1938) Texas Independence Centennial

	Distribution	AU-50	MS-60	MS-63	MS-65
1934, Texas Independence Centennial	61,463	$75	$80	$90	$135
1935, Texas Independence Centennial (same as 1934)	9,996				
1935D, Same type, D mint	10,007	Set:	200	225	335
1935S, Same type, S mint	10,008				
1936, Texas Independence Centennial (same as 1934)	8,911				
1936D, Same type, D mint	9,039	Set:	200	225	335
1936S, Same type, S mint	9,055				
1937, Texas Independence Centennial (same as 1934)	6,571				
1937D, Same type, D mint	6,605	Set:	200	225	335
1937S, Same type, S mint	6,637				

	Distribution	AU-50	MS-60	MS-63	MS-65
1938, Texas Independence Centennial (same as 1934) 3,780					
1938D, Same type, D mint 3,775		*Set:*	$350	$380	$700
1938S, Same type, S mint 3,814					
Texas Independence Centennial, single type coin		$75	80	90	135

(1934–1938) Daniel Boone Bicentennial   1934 Added on Reverse

	Distribution	AU-50	MS-60	MS-63	MS-65
1934, Daniel Boone Bicentennial 10,007		$75	$85	$95	$140
1935, Same type 10,010					
1935D, Same type, D mint 5,005		*Set:*	200	250	390
1935S, Same type, S mint 5,005					
1935, Same as 1934, but 1934 on Reverse 10,008					
1935D, Same type, D mint 2,003		*Set:*	400	475	1,100
1935S, Same type, S mint 2,004					
1936, Daniel Boone (same as preceding) .12,012					
1936D, Same type, D mint 5,005		*Set:*	200	250	390
1936S, Same type, S mint 5,006					
1937, Daniel Boone (same as preceding) .9,810					
1937D, Same type, D mint 2,506		*Set:*	380	450	800
1937S, Same type, S mint 2,506					
1938, Daniel Boone (same as preceding) .2,100					
1938D, Same type, D mint 2,100		*Set:*	500	675	900
1938S, Same type, S mint 2,100					
Daniel Boone Bicentennial, single type coin		75	85	95	140

(1935) Connecticut Tercentenary

	Distribution	AU-50	MS-60	MS-63	MS-65
1935, Connecticut Tercentenary 25,018		$135	$165	$180	$300

(1935–1939)
Arkansas Centennial

	Distribution	AU-50	MS-60	MS-63	MS-65
1935, Arkansas Centennial 13,012					
1935D, Same type, D mint 5,505	*Set:*	$165	$220	$400
1935S, Same type, S mint 5,506					
1936, Arkansas Centennial (same as 1935; date 1936 on reverse) . .9,660					
1936D, Same type, D mint 9,660	*Set:*	165	220	425
1936S, Same type, S mint 9,662					
1937, Arkansas Centennial (same as 1935) 5,505					
1937D, Same type, D mint 5,505	*Set:*	180	225	500
1937S, Same type S mint 5,506					
1938, Arkansas Centennial (same as 1935) 3,156					
1938D, Same type, D mint 3,155	*Set:*	225	250	850
1938S, Same type, S mint 3,156					
1939, Arkansas Centennial (same as 1935) 2,104					
1939D, Same type, D mint 2,104	*Set:*	460	600	1,650
1939S, Same type, S mint 2,105					
Arkansas Centennial, single type coin	$45	60	70	130

(1936) Arkansas
Centennial – Robinson

	Distribution	AU-50	MS-60	MS-63	MS-65
1936, Arkansas Centennial (Robinson) 25,265	$75	$85	$95	$215

(1935) Hudson, New
York, Sesquicentennial

	Distribution	AU-50	MS-60	MS-63	MS-65
1935, Hudson, New York, Sesquicentennial 10,008	$360	$475	$650	$1,150

COMMEMORATIVES

(1935–1936) California–Pacific International Exposition

	Distribution	AU-50	MS-60	MS-63	MS-65
1935S, California-Pacific International Exposition 70,132		$50	$65	$80	$95
1936D, California-Pacific International Exposition 30,092		50	75	85	100

(1935) Old Spanish Trail

	Distribution	AU-50	MS-60	MS-63	MS-65
1935, Old Spanish Trail 10,008		$530	$675	$760	$1,100

(1936) Providence, Rhode Island, Tercentenary

	Distribution	AU-50	MS-60	MS-63	MS-65
1936, Providence, Rhode Island, Tercentenary 20,013					
1936D, Same type, D mint 15,010		*Set:*	$170	$190	$410
1936S, Same type, S mint 15,011					
Providence, Rhode Island, Tercentenary, single type coin		$55	60	70	140

(1936) Cleveland Centennial / Great Lakes Exposition

	Distribution	AU-50	MS-60	MS-63	MS-65
1936, Cleveland Centennial / Great Lakes Exposition 50,030		$70	$75	$80	$110

(1936) Wisconsin Territorial Centennial

	Distribution	AU-50	MS-60	MS-63	MS-65
1936, Wisconsin Territorial Centennial 25,015		$120	$140	$150	$200

(1936) Cincinnati Music Center

	Distribution	AU-50	MS-60	MS-63	MS-65
1936, Cincinnati Music Center 5,005					
1936D, Same type, D mint 5,005		*Set:*	$450	$500	$1,200
1936S, Same type, S mint 5,006					
Cincinnati Music Center, single type coin		$140	150	160	390

(1936) Long Island Tercentenary

	Distribution	AU-50	MS-60	MS-63	MS-65
1936, Long Island Tercentenary	81,826	$50	$60	$65	$225

(1936) York County, Maine, Tercentenary

	Distribution	AU-50	MS-60	MS-63	MS-65
1936, York County, Maine, Tercentenary	25,015	$120	$130	$150	$175

(1936) Bridgeport, Connecticut, Centennial

	Distribution	AU-50	MS-60	MS-63	MS-65
1936, Bridgeport, Connecticut, Centennial	25,015	$75	$85	$110	$160

(1936) Lynchburg, Virginia, Sesquicentennial

	Distribution	AU-50	MS-60	MS-63	MS-65
1936, Lynchburg, Virginia, Sesquicentennial	20,013	$125	$140	$160	$210

(1936) Elgin, Illinois, Centennial

	Distribution	AU-50	MS-60	MS-63	MS-65
1936, Elgin, Illinois, Centennial	20,015	$125	$140	$165	$190

(1936) Albany, New York, Charter

	Distribution	AU-50	MS-60	MS-63	MS-65
1936, Albany, New York, Charter	17,671	$170	$185	$200	$235

(1936) San Francisco – Oakland Bay Bridge Opening

	Distribution	AU-50	MS-60	MS-63	MS-65
1936S, San Francisco–Oakland Bay Bridge Opening	71,424	$90	$100	$120	$210

(1936) Delaware Tercentenary

	Distribution	AU-50	MS-60	MS-63	MS-65
1936, Delaware Tercentenary	20,993	$160	$180	$200	$250

(1936) Columbia, South Carolina, Sesquicentennial

	Distribution	AU-50	MS-60	MS-63	MS-65
1936, Columbia, South Carolina, Sesquicentennial 9,007					
1936D, Same type, D mint 8,009		*Set:*	$425	$475	$600
1936S, Same type, S mint 8,007					
Columbia, South Carolina, Sesquicentennial, single type coin		$145	150	175	200

(1936) Battle of Gettysburg Anniversary

	Distribution	AU-50	MS-60	MS-63	MS-65
1936, Battle of Gettysburg Anniversary 26,928		$235	$275	$300	$450

(1936) Norfolk, Virginia, Bicentennial

	Distribution	AU-50	MS-60	MS-63	MS-65
1936, Norfolk, Virginia, Bicentennial 16,936		$260	$275	$300	$360

(1937) Roanoke Island, North Carolina, 350th Anniversary

	Distribution	AU-50	MS-60	MS-63	MS-65
1937, Roanoke Island, North Carolina, 350th Anniversary 29,030		$135	$150	$160	$175

(1937) Battle of Antietam Anniversary

	Distribution	AU-50	MS-60	MS-63	MS-65
1937, Battle of Antietam Anniversary 18,028		$365	$400	$450	$510

(1938) New Rochelle, New York, 250th Anniversary

	Distribution	AU-50	MS-60	MS-63	MS-65
1938, New Rochelle, New York, 250th Anniversary 15,266		$215	$225	$250	$315

(1946) Iowa Centennial

	Distribution	AU-50	MS-60	MS-63	MS-65
1946, Iowa Centennial 100,057		$65	$70	$80	$125

(1946–1951) Booker T. Washington Memorial

	Distribution		MS-60	MS-65
1946, Booker T. Washington Memorial **(a)**	700,546			
1946D, Same type, D mint	50,000	Set:	$32	$90
1946S, Same type, S mint	500,279			
1947, Same type as 1946	6,000			
1947D, Same type, D mint	6,000	Set:	45	140
1947S, Same type, S mint	6,000			
1948, Same type as 1946	8,005			
1948D, Same type, D mint	8,005	Set:	85	150
1948S, Same type, S mint	8,005			
1949, Same type as 1946	6,004			
1949D, Same type, D mint	6,004	Set:	130	185
1949S, Same type, S mint	6,004			
1950, Same type as 1946	6,004			
1950D, Same type, D mint	6,004	Set:	75	125
1950S, Same type, S mint	62,091			
1951, Same type as 1946	210,082			
1951D, Same type, D mint	7,004	Set:	55	110
1951S, Same type, S mint	7,004			
Booker T. Washington Memorial, single type coin			10	25

a. Minted; quantity melted unknown.

(1951–1954) Carver/Washington Commemorative

	Distribution	AU-50	MS-60	MS-63	MS-65
1951, Carver/Washington	20,018				
1951D, Same type, D mint	10,004	Set:	$55	$75	$310
1951S, Same type, S mint	10,004				
1952, Same type as 1951	1,106,292				
1952D, Same type, D mint	8,006	Set:	55	70	240
1952S, Same type, S mint	8,006				

Chart continued on next page.

	Distribution	AU-50	MS-60	MS-63	MS-65
1953, Same type as 1951	8,003				
1953D, Same type, D mint	8,003	Set:	$55	$75	$300
1953S, Same type, S mint	88,020				
1954, Same type as 1951	12,006				
1954D, Same type, D mint	12,006	Set:	50	70	240
1954S, Same type, S mint	42,024				
Carver/Washington, single type coin		$9	12	15	26

MODERN COMMEMORATIVES

(1982) George Washington 250th Anniversary of Birth

	Distribution	MS-67	PF-67
1982D, George Washington, 250th Anniversary half dollar	2,210,458	$5	
1982S, Same type, S mint, Proof	(4,894,044)		$5

(1983–1984) Los Angeles Olympiad

	Distribution	MS-67	PF-67
1983P, Discus Thrower silver dollar	294,543	$14	
1983D, Same type, D mint	174,014	14	
1983S, Same type, S mint	(1,577,025) 174,014	14	$14

COMMEMORATIVES

(1983–1984) Los Angeles Olympiad

	Distribution	MS-67	PF-67
1984P, Olympic Coliseum silver dollar	294,543	$14	
1984D, Same type, D mint	174,014	14	
1984S, Same type, S mint	(1,577,025) 174,014	14	$14
1984P, Olympic gold $10	(33,309)		470
1984D, Same type, D mint	(34,533)		470
1984S, Same type, S mint	(48,551)		470
1984W, Same type, W mint	(381,085) 75,886	470	470

(1986) Statue of Liberty

	Distribution	MS-67	PF-67
1986D, Statue of Liberty half dollar	928,008	$4.50	
1986S, Same type, S mint, Proof	(6,925,627)		$4.50
1986P, Statue of Liberty silver dollar	723,635	14.00	
1986S, Same type, S mint, Proof	(6,414,638)		14.00
1986W, Statue of Liberty gold $5	(404,013) 95,248	240.00	240.00

(1987) U.S. Constitution Bicentennial

	Distribution	MS-67	PF-67
1987P, U.S. Constitution Bicentennial silver dollar	.451,629	$14	
1987S, Same type, S mint, Proof	.(2,747,116)		$14
1987W, U.S. Constitution Bicentennial gold $5	(651,659) 214,225	240	240

(1988) Seoul Olympiad

	Distribution	MS-67	PF-67
1988D, Seoul Olympiad silver dollar	.191,368	$14	
1988S, Same type, S mint, Proof	.(1,359,366)		$14
1988W, Seoul Olympiad gold $5	(281,465) 62,913	240	240

(1989) Congress Bicentennial

	Distribution	MS-67	PF-67
1989D, Congress Bicentennial half dollar 163,753		$6	
1989S, Same type, S mint, Proof ....(767,897)			$6
1989D, Congress Bicentennial silver dollar 135,203		17	
1989S, Same type, S mint, Proof ....(762,198)			18
1989W, Congress Bicentennial gold $5 ....(164,690) 46,899		250	250

(1990) Eisenhower Centennial

	Distribution	MS-67	PF-67
1990W, Eisenhower Centennial silver dollar 241,669		$15	
1990P, Same type, P mint, Proof ....(1,144,461)			$16

(1991) Mount Rushmore Golden Anniversary

	Distribution	MS-67	PF-67
1991D, Mount Rushmore Golden Anniversary half dollar 172,754		$15	
1991S, Same type, S mint, Proof . . . .(753,257)			$14
1991P, Mount Rushmore Golden Anniversary silver dollar 133,139		22	
1991S, Same type, S mint, Proof . . . .(738,419)			19
1991W, Mount Rushmore Golden Anniversary gold $5 . . . .(111,991) 31,959		250	240

(1991) Korean War Memorial

	Distribution	MS-67	PF-67
1991D, Korean War Memorial silver dollar 213,049		$16	
1991P, Same type, P mint, Proof . . . .(618,488)			$17

(1991) United Service Organizations

	Distribution	MS-67	PF-67
1991D United Service Organizations silver dollar 124,958		$15	
1991S, Same type, S mint, Proof ....(321,275)			$16

(1992) XXV Olympiad

	Distribution	MS-67	PF-67
1992P, XXV Olympiad clad half dollar 161,607		$7	
1992S, Same type, S mint, Proof ....(519,645)			$7.50
1992D, XXV Olympiad silver dollar 187,552		18	
1992S, Same type, S mint, Proof ....(504,505)			18.00
1992W, XXV Olympiad gold $5 ....(77,313) 27,732		240	240.00

(1992) **White House 200th Anniversary**

	Distribution	MS-67	PF-67
1992D, White House 200th Anniversary silver dollar 123,803		$20	
1992W, Same type, W Mint, Proof ....(375,851)			$20

(1992) **Christopher Columbus Quincentenary**

	Distribution	MS-67	PF-67
1992D, Christopher Columbus Quincentenary half dollar 135,702		$9	
1992S, Same type, S mint, Proof ....(390,154)			$8
1992D, Christopher Columbus Quincentenary silver dollar 106,949		21	
1992P, Same type, P mint, Proof ....(385,241)			24
1992W, Christopher Columbus Quincentenary gold $5 ....(79,730) 24,329		270	250

(1993) Bill of Rights

	Distribution	MS-67	PF-67
1993W, Bill of Rights silver half dollar	193,346	$14	
1993S, Same type, S mint, Proof	(586,315)		$12
1993D, Bill of Rights silver dollar	98,383	14	
1993S, Same type, S mint, Proof	(534,001)		15
1993W, Bill of Rights gold $5	(78,651) 23,266	275	240

(1991–1995) 50th Anniversary of World War II

	Distribution	MS-67	PF-67
(1993P) 1991–1995 World War II clad half dollar	(317,396) 197,072	$22	$20

Entry continued on next page.

(1991–1995) 50th Anniversary of World War II

	Distribution	MS-67	PF-67
(1993D) 1991–1995 World War II silver dollar	107,240	$24	
(1993W) Same type, W mint, Proof	(342,041)		$30
(1993W) 1991–1995 World War II gold $5	(67,026) ... 23,672	275	260

(1994) World Cup Tournament

	Distribution	MS-67	PF-67
1994D, World Cup Tournament clad half dollar	168,208	$7	
1994P, Same type, P mint, Proof	(609,354)		$6
1994D, World Cup Tournament silver dollar	81,524	17	
1994S, Same type, S mint, Proof	(577,090)		18
1994W, World Cup Tournament gold $5	(89,614) ... 22,447	270	240

(1993 [1994]) Thomas Jefferson

	Distribution	MS-67	PF-67
1993 (1994) Thomas Jefferson silver dollar	266,927	$16	
1993 (1994) Same type, S mint, Proof	(332,891)		$17

(1994) Vietnam Veterans Memorial

	Distribution	MS-67	PF-67
1994W, Vietnam Veterans Memorial silver dollar	57,290	$65	
1994P, Same type, P mint, Proof	(227,671)		$52

(1994) U.S. Prisoner of War Museum

	Distribution	MS-67	PF-67
1994W, U.S. Prisoner of War Museum silver dollar	54,893	$70	
1994P, Same type, P mint, Proof	(224,449)		$32

(1994) Women in Military Service Memorial

	Distribution	MS-67	PF-67
1994W, Women in Military Service Memorial silver dollar	69,860	$30	
1994P, Same type, P mint, Proof	(241,278)		$30

(1994) U.S. Capitol Bicentennial

	Distribution	MS-67	PF-67
1994D, U.S. Capitol Bicentennial silver dollar	68,332	$15	
1994S, Same type, S mint, Proof	(279,579)		$16

(1995) Civil War Battlefield Preservation

	Distribution	MS-67	PF-67
1995S, Civil War Battlefield Preservation clad half dollar	119,520	$32	
1995S, Same type, S mint, Proof	(330,002)		$30

(1995) Civil War Battlefield Preservation

	Distribution	MS-67	PF-67
1995P, Civil War Battlefield Preservation silver dollar	45,866	$55	
1995S, Same type, S mint, Proof	(437,114)		$55
1995W, Civil War Battlefield Preservation gold $5	12,735	700	
1995W, Same type, W mint, Proof	(55,246)		300

(1995) XXVI Olympiad

	Distribution	MS-67	PF-67
1995S, XXVI Olympiad, Basketball clad half dollar	171,001	$15	
1995S, Same type, S mint, Proof	(169,655)		$13
1995S, XXVI Olympiad, Baseball clad half dollar	164,605	15	
1995S, Same type, S mint, Proof	(118,087)		14
1996S, XXVI Olympiad, Swimming clad half dollar	49,533	110	
1996S, Same type, S mint, Proof	(114,315)		25
1996S, XXVI Olympiad, Soccer clad half dollar	52,836	110	
1996S, Same type, S mint, Proof	(112,412)		75
1995D, XXVI Olympiad, Gymnastics silver dollar	42,497	50	
1995P, Same type, P mint, Proof	(182,676)		35

Entry continued on next page.

(1995) XXVI Olympiad

	Distribution	MS-67	PF-67
1995D, XXVI Olympiad, Paralympics silver dollar 28,649		$60	
1995P, Same type, P mint, Proof . . . .(138,337)			$40
1995D, XXVI Olympiad, Track and Field silver dollar 24,976		70	
1995P, Same type, P mint, Proof . . . .(136,935)			38
1995D, XXVI Olympiad, Cycling silver dollar 19,662		110	
1995P, Same type, P mint, Proof . . . .(118,795)			35
1996D, XXVI Olympiad, Tennis silver dollar 15,983		250	
1996P, Same type, P mint, Proof . . . .(92,016)			68
1996D, XXVI Olympiad, Paralympics silver dollar 14,497		275	
1996P, Same type, P mint, Proof . . . .(84,280)			66
1996D, XXVI Olympiad, Rowing silver dollar 16,258		260	
1996P, Same type, P mint, Proof . . . .(151,890)			50
1996D, XXVI Olympiad, High Jump silver dollar 15,697		300	
1996P, Same type, P mint, Proof . . . .(124,502)			45
1995W, XXVI Olympiad, Torch Runner gold $5 14,675		680	
1995W, Same type, W mint, Proof . . . .(57,442)			300
1995W, XXVI Olympiad, Stadium gold $5 10,579		990	
1995W, Same type, W mint, Proof . . . .(43,124)			450
1996W, XXVI Olympiad, Flag Bearer gold $5 9,174		875	
1996W, Same type, W mint, Proof . . . .(32,886)			525
1996W, XXVI Olympiad, Cauldron gold $5 9,210		850	
1996W, Same type, W mint, Proof . . . .(38,555)			525

(1995) Special Olympics World Games

	Distribution	MS-67	PF-67
1995W, Special Olympics World Games silver dollar 89,301		$23	
1995P, Same type, P mint, Proof . . . .(351,764)			$19

(1996) National Community Service

	Distribution	MS-67	PF-67
1996S, National Community Service silver dollar	23,500	$160	
1996S, Same type, S mint, Proof	(101,543)		$60

(1996) Smithsonian Institution 150th Anniversary

	Distribution	MS-67	PF-67
1996D, Smithsonian Institution 150th Anniversary silver dollar	31,320	$110	
1996P, Same type, P mint, Proof	(129,152)		$50
1996W, Smithsonian Institution 150th Anniversary gold $5	9,068	950	
1996W, Same type, W mint, Proof	(21,772)		435

(1997) Botanic Garden

	Distribution	MS-67	PF-67
1997P, Botanic Garden silver dollar	58,505	$32	
1997P, Same type, P mint, Proof	(189,671)		$30

(1997) Jackie Robinson

	Distribution	MS-67	PF-67
1997S, Jackie Robinson silver dollar	30,180	$80	
1997S, Same type, S mint, Proof	(110,002)		$70
1997W, Jackie Robinson gold $5	5,174	4,300	
1997W, Same type, W mint, Proof	(24,072)		650

(1997) Franklin D. Roosevelt

	Distribution	MS-67	PF-67
1997W, Franklin D. Roosevelt gold $5	11,894	$675	
1997W, Same type, W mint, Proof	(29,474)		$375

(1997) National Law Enforcement Officers Memorial

	Distribution	MS-67	PF-67
1997P, National Law Enforcement Officers Memorial silver dollar	28,575	$125	
1997P, Same type, P mint, Proof	(110,428)		$90

(1998) Robert F. Kennedy

	Distribution	MS-67	PF-67
1998S, Robert F. Kennedy silver dollar	106,422	$25	
1998S, Same type, S mint, Proof	(99,020)		$34

(1998) Black Revolutionary War Patriots

	Distribution	MS-67	PF-67
1998S, Black Revolutionary War Patriots silver dollar	37,210	$125	
1998S, Same type, S mint, Proof	(75,070)		$80

(1999) Dolley Madison Commemorative

	Distribution	MS-67	PF-67
1999P, Dolley Madison silver dollar	89,104	$30	
1999P, Same type, P mint, Proof	(224,403)		$28

(1999) George Washington Death Bicentennial

	Distribution	MS-67	PF-67
1999W, George Washington Death Bicentennial gold $5	22,511	$315	
1999W, Same type, W mint, Proof	(41,693)		$275

(1999) Yellowstone National Park

	Distribution	MS-67	PF-67
1999P, Yellowstone National Park silver dollar	82,563	$40	
1999S, Same type, S mint, Proof	(187,595)		$39

(2000) Library of Congress Bicentennial

	Distribution	MS-67	PF-67
2000P, Library of Congress Bicentennial silver dollar	53,264	$37	
2000P, Same type, P mint, Proof	(198,503)		$37
2000W, Library of Congress Bicentennial bimetallic (gold/platinum) $10	7,261	2,500	
2000W, Same type, W mint, Proof	(27,445)		850

(2000) Leif Ericson Millennium

	Distribution	MS-67	PF-67
2000P, Leif Ericson Millennium silver dollar 28,150		$75	
2000P, Same type, P mint, Proof . . . .(144,748)			$60

(2001) American Buffalo Commemorative

	Distribution	MS-67	PF-67
2001D, American Buffalo silver dollar 227,131		$200	
2001P, Same type, P mint, Proof . . . .(272,869)			$225

(2001) Capitol Visitor Center

	Distribution	MS-67	PF-67
2001P, Capitol Visitor Center clad half dollar 99,157		$10	
2001P, Same type, P mint, Proof . . . .(77,962)			$13

Entry continued on next page.

(2001) Capitol Visitor Center

	Distribution	MS-67	PF-67
2001P, Capitol Visitor Center silver dollar	35,380	$24	
2001P, Same type, P mint, Proof	(143,793)		$30
2001W, Capitol Visitor Center gold $5	6,761	1,100	
2001W, Same type, W mint, Proof	(27,652)		300

(2002) Salt Lake City Olympic Games

	Distribution	MS-67	PF-67
2002D, Salt Lake Olympics silver dollar	40,257	$27	
2002P, Same type, P mint, Proof	(166,864)		$31
2002W, Salt Lake Olympics gold $5	10,585	400	
2002W, Same type, W mint, Proof	(32,877)		300

(2002) West Point Bicentennial

	Distribution	MS-67	PF-67
2002W, West Point Bicentennial silver dollar	103,201	$15	
2002W, Same type, W mint, Proof	(288,293)		$15

(2003) First Flight Centennial

	Distribution	MS-67	PF-67
2003P, First Flight Centennial clad half dollar	57,122	$11	
2003P, Same type, P mint, Proof	(109,710)		$12
2003P, First Flight Centennial silver dollar	53,533	26	
2003P, Same type, P mint, Proof	(190,240)		23
2003W, First Flight Centennial gold $10	10,009	490	
2003W, Same type, W mint, Proof	(21,676)		470

(2004) Thomas Alva Edison

	Distribution	MS-67	PF-67
2004P, Thomas Alva Edison silver dollar	92,510	$26	
2004P, Same type, P mint, Proof	(211,055)		$27

(2004) Lewis and Clark Bicentennial

	Distribution	MS-67	PF-67
2004P, Lewis and Clark Bicentennial silver dollar	142,015	$24	
2004P, Same type, P mint, Proof	(351,989)		$22

(2005) Chief Justice John Marshall

	Distribution	MS-67	PF-67
2005P, Chief Justice John Marshall silver dollar	67,096	$25	
2005P, Same type, P mint, Proof	(196,753)		$28

(2005) Marine Corps 230th Anniversary

	Distribution	MS-67	PF-67
2005P, Marine Corps 230th Anniversary silver dollar	49,671	$30	
2005P, Same type, P mint, Proof	(548,810)		$30

(2006) Benjamin Franklin

	Distribution	MS-67	PF-67
2006P, Benjamin Franklin "Scientist" silver dollar	58,000	$25	
2006P, Same type, P mint, Proof	(142,000)		$35
2006P, Benjamin Franklin "Founding Father" silver dollar	58,000	25	
2006P, Same type, P mint, Proof	(142,000)		35

(2006) San Francisco Old Mint

	Distribution	MS-67	PF-67
2006S, San Francisco Old Mint silver dollar	67,100	$33	
2006S, Same type, S mint, Proof	(160,870)		$33
2006S, San Francisco Old Mint gold $5	17,500	250	
2006S, Same type, S mint, Proof	(44,174)		250

(2007) Jamestown 400th Anniversary

	Distribution	MS-67	PF-67
2007P, Jamestown 400th Anniversary silver dollar		$30	
2007P, Same type, P mint, Proof			$32
2007W, Jamestown 400th Anniversary gold $5		250	
2007W, Same type, W mint, Proof			250

(2007) Little Rock Central High School Desegregation

	Distribution	MS-67	PF-67
2007P, Little Rock Central High School Desegregation silver dollar		$30	
2007P, Same type, P mint, Proof			$32

(2008) Bald Eagle

	Distribution	MS-67	PF-67
2008S, Bald Eagle clad half dollar		$7	
2008S, Same type, S mint, Proof			$8
2008S, Bald Eagle silver dollar		24	
2008S, Same type, S mint, Proof			25
2008W, Bald Eagle gold $5		250	
2008W, Same type, W mint, Proof			250

(2009) Louis Braille Bicentennial

	Distribution	MS-67	PF-67
2009P, Louis Braille Bicentennial silver dollar		$24	
2009P, Same type, P Mint, Proof			$25

(2009) Abraham Lincoln Bicentennial

	Distribution	MS-67	PF-67
2009P, Abraham Lincoln Bicentennial silver dollar		$24	
2009P, Same type, P Mint, Proof			$25

GOVERNMENT COMMEMORATIVE SETS

Values are for commemorative coins and sets in all of their original packaging.

	Value
(1983–1984) Los Angeles Olympiad	
1983 and 1984 Proof dollars	$30
1983 and 1984 6-coin set. One each of 1983 and 1984 dollars, both Proof and Uncirculated gold $10 **(a)**	1,000
1983 3-piece collector set. 1983 P, D, and S Uncirculated dollars	45
1984 3-piece collector set. 1984 P, D, and S Uncirculated dollars	45
1983 and 1984 gold and silver Uncirculated set. One each of 1983 and 1984 Uncirculated dollar and one 1984 Uncirculated gold $10	500
1983 and 1984 gold and silver Proof set. One each of 1983 and 1984 Proof dollars and one 1984 Proof gold $10	500

a. Packaged in cherrywood box.

COMMEMORATIVES

	Value
(1986) Statue of Liberty	
2-coin set. Proof silver dollar and clad half dollar	$20
3-coin set. Proof silver dollar, clad half dollar, and gold $5	260
2-coin set. Uncirculated silver dollar and clad half dollar	20
2-coin set. Uncirculated and Proof gold $5	500
3-coin set. Uncirculated silver dollar, clad half dollar, and gold $5	260
6-coin set. One each of Proof and Uncirculated half dollar, silver dollar, and gold $5 **(a)**	525
(1987) Constitution	
2-coin set. Uncirculated silver dollar and gold $5	260
2-coin set. Proof silver dollar and gold $5	260
4-coin set. One each of Proof and Uncirculated silver dollar and gold $5 **(a)**	520
(1988) Seoul Olympiad	
2-coin set. Uncirculated silver dollar and gold $5	260
2-coin set. Proof silver dollar and gold $5	260
4-coin set. One each of Proof and Uncirculated silver dollar and gold $5 **(a)**	520
(1989) Congress	
2-coin set. Proof clad half dollar and silver dollar	26
3-coin set. Proof clad half dollar, silver dollar, and gold $5	275
2-coin set. Uncirculated clad half dollar and silver dollar	25
3-coin set. Uncirculated clad half dollar, silver dollar, and gold $5	275
6-coin set. One each of Proof and Uncirculated clad half dollar, silver dollar, and gold $5 **(a)**	550
(1991) Mount Rushmore	
2-coin set. Uncirculated clad half dollar and silver dollar	30
2-coin set. Proof clad half dollar and silver dollar	35
3-coin set. Uncirculated clad half dollar, silver dollar, and gold $5	290
3-coin set. Proof half dollar, silver dollar, and gold $5	275
6-coin set. One each of Proof and Uncirculated clad half dollar, silver dollar, and gold $5 **(a)**	565
(1992) XXV Olympiad	
2-coin set. Uncirculated clad half dollar and silver dollar	25
2-coin set. Proof clad half dollar and silver dollar	26
3-coin set. Uncirculated clad half dollar, silver dollar, and gold $5	275
3-coin set. Proof half dollar, silver dollar, and gold $5	275
6-coin set. One each of Proof and Uncirculated clad half dollar, silver dollar, and gold $5 **(a)**	550
(1992) Christopher Columbus	
2-coin set. Uncirculated clad half dollar and silver dollar	30
2-coin set. Proof clad half dollar and silver dollar	32
3-coin set. Uncirculated clad half dollar, silver dollar, and gold $5	300
3-coin set. Proof half dollar, silver dollar, and gold $5	290
6-coin set. One each of Proof and Uncirculated clad half dollar, silver dollar, and gold $5 **(a)**	590
(1993) Bill of Rights	
2-coin set. Uncirculated silver half dollar and silver dollar	30
2-coin set. Proof silver half dollar and silver dollar	30
3-coin set. Uncirculated silver half dollar, silver dollar, and gold $5	305
3-coin set. Proof half dollar, silver dollar, and gold $5	270
6-coin set. One each of Proof and Uncirculated silver half dollar, silver dollar, and gold $5 **(a)**	575
"Young Collector" set. Silver half dollar	15
Educational set. Silver half dollar and James Madison medal	16
Proof silver half dollar and 25-cent stamp	15

a. Packaged in cherrywood box.

	Value
(1993) World War II	
2-coin set. Uncirculated clad half dollar and silver dollar	$45
2-coin set. Proof clad half dollar and silver dollar	50
3-coin set. Uncirculated clad half dollar, silver dollar, and gold $5	320
3-coin set. Proof clad half dollar, silver dollar, and gold $5	310
6-coin set. One each of Proof and Uncirculated clad half dollar, silver dollar, and gold $5 **(a)**	630
"Young Collector" set. Clad half dollar	23
"Victory" set. Silver dollar and French franc	24
Victory Medal set. Uncirculated clad half dollar and reproduction medal	25
(1993) Thomas Jefferson	
3-piece set (issued in 1994). Silver dollar, Jefferson nickel, and $2 note	65
(1994) World Cup Soccer	
2-coin set. Uncirculated clad half dollar and silver dollar	23
2-coin set. Proof clad half dollar and silver dollar	24
3-coin set. Uncirculated clad half dollar, silver dollar, and gold $5	295
3-coin set. Proof clad half dollar, silver dollar, and gold $5	275
6-coin set. One each of Proof and Uncirculated clad half dollar, silver dollar, and gold $5 **(a)**	570
"Young Collector" set. Uncirculated clad half dollar	9
"Special Edition" set. Proof clad half dollar and silver dollar	26
(1994) U.S. Veterans	
3-coin set. Uncirculated POW, Vietnam, and Women in Military Service silver dollars	165
3-coin set. Proof POW, Vietnam, and Women in Military Service silver dollars	115
(1995) Special Olympics	
2-coin set. Proof Special Olympics silver dollar, 1995S Kennedy half dollar	60
(1995) Civil War Battlefield Preservation	
2-coin set. Uncirculated clad half dollar and silver dollar	82
2-coin set. Proof clad half dollar and silver dollar	90
3-coin set. Uncirculated clad half dollar, silver dollar, and gold $5	780
3-coin set. Proof clad half dollar, silver dollar, and gold $5	420
6-coin set. One each of Proof and Uncirculated clad half dollar, silver dollar, and gold $5 **(a)**	1,200
"Young Collector" set. Uncirculated clad half dollar	35
2-coin "Union" set. Clad half dollar and silver dollar	85
3-coin "Union" set. Clad half dollar, silver dollar, and gold $5	525
(1995–1996) Centennial Olympic Games	
4-coin set #1. Uncirculated half dollar (Basketball), dollars (Gymnastics, Paralympics), gold $5 (Torch Bearer)	750
4-coin set #2. Proof half dollar (Basketball), dollars (Gymnastics, Paralympics), gold $5 (Torch Bearer)	360
2-coin set #1: Proof silver dollars (Gymnastics, Paralympics)	75
"Young Collector" set. Uncirculated Basketball, Baseball, Swimming, or Soccer half dollar	—
1995–1996 16-coin Uncirculated set. One each of all Uncirculated coins **(a)**	5,000
1995–1996 16-coin Proof set. One each of all Proof coins **(a)**	2,380
1995–1996 8-coin Proof set. One each of Proof dollar coins **(a)**	375
1995–1996 32-coin set. One each of all Uncirculated and Proof coins **(a)**	7,380
(1996) National Community Service	
Proof silver dollar and Saint-Gaudens stamp	70

a. Packaged in cherrywood box.

COMMEMORATIVES

	Value

(1996) Smithsonian Institution 150th Anniversary

2-coin set. Proof silver dollar and gold $5 . . . . $485

4-coin set. One each of Proof and Uncirculated silver dollar and gold $5 **(a)** 1,550

"Young Collector" set. Proof silver dollar 50

(1997) Botanic Garden

"Coinage and Currency" set. Uncirculated silver dollar, Jefferson nickel, and $1 note 135

(1997) Jackie Robinson

2-coin set. Proof silver dollar and gold $5 725

4-coin set. One each of Proof and Uncirculated silver dollar and gold $5 **(a)** 5,125

3-piece "Legacy" set. Baseball card, pin, and gold $5 660

(1997) National Law Enforcement Officers Memorial

Insignia set. Silver dollar, lapel pin, and patch 150

(1998) Robert F. Kennedy

2-coin set. RFK silver dollar and JFK silver half dollar 250

2-coin set. Proof and Uncirculated RFK silver dollars 60

(1998) Black Revolutionary War Patriots

2-coin set. Proof and Uncirculated silver dollars 210

"Young Collector" set. Uncirculated silver dollar 130

Black Revolutionary War Patriots set. Silver dollar and four stamps 100

(1999) Dolley Madison Commemorative

2-coin set. Proof and Uncirculated silver dollars 60

(1999) George Washington Death

2-coin set. One each of Proof and Uncirculated gold $5 600

(1999) Yellowstone National Park

2-coin set. One each of Proof and Uncirculated silver dollars 80

(2000) Leif Ericson Millennium

2-coin set. Proof silver dollar and Icelandic 1,000 kronur 90

(2000) Millennium Coin and Currency Set

3-piece set. Uncirculated 2000 Sacagawea dollar; Uncirculated 2000 Silver Eagle; George

Washington $1 note, series 1999 65

(2001) American Buffalo

2-coin set. One each of Proof and Uncirculated silver dollar 425

"Coinage and Currency" set. Uncirculated American Buffalo silver dollar, face reprint of 1899 $5 Indian

Chief Silver Certificate, 1987 Chief Red Cloud 10¢ stamp, 2001 Bison 21¢ stamp 225

(2001) Capitol Visitor Center

3-coin set. Proof clad half dollar, silver dollar, and gold $5 345

(2002) Salt Lake Olympic Games

2-coin set. Proof silver dollar and gold $5 335

4-coin set. One each of Proof and Uncirculated silver dollar and gold $5 760

(2004) Thomas A. Edison

Edison set. Uncirculated silver dollar and light bulb 38

a. Packaged in cherrywood box.

	Value

(2004) Lewis and Clark
Coin and Pouch set. Proof silver dollar and beaded pouch $115
"Coinage and Currency" set. Uncirculated silver dollar, Sacagawea golden dollar, two 2005 nickels,
replica 1901 $10 Bison note, silver-plated Peace Medal replica, three stamps, two booklets 50

(2004) Westward Journey Nickel Series™
Westward Journey Nickel Series™ Coin and Medal set. Proof Sacagawea golden dollar, two 2004 Proof
nickels, silver-plated Peace Medal replica 30

(2005) Westward Journey Nickel Series™
Westward Journey Nickel Series™ Coin and Medal set. Proof Sacagawea golden dollar, two 2005 Proof
nickels, silver-plated Peace Medal replica 35

(2005) Chief Justice John Marshall
"Coin and Chronicles" set. Uncirculated silver dollar, booklet, BEP intaglio portrait 35

(2005) American Legacy
American Legacy Collection. Proof Marine Corps dollar, Proof John Marshall dollar, 10-piece Proof set . . 100

(2005) Marine Corps 230th Anniversary
Marine Corps Uncirculated silver dollar and stamp set 35

(2006) Benjamin Franklin
"Coin and Chronicles" set. Uncirculated "Scientist" silver dollar, four stamps, *Poor Richard's Almanack*
replica, intaglio print 40

(2006) American Legacy
American Legacy Collection. Proof 2006P Benjamin Franklin, Founding Father silver dollar; Proof 2006S
San Francisco Old Mint silver dollar; Proof cent, nickel, dime, quarter, half dollar, and dollar 100

(2007) American Legacy
American Legacy Collection. 16 Proof coins for 2007: five state quarters; four Presidential dollars;
Jamestown and Little Rock Central High School Desegregation silver dollars; Proof cent, nickel, dime,
half dollar, and dollar 70

(2007) Little Rock Central High School Desegregation
Little Rock Coin and Medal Set. Proof 2007P silver dollar, bronze medal 120

(2008) Bald Eagle
3-Piece set. Proof clad half dollar, silver dollar, and gold $5 275
Bald Eagle Coin and Medal Set. Uncirculated silver dollar, bronze medal 20
"Young Collector" set. Uncirculated clad half dollar 20

(2008) American Legacy
American Legacy Collection. 15 Proof coins for 2008: cent, nickel, dime, half dollar, and dollar;
five state quarters; four Presidential dollars; Bald Eagle dollar 100

PROOF COINS AND SETS

Proof coins can usually be distinguished by their sharpness of detail, high wire edge, and extremely brilliant, mirrorlike surface. Proofs are sold by the Mint at a premium.

Proof coins were not struck during 1943–1949 or 1965–1967. Sets from 1936 through 1972 include the cent, nickel, dime, quarter, and half dollar; from 1973 through 1981 the dollar was also included. *Values shown are for original unblemished sets.*

Figures in parentheses represent the total number of full sets minted.

Year	Mintage	Issue Price	Current Value	Year	Mintage	Issue Price	Current Value
1936	(3,837)	$1.89	$5,000.00	1978S	(3,127,781)	$9.00	$5.00
1937	(5,542)	1.89	2,500.00	1979S	(3,677,175)	9.00	5.00
1938	(8,045)	1.89	1,200.00	1979S	*	9.00	60.00
1939	(8,795)	1.89	1,000.00	1980S	(3,554,806)	10.00	4.00
1940	(11,246)	1.89	900.00	1981S	(4,063,083)	11.00	4.00
1941	(15,287)	1.89	900.00	1982S	(3,857,479)	11.00	2.00
1942, Both nickels	(21,120)	1.89	825.00	1983S	(3,138,765)	11.00	3.00
1942, One nickel	*	1.89	800.00	1983S, Prestige Set			
1950	(51,386)	2.10	500.00	(Olympic dollar)	(140,361)	59.00	43.00
1951	(57,500)	2.10	400.00	1984S	(2,748,430)	11.00	4.00
1952	(81,980)	2.10	175.00	1984S, Prestige Set			
1953	(128,800)	2.10	160.00	(Olympic dollar)	(316,680)	59.00	15.00
1954	(233,300)	2.10	72.00	1985S	(3,362,821)	11.00	2.90
1955, Box pack	(378,200)	2.10	75.00	1986S	(2,411,180)	11.00	3.00
1955, Flat pack	*	2.10	75.00	1986S, Prestige Set (Statue			
1956	(669,384)	2.10	35.00	of Liberty half, dollar)	(599,317)	48.50	16.00
1957	(1,247,952)	2.10	16.00	1987S	(3,792,233)	11.00	3.00
1958	(875,652)	2.10	32.00	1987S, Prestige Set			
1959	(1,149,291)	2.10	15.00	(Constitution dollar)	(435,495)	45.00	14.00
1960, With Lg Date cent	(1,691,602)	2.10	12.00	1988S	(3,031,287)	11.00	3.00
1960, With Sm Date cent	*	2.10	18.00	1988S, Prestige Set			
1961	(3,028,244)	2.10	10.00	(Olympic dollar)	(231,661)	45.00	20.00
1962	(3,218,019)	2.10	10.00	1989S	(3,009,107)	11.00	4.00
1963	(3,075,645)	2.10	11.00	1989S, Prestige Set			
1964	(3,950,762)	2.10	10.00	(Congressional half,			
1968S	(3,041,506)	5.00	4.00	dollar)	(211,807)	45.00	22.00
1969S	(2,934,631)	5.00	4.50	1990S	(2,793,433)	11.00	3.00
1970S	(2,632,810)	5.00	5.00	1990S, With No S cent	(3,555)	11.00	4,200.00
1970S, With Sm Date cent	*	5.00	55.00	1990S, With No S cent			
1971S	(3,220,733)	5.00	2.00	(Prestige Set)	*	45.00	4,500.00
1972S	(3,260,996)	5.00	2.00	1990S, Prestige Set			
1973S	(2,760,339)	7.00	4.00	(Eisenhower dollar)	(506,126)	45.00	16.75
1974S	(2,612,568)	7.00	5.00	1991S	(2,610,833)	11.00	7.00
1975S, With 1976 quarter,				1991S, Prestige Set (Mt.			
half, and dollar	(2,845,450)	7.00	5.00	Rushmore half, dollar)	(256,954)	59.00	37.00
1976S	(4,149,730)	7.00	5.00	1992S	(2,675,618)	11.00	3.00
1976S, 3-piece set	(3,998,621)	15.00	9.00	1992S, Prestige Set			
1977S	(3,251,152)	9.00	4.00	(Olympic half, dollar)	(183,293)	56.00	43.00

* Included in number above.

Chart continued on next page.

Year	Mintage	Issue Price	Current Value
1992S, Silver . . . .(1,009,586)	$21.00	$10.00
1992S, Silver Premier Set . .(308,055)	37.00	11.00
1993S . . . .(2,409,394)	12.50	6.00
1993S, Prestige Set		
(Madison half, dollar) . .(224,045)	57.00	20.00
1993S, Silver . . . .(570,213)	21.00	19.00
1993S, Silver Premier Set . .(191,140)	37.50	19.00
1994S . . . .(2,308,701)	12.50	6.00
1994S, Prestige Set (World		
Cup half, dollar) . . . . . .(175,893)	57.00	25.00
1994S, Silver . . . .(636,009)	21.00	23.00
1994S Silver Premier Set . . .(149,320)	37.50	23.00
1995S . . . .(2,010,384)	12.50	19.00
1995S, Prestige Set (Civil		
War half, dollar) . . . . . .(107,112)	57.00	80.00
1995S, Silver . . . .(549,878)	21.00	50.00
1995S, Silver Premier Set . .(130,107)	37.50	50.00
1996S . . . .(1,695,244)	12.50	8.00
1996S, Prestige Set		
(Olympic half, dollar) . . .(55,000)	57.00	275.00
1996S, Silver . . . .(623,655)	21.00	22.00
1996S, Silver Premier Set . .(151,366)	37.50	25.00
1997S . . . .(1,975,000)	12.50	18.00
1997S, Prestige Set		
(Botanic dollar) . . . .(80,000)	48.00	90.00
1997S, Silver . . . .(605,473)	21.00	35.00
1997S, Silver Premier Set . .(136,205)	37.50	36.00
1998S . . . .(2,086,507)	12.50	10.00
1998S, Silver . . . .(638,134)	21.00	16.00
1998S, Silver Premier Set . .(240,658)	37.50	17.00
1999S, 9-piece set . . . . .(2,543,401)	19.95	30.00
1999S, 5-piece quarter set (1,169,958)	13.95	32.00
1999S, Silver 9-piece set . .(804,565)	31.95	200.00
2000S, 10-piece set . . . . .(3,082,572)	19.95	10.00
2000S, 5-piece quarter set . .(937,600)	13.95	5.00
2000S, Silver 10-piece set . .(965,421)	31.95	20.00

Year	Mintage	Issue Price	Current Value
2001S, 10-piece set . . . . .(2,294,909)	$19.95	$60.00
2001S, 5-piece quarter set . .(799,231)	13.95	32.00
2001S, Silver 10-piece set . .(889,697)	31.95	75.00
2002S, 10-piece set . . . . .(2,319,766)	19.95	20.00
2002S, 5-piece quarter set . .(764,479)	13.95	12.00
2002S, Silver 10-piece set . .(892,229)	31.95	36.00
2003S, 10-piece set . . . . .(2,172,684)	19.95	13.00
2003S, 5-piece quarter set (1,235,832)	13.95	9.00
2003S, Silver 10-piece set (1,125,755)	31.95	20.00
2004S, 11-piece set . . . . .(1,789,488)	22.95	28.00
2004S, 5-piece quarter set . .(951,196)	15.95	10.00
2004S, Silver 11-piece set (1,175,934)	37.95	24.00
2004S, Silver 5-piece		
quarter set . . . .(593,852)	23.95	16.00
2005S, 11-piece set . . . . .(2,275,000)	22.95	111.00
2005S, 5-piece quarter set . .(987,960)	15.95	8.00
2005S, Silver 11-piece set (1,069,679)	37.95	22.00
2005S, Silver 5-piece		
quarter set . . . .(608,970)	23.95	16.00
2006S, 10-piece set . . . . .(2,000,428)	22.95	18.00
2006S, 5-piece quarter set . .(882,000)	15.95	11.00
2006S, Silver 10-piece set (1,054,008)	37.95	16.00
2006S, Silver 5-piece		
quarter set . . . .(531,000)	23.95	15.00
2007S, 14-piece set . . . . .(1,384,797)	26.95	19.00
2007S, 5-piece quarter set . .(618,015)	13.95	10.00
2007S, 4-piece		
Presidential set . . . . .(1,102,390)	14.95	11.00
2007S, Silver 14-piece set . .(677,996)	44.95	30.00
2007S, Silver 5-piece		
quarter set . . . .(416,997)	25.95	15.00
2008S, 14-piece set	26.95	20.00
2008S, 5-piece quarter set	13.95	10.00
2008S, 4-piece Presidential set	14.95	11.00
2008S, Silver 14-piece set	44.95	32.00
2008S, Silver 5-piece quarter set	25.95	15.00

* Included in number above.

UNCIRCULATED MINT SETS

Official Mint Sets are specially packaged by the government for sale to collectors. They contain uncirculated specimens of each year's coins for every denomination issued from each mint. Sets from 1947 through 1958 contain two examples of each regular-issue coin. No official sets were produced in 1950, 1982, or 1983. Privately assembled sets are valued according to individual coin prices. Only official sets are included in the following list. Unlike the Proof sets, these are normal coins intended for circulation and are not minted with any special consideration for quality.

Year	Mintage	Issue Price	Current Value	Year	Mintage	Issue Price	Current Value
1947 P-D-S	5,000	$4.87	$850.00	1978 P-D	2,162,609	$7.00	$4.00
1948 P-D-S	6,000	4.92	425.00	1979 P-D	2,526,000	8.00	3.75
1949 P-D-S	5,000	5.45	575.00	1980 P-D-S	2,815,066	9.00	4.85
1951 P-D-S	8,654	6.75	550.00	1981 P-D-S	2,908,145	11.00	8.50
1952 P-D-S	11,499	6.14	490.00	1984 P-D	1,832,857	7.00	4.00
1953 P-D-S	15,538	6.14	325.00	1985 P-D	1,710,571	7.00	4.00
1954 P-D-S	25,599	6.19	140.00	1986 P-D	1,153,536	7.00	7.00
1955 P-D-S	49,656	3.57	95.00	1987 P-D	2,890,758	7.00	4.00
1956 P-D	45,475	3.34	90.00	1988 P-D	1,646,204	7.00	4.00
1957 P-D	34,324	4.40	155.00	1989 P-D	1,987,915	7.00	4.00
1958 P-D	50,314	4.43	90.00	1990 P-D	1,809,184	7.00	4.00
1959 P-D	187,000	2.40	33.00	1991 P-D	1,352,101	7.00	5.00
1960 P-D	260,485	2.40	18.00	1992 P-D	1,500,143	7.00	4.00
1961 P-D	223,704	2.40	27.00	1993 P-D	1,297,431	8.00	4.50
1962 P-D	385,285	2.40	15.00	1994 P-D	1,234,813	8.00	4.50
1963 P-D	606,612	2.40	15.00	1995 P-D	1,038,787	8.00	9.00
1964 P-D	1,008,108	2.40	15.00	1996 P-D, Plus			
1965*	2,360,000	4.00	2.50	1996W dime	1,457,949	8.00	15.00
1966*	2,261,583	4.00	3.00	1997 P-D	950,473	8.00	13.00
1967*	1,863,344	4.00	8.00	1998 P-D	1,187,325	8.00	4.25
1968 P-D-S	2,105,128	2.50	3.00	1999 P-D (18 pieces)	1,243,867	14.95	15.00
1969 P-D-S	1,817,392	2.50	3.00	2000 P-D (20 pieces)	1,490,160	14.95	6.00
1970 P-D-S	2,038,134	2.50	9.00	2001 P-D (20 pieces)	1,116,915	14.95	11.00
1971 P-D-S	2,193,396	3.50	2.50	2002 P-D (20 pieces)	1,139,388	14.95	13.00
1972 P-D-S	2,750,000	3.50	2.50	2003 P-D (20 pieces)	1,001,532	14.95	12.00
1973 P-D-S	1,767,691	6.00	10.00	2004 P-D (22 pieces)	842,507	16.95	30.00
1974 P-D-S	1,975,981	6.00	4.00	2005 P-D (22 pieces)	1,160,000	16.95	7.00
1975 P-D	1,921,488	6.00	5.00	2006 P-D (20 pieces)	847,361	16.95	8.00
1776-1976 (3-piece set)	4,908,319	9.00	9.00	2007 P-D (28 pieces)		22.95	15.00
1976 P-D	1,892,513	6.00	4.00	2008 P-D (28 pieces)		22.95	15.00
1977 P-D	2,006,869	7.00	5.00				

Note: Sets issued from 2005 onward have a special Satin Finish that is somewhat different from the finish on Uncirculated coins made for general circulation. * Special Mint Set.

$1 SILVER EAGLES

Values below are based on spot silver value of $16 per ounce.

	Mintage	Unc.	PF		Mintage	Unc.	PF
$1 1986	5,393,005	$16		$1 1999	7,408,640	$16	
$1 1986S	(1,446,778)		$25	$1 1999P	(549,769)		$26
$1 1987	11,442,335	16		$1 2000(W)	9,239,132	16	
$1 1987S	(904,732)		25	$1 2000P	(600,000)		
$1 1988	5,004,646	16		$1 2001(W)	9,001,711	16	
$1 1988S	(557,370)		29	$1 2001W	(746,398)		26
$1 1989	5,203,327	16		$1 2002(W)	10,539,026	16	
$1 1989S	(617,694)		25	$1 2002W	(647,342)		25
$1 1990	5,840,210	16		$1 2003(W)	8,495,008	16	
$1 1990S	(695,510)		25	$1 2003W	(747,831)		25
$1 1991	7,191,066	16		$1 2004(W)	8,882,754	16	
$1 1991S	(511,925)		28	$1 2004W	(801,602)		25
$1 1992	5,540,068	16		$1 2005(W)	8,891,025	16	
$1 1992S	(498,654)		25	$1 2005W	(701,606)		25
$1 1993	6,763,762	16		$1 2006(W)		16	
$1 1993P	(405,913)		75	$1 2006W, Burnished		35	
$1 1994	4,227,319	18		$1 2006W			25
$1 1994P	(372,168)		120	$1 2006P, Reverse Proof			125
$1 1995	4,672,051	17		$1 2007(W)		16	
$1 1995P	(438,511)		95	$1 2007W, Burnished		20	
$1 1995W	(30,125)		2,500	$1 2007W			25
$1 1996	3,603,386	25		$1 2008(W)		16	
$1 1996P	(500,000)		45	$1 2008W, Burnished		20	
$1 1997	4,295,004	19		$1 2008W			25
$1 1997P	(435,368)		65	$1 2009(W)		16	
$1 1998	4,847,549	17		$1 2009W, Burnished		20	
$1 1998P	(450,000)		26	$1 2009W			25

Starting in 2006, special American Eagle Uncirculated coins in silver, gold, and platinum have been sold directly from the United States Mint. The term "Uncirculated-burnished" refers to the specialized minting process used to create these coins. Although they are similar in appearance to the ordinary Uncirculated American Eagle bullion coins, the Uncirculated-burnished coins can be distinguished by the addition of a mintmark and by the use of burnished coin blanks. Proof coins, which also have a mintmark, have a highly reflective, mirrorlike surface.

AMERICAN EAGLE GOLD COINS

Bullion values are based on spot gold at $950 per ounce.

$5 Tenth-Ounce Gold

	Mintage	Unc.	PF
$5 MCMLXXXVI (1986)	.912,609	$95	
$5 MCMLXXXVII (1987)	.580,266	95	
$5 MCMLXXXVIII (1988)	.159,500	120	
$5 MCMLXXXVIII (1988)P	.(143,881)		$100
$5 MCMLXXXIX (1989)	.264,790	95	
$5 MCMLXXXIX (1989)P	.(84,647)		100
$5 MCMXC (1990)	.210,210	95	
$5 MCMXC (1990)P	.(99,349)		100
$5 MCMXCI (1991)	.165,200	95	
$5 MCMXCI (1991)P	.(70,334)		100
$5 1992	.209,300	95	
$5 1992P	.(64,874)		100
$5 1993	.210,709	95	
$5 1993P	.(58,649)		100
$5 1994	.206,380	95	
$5 1994W	.(62,849)		100
$5 1995	.223,025	95	
$5 1995W	.(62,673)		100
$5 1996	.401,964	95	
$5 1996W	.(56,700)		100
$5 1997	.528,266	95	
$5 1997W	.(34,984)		110
$5 1998	.1,344,520	95	
$5 1998W	.(20,000)		110

	Mintage	Unc.	PF
$5 1999	.2,750,338	$95	
$5 1999W	.(48,426)		$115
$5 2000	.569,153	95	
$5 2000W	.(49,970)		100
$5 2001	.269,147	95	
$5 2001W	.(37,547)		100
$5 2002	.230,027	95	
$5 2002W	.(40,864)		100
$5 2003	.245,029	95	
$5 2003W	.(46,000)		100
$5 2004	.250,016	95	
$5 2004W	.(15,636)		100
$5 2005	.300,043	95	
$5 2005W	.(17,546)		100
$5 2006W, Burnished		95	
$5 2006(W)		95	
$5 2006W			100
$5 2007(W)		95	
$5 2007W, Burnished		110	
$5 2007W			100
$5 2008		95	
$5 2008W, Burnished		95	
$5 2008W			100

$10 Quarter-Ounce Gold

	Mintage	Unc.	PF
$10 MCMLXXXVI (1986)	.726,031	$235	
$10 MCMLXXXVII (1987)	.269,255	235	
$10 MCMLXXXVIII (1988)	.49,000	235	
$10 MCMLXXXVIII (1988)P	.(98,028)		$245
$10 MCMLXXXIX (1989)	.81,789	235	
$10 MCMLXXXIX (1989)P	.(54,170)		245
$10 MCMXC (1990)	.41,000	235	
$10 MCMXC (1990)P	.(62,674)		245
$10 MCMXCI (1991)	.36,100	245	
$10 MCMXCI (1991)P	.(50,839)		245

	Mintage	Unc.	PF
$10 1992	.59,546	$235	
$10 1992P	.(46,269)		$245
$10 1993	.71,864	235	
$10 1993P	.(46,464)		245
$10 1994	.72,650	235	
$10 1994W	.(48,172)		245
$10 1995	.83,752	235	
$10 1995W	.(47,484)		245
$10 1996	.60,318	235	
$10 1996W	.(37,900)		245

Chart continued on next page.

	Mintage	Unc.	PF		Mintage	Unc.	PF
$10 1997	108,805	$235		$10 2004	72,014	$235	
$10 1997W	(29,808)		$255	$10 2004W	(9,344)		$245
$10 1998	309,829	235		$10 2005	72,015	235	
$10 1998W	(29,733)		255	$10 2005W	(7,992)		245
$10 1999	564,232	235		$10 2006(W)		235	
$10 1999W	(34,416)		245	$10 2006W, Burnished		245	
$10 2000	128,964	235		$10 2006W			245
$10 2000W	(36,033)		245	$10 2007(W)		235	
$10 2001	71,280	235		$10 2007W, Burnished		245	
$10 2001W	(25,630)		255	$10 2007W			245
$10 2002	62,027	235		$10 2008		235	
$10 2002W	(29,242)		245	$10 2008W, Burnished		245	
$10 2003	74,029	235		$10 2008W			245
$10 2003W	(31,000)		245				

$25 Half-Ounce Gold

	Mintage	Unc.	PF		Mintage	Unc.	PF
$25 MCMLXXXVI (1986)	599,566	$470		$25 1998W	(25,549)		$480
$25 MCMLXXXVII (1987)	131,255	470		$25 1999	263,013	$470	
$25 MCMLXXXVII (1987)P	(143,398)		$480	$25 1999W	(30,452)		480
$25 MCMLXXXVIII (1988)	45,000	475		$25 2000	79,287	470	
$25 MCMLXXXVIII (1988)P	(76,528)		480	$25 2000W	(32,027)		480
$25 MCMLXXXIX (1989)	44,829	480		$25 2001	48,047	470	
$25 MCMLXXXIX (1989)P	(44,798)		480	$25 2001W	(23,261)		480
$25 MCMXC (1990)	31,000	490		$25 2002	70,027	470	
$25 MCMXC (1990)P	(51,636)		480	$25 2002W	(26,646)		480
$25 MCMXCI (1991)	24,100	750		$25 2003	79,029	470	
$25 MCMXCI (1991)P	(53,125)		480	$25 2003W	(33,000)		480
$25 1992	54,404	470		$25 2004	98,040	470	
$25 1992P	(40,976)		480	$25 2004W	(7,835)		480
$25 1993	73,324	470		$25 2005	80,023	470	
$25 1993P	(43,319)		480	$25 2005W	(7,054)		480
$25 1994	62,400	470		$25 2006(W)		470	
$25 1994W	(44,584)		480	$25 2006W, Burnished		500	
$25 1995	53,474	470		$25 2006W			480
$25 1995W	(45,442)		480	$25 2007W, Burnished		480	
$25 1996	39,287	470		$25 2007(W)		470	
$25 1996W	(34,700)		480	$25 2007W			480
$25 1997	79,605	470		$25 2008(W)		470	
$25 1997W	(26,801)		480	$25 2008W, Burnished		480	
$25 1998	169,029	470		$25 2008W			480

$50 One-Ounce Gold

	Mintage	Unc.	PF		Mintage	Unc.	PF
$50 MCMLXXXVI (1986)	1,362,650	$950		$50 MCMLXXXIX (1989)W	(54,570)		$975
$50 MCMLXXXVI (1986)W	(446,290)		$975	$50 MCMXC (1990)	373,210	$950	
$50 MCMLXXXVII (1987)	1,045,500	950		$50 MCMXC (1990)W	(62,401)		975
$50 MCMLXXXVII (1987)W	(147,498)		975	$50 MCMXCI (1991)	243,100	950	
$50 MCMLXXXVIII (1988)	465,000	950		$50 MCMXCI (1991)W	(50,411)		975
$50 MCMLXXXVIII (1988)W	(87,133)		975	$50 1992	275,000	950	
$50 MCMLXXXIX (1989)	415,790	950		$50 1992W	(44,826)		975

GOLD BULLION

	Mintage	Unc.	PF
$50 1993	480,192	$950	
$50 1993W	(34,389)		$975
$50 1994	221,633	950	
$50 1994W	(46,674)		975
$50 1995	200,636	950	
$50 1995W	(46,484)		975
$50 1996	189,148	950	
$50 1996W	(36,000)		975
$50 1997	664,508	950	
$50 1997W	(27,554)		1,000
$50 1998	1,468,530	950	
$50 1998W	(26,060)		1,000
$50 1999	1,505,026	950	
$50 1999W	(31,446)		975
$50 2000	433,319	950	
$50 2000W	(33,006)		975
$50 2001	143,605	950	
$50 2001W	(24,580)		1,000
$50 2002	222,029	950	
$50 2002W	(27,499)		975

	Mintage	Unc.	PF
$50 2003	416,032	$950	
$50 2003W	(33,000)		$975
$50 2004	417,019	950	
$50 2004W	(8,720)		975
$50 2005	356,555	950	
$50 2005W	(9,784)		975
$50 2006(W)		950	
$50 2006W, Burnished		950	
$50 2006W			975
$50 2006W, Reverse Proof			1,800
$50 2007(W)		950	
$50 2007W, Burnished		950	
$50 2007W			975
$50 2008		950	
$50 2008W, Burnished		950	
$50 2008W			975
$50 2009		950	
$50 2009W, Burnished		950	
$50 2009W			975

Gold Bullion Sets

	PF
1987 Gold Set. $50, $25	$1,450
1988 Gold Set. $50, $25, $10, $5	1,800
1989 Gold Set. $50, $25, $10, $5	1,800
1990 Gold Set. $50, $25, $10, $5	1,800
1991 Gold Set. $50, $25, $10, $5	1,800
1992 Gold Set. $50, $25, $10, $5	1,800
1993 Gold Set. $50, $25, $10, $5	1,800
1993 Bicentennial Gold Set. $25, $10, $5, $1 silver eagle, and medal	850
1994 Gold Set. $50, $25, $10, $5	1,800
1995 Gold Set. $50, $25, $10, $5	1,800
1995 Anniversary Gold Set. $50, $25, $10, $5, and $1 silver eagle	5,000
1996 Gold Set. $50, $25, $10, $5	1,800

	PF
1997 Gold Set. $50, $25, $10, $5	$1,850
1997 Impressions of Liberty Set. $100 platinum, $50 gold, $1 silver	2,850
1998 Gold Set. $50, $25, $10, $5	1,800
1999 Gold Set. $50, $25, $10, $5	1,800
2000 Gold Set. $50, $25, $10, $5	1,800
2001 Gold Set. $50, $25, $10, $5	1,800
2002 Gold Set. $50, $25, $10, $5	1,800
2003 Gold Set. $50, $25, $10, $5	1,800
2004 Gold Set. $50, $25, $10, $5	1,800
2005 Gold Set. $50, $25, $10, $5	1,800
2006 Gold Set. $50, $25, $10, $5	1,800
2007 Gold Set. $50, $25, $10, $5	1,800
2008 Gold Set. $50, $25, $10, $5	1,800

2006 20th Anniversary Sets

2006W $50 Gold Set. Uncirculated, Proof, Reverse Proof	$4,500
2006 Silver Dollars. Uncirculated, Proof, Reverse Proof	200

2006W 1-oz. Gold- and Silver-Dollar Set. Uncirculated	$975

AMERICAN BUFFALO .9999 FINE GOLD BULLION COINS

	Unc.	PF
$5 2008W	$100	
$5 2008W		$110
$10 2008W	250	
$10 2008W		270
$25 2008W	495	
$25 2008W		510
$50 2006W	950	
$50 2006W		975
$50 2007W	950	

	Unc.	PF
$50 2007W		$975
$50 2008W	$950	
$50 2008W		975
$50 2009W		975
2008W Four-coin set	1,800	1,875
2009W Four-coin set	1,800	1,875
2008W Double Prosperity set. Uncirculated $25 Buffalo gold and $25 American Eagle coins	1,500	

FIRST SPOUSE $10 GOLD BULLION COINS
Half-Ounce 24-Karat Gold

Martha Washington   Abigail Adams   Jefferson's Liberty   Dolley Madison

	Unc.	PF
$10 2007, Martha Washington	$470	$480
$10 2007, Abigail Adams	470	480

	Unc.	PF
$10 2007, Thomas Jefferson's Liberty	$470	$480
$10 2007, Dolley Madison	470	480

Elizabeth Monroe   **Louisa Adams**   **Jackson's Liberty**   **Van Buren's Liberty**

	Unc.	PF
$10 2008, Elizabeth Monroe	$470	$480
$10 2008, Louisa Adams	470	480

	Unc.	PF
$10 2008, Andrew Jackson's Liberty	$470	$480
$10 2008, Martin Van Buren's Liberty	470	480

Anna Harrison

Letitia Tyler

Julia Tyler

Sarah Polk

Margaret Taylor

U.S. Mint artist renderings.

	Unc.	PF
$10 2009, Anna Harrison	$470	$480
$10 2009, Letitia Tyler	470	480
$10 2009, Julia Tyler	470	480

	Unc.	PF
$10 2009, Sarah Polk	$470	$480
$10 2009, Margaret Taylor	470	480

MMIX ULTRA HIGH RELIEF GOLD COIN

A modern version of the famous United States 1907 Ultra High Relief double eagle gold pattern was produced in 2009 at the Philadelphia Mint. It was made as a tour de force to demonstrate how technical advances in minting techniques can now accommodate manufacturing such a coin. The original design was never made for commercial use because it was at that time impossible to make it in sufficient quantities

The original striding-Liberty design used on these coins was the artistry of Augustus Saint-Gaudens. A version of it in much lower relief was used on double eagle coins minted from 1907 to 1933. In recreating the artist's attempt to mint a stunning coin in ultra high relief, the 2009 version was made in a slightly smaller diameter, and composed of 24-karat gold, thus making it easier to strike and maintain the fidelity of the design. Through 21st-century technology the original Saint-Gaudens plasters were digitally mapped by the Mint and used in the die-making process. The date was changed to 2009, and four additional stars were added to represent the current 50 states. Also included was the inscription "In God We Trust" which was not used on the 1907 version.

The MMIX Ultra High Relief gold coins are 4 mm thick and contain one ounce of .999 fine gold. All are Uncirculated (business strikes). All are made at the West Point Mint, and packaged by the Mint in a special mahogany box.

MMIX Ultra High Relief Gold Coin
Photographed at an angle to show the edge, lettered E PLURIBUS UNUM, and the depth of relief.

MMIX Ultra High Relief Gold Coin $1,000

AMERICAN EAGLE PLATINUM COINS

The one-ounce American Eagle platinum coin is designated $100 and contains one ounce of pure platinum. Fractional denominations containing 1/2 ounce, 1/4 ounce, or 1/10 ounce are called $50, $25, and $10, respectively.

Bullion values are based on spot platinum at $1,200 per ounce.

Obverse for Bullion and Proof, All Years

Reverse for Bullion, All Years; for Proof in 1997

Vistas of Liberty Reverse Designs

1998, Eagle Over New England

1999, Eagle Above Southeastern Wetlands

2000, Eagle Above America's Heartland

2001, Eagle Above America's Southwest

2002, Eagle Fishing in America's Northwest

$10 Tenth-Ounce Platinum

	Mintage	Unc.	PF		Mintage	Unc.	PF
$10 1997	70,250	$120		$10 2001W	(25,000)		$130
$10 1997W	(37,025)		$130	$10 2002	23,005	$120	
$10 1998	39,525	120		$10 2002W	(12,365)		130
$10 1998W	(19,832)		130	$10 2003	22,007	120	
$10 1999	55,955	120		$10 2003W	(9,249)		130
$10 1999W	(19,123)		130	$10 2004	15,010	120	
$10 2000	34,027	120		$10 2004W	(3,171)		250
$10 2000W	(15,651)		130	$10 2005	14,013	120	
$10 2001	52,017	120		$10 2005W	(2,583)		130

Chart continued on next page.

PLATINUM BULLION

	Mintage	Unc.	PF
$10 2006(W)		$120	
$10 2006W, Burnished		170	
$10 2006W			$130
$10 2007(W)		120	
$10 2007W, Burnished		150	

	Mintage	Unc.	PF
$10 2007W			$130
$10 2008(W)		$120	
$10 2008W, Burnished		150	
$10 2008W			130

$25 Quarter-Ounce Platinum

	Mintage	Unc.	PF
$25 1997	27,100	$300	
$25 1997W	(18,661)		$310
$25 1998	38,887	300	
$25 1998W	(14,860)		310
$25 1999	39,734	300	
$25 1999W	(13,514)		310
$25 2000	20,054	300	
$25 2000W	(11,995)		310
$25 2001	21,815	300	
$25 2001W	(8,858)		310
$25 2002	27,405	300	
$25 2002W	(9,282)		310
$25 2003	25,207	300	
$25 2003W	(6,829)		310

	Mintage	Unc.	PF
$25 2004	18,010	$300	
$25 2004W	(2,583)		$800
$25 2005	12,013	300	
$25 2005W	(932)		400
$25 2006(W)		300	
$25 2006W, Burnished		400	
$25 2006W			310
$25 2007(W)		300	
$25 2007W, Burnished		300	
$25 2007W			310
$25 2008(W)		300	
$25 2008W, Burnished		300	
$25 2008W			310

$50 Half-Ounce Platinum

	Mintage	Unc.	PF
$50 1997	20,500	$600	
$50 1997W	(15,463)		$610
$50 1998	32,415	600	
$50 1998W	(13,821)		610
$50 1999	32,309	600	
$50 1999W	(11,098)		610
$50 2000	18,892	600	
$50 2000W	(11,049)		610
$50 2001	12,815	600	
$50 2001W	(8,268)		610
$50 2002	24,005	600	
$50 2002W	(8,772)		610
$50 2003	17,409	600	
$50 2003W	(6,963)		610

	Mintage	Unc.	PF
$50 2004	13,236	$600	
$50 2004W	(1,073)		$1,400
$50 2005	9,013	600	
$50 2005W	(846)		800
$50 2006(W)		600	
$50 2006W, Burnished		620	
$50 2006W			610
$50 2007(W)		600	
$50 2007W, Burnished		620	
$50 2007W			610
$50 2008(W)		600	
$50 2008W, Burnished		620	
$50 2008W			610

$100 One-Ounce Platinum

	Mintage	Unc.	PF		Mintage	Unc.	PF
$100 1997	56,000	$1,200		$100 2004	7,009	$1,200	
$100 1997W	(18,000)		$1,220	$100 2004W	(2,017)		$1,300
$100 1998	133,002	1,200		$100 2005	6,310	1,200	
$100 1998W	(14,203)		1,220	$100 2005W	(1,663)		1,250
$100 1999	56,707	1,200		$100 2006(W)		1,200	
$100 1999W	(12,351)		1,220	$100 2006W, Burnished		1,220	
$100 2000	10,003	1,200		$100 2006W			1,220
$100 2000W	(12,453)		1,220	$100 2007(W)		1,200	
$100 2001	14,070	1,200		$100 2007W, Burnished		1,220	
$100 2001W	(8,990)		1,220	$100 2007W			1,220
$100 2002	11,502	1,200		$100 2008(W)		1,200	
$100 2002W	(9,834)		1,220	$100 2008W, Burnished		1,220	
$100 2003	8,007	1,200		$100 2008W			1,220
$100 2003W	(8,106)		1,220	$100 2009W			1,220

Platinum Bullion Sets

1997 Platinum Set. $100, $50, $25, $10	$2,275
1998 Platinum Set. $100, $50, $25, $10	2,275
1999 Platinum Set. $100, $50, $25, $10	2,275
2000 Platinum Set. $100, $50, $25, $10	2,275
2001 Platinum Set. $100, $50, $25, $10	2,275
2002 Platinum Set. $100, $50, $25, $10	2,275
2003 Platinum Set. $100, $50, $25, $10	2,275
2004W Platinum Set. $100, $50, $25, $10	3,750
2005W Platinum Set. $100, $50, $25, $10	2,275
2006W Platinum Set. $100, $50, $25, $10	2,275
2007W Platinum Set. $100, $50, $25, $10	2,275
2008W Platinum Set. $100, $50, $25, $10	2,275

Prices are for original Uncirculated or Proof pieces with box and papers.

Private coins were circulated in most instances because of a shortage of regular coinage. Some numismatists use the general term *private gold* to refer to coins struck outside of the United States Mint. In the sense that no state or territory had authority to coin money, *private gold* simply refers to those interesting necessity pieces of various shapes, denominations, and degrees of intrinsic worth which were circulated in isolated areas of our country by individuals, assayers, bankers, etc. Some will use the words "Territorial" and "State" to cover certain issues because they were coined and circulated in a territory or state. While the state of California properly sanctioned the ingots stamped by F.D. Kohler as state assayer, in no instance were any of the gold pieces struck by authority of any of the territorial governments.

The stamped ingots put out by Augustus Humbert, the United States assayer of gold, were not recognized at the United States Mint as an official issue of coins, but simply as ingots, though Humbert placed the value and fineness on the pieces as an official agent of the federal government.

TEMPLETON REID
Georgia Gold 1830

The first private gold coinage under the Constitution was struck by Templeton Reid, a jeweler and gunsmith, in Milledgeville, Georgia in July 1830. To be closer to the mines, he moved to Gainesville, where most of his coins were made. Although weights were accurate, Reid's assays were not, and his coins were slightly short of claimed value. Accordingly, he was severely attacked in the newspapers and soon lost the public's confidence.

	VG	VF
1830, $2.50	$30,000	$50,000
1830, $5	75,000	125,000
1830, TEN DOLLARS	135,000	225,000
(No Date) TEN DOLLARS	120,000	180,000

California Gold 1849

1849, TEN DOLLAR CALIFORNIA GOLD *(unique, in Smithsonian)* . . . .

THE BECHTLERS
RUTHERFORD COUNTY, NC, 1831–1852

Two skilled German metallurgists, Christopher Bechtler and his son August, and later Christopher Bechtler, Junior, a nephew of Christopher the elder, operated a private mint at Rutherfordton, North Carolina. Rutherford County, in which Rutherfordton is located, was the principal source of the nation's gold supply from 1790 to 1848.

Christopher Bechtler

	VF	EF	AU	Unc.
ONE DOLLAR CAROLINA, 28.G, N Reversed	$1,200	$2,000	$2,600	$5,250
ONE GOLD DOLLAR N. CAROLINA, 28.G, No Star	2,500	3,500	4,750	10,000
ONE GOLD DOLLAR N. CAROLINA, 30.G.	1,500	2,250	3,300	8,000
2.50 CAROLINA, 67.G., 21 CARATS	3,200	5,200	6,250	12,000
2.50 CAROLINA, 70.G, 20 CARATS	3,400	5,750	6,750	14,000
2.50 GEORGIA, 64.G, 22 CARATS	3,700	6,750	7,000	16,000
2.50 NORTH CAROLINA, 75.G., 20 CARATS. RUTHERFORD in a Circle. Border of Large Beads	9,000	12,000	19,000	30,000
2.50 NORTH CAROLINA, 20 C. Without 75.G	9,000	13,000	20,000	32,000

Without 150.G.

	VF	EF	AU	Unc.
5 DOLLARS NORTH CAROLINA GOLD, 150.G., 20 CARATS	$9,500	$13,000	$21,000	$36,000
Similar, Without 150.G.		—	—	
5 DOLLARS CAROLINA, RUTHERFORD, 140.G., 20 CARATS				
Plain Edge	3,500	5,250	6,750	12,000
Reeded Edge	8,000	14,000	19,000	29,000
5 DOLLARS CAROLINA GOLD, RUTHERF., 140.G., 20 CARATS,				
AUGUST 1, 1834	3,750	5,200	6,750	12,000
Similar, but "20" Distant From CARATS	4,000	5,750	7,000	14,000
5 DOLLARS CAROLINA GOLD, 134.G., 21 CARATS, With Star	3,250	4,250	6,000	10,000
5 DOLLARS GEORGIA GOLD, RUTHERFORD, 128.G., 22 CARATS	3,500	5,000	8,000	14,000
5 DOLLARS GEORGIA GOLD, RUTHERF., 128.G., 22 CARATS	3,500	5,000	8,000	14,000

August Bechtler

	VF	EF	AU	Unc.
1 DOL:, CAROLINA GOLD, 27.G., 21.C	$800	$1,200	$1,600	$2,750
5 DOLLARS, CAROLINA GOLD, 134.G:, 21 CARATS	3,000	4,500	6,250	17,500

	VF	EF	AU	Unc.
5 DOLLARS, CAROLINA GOLD, 128.G., 22 CARATS	$6,000	$8,000	$12,000	$18,000
5 DOLLARS, CAROLINA GOLD, 141.G., 20 CARATS	6,000	8,000	12,000	20,000

NORRIS, GREGG & NORRIS
SAN FRANCISCO 1849

These pieces are considered the first of the California private gold coins. A newspaper account dated May 31, 1849, described a five-dollar gold coin struck at Benicia City, though with the imprint San Francisco, and the private stamp of Norris, Gregg & Norris.

	F	VF	EF	AU	Unc.
1849, Half Eagle, Plain Edge	$2,600	$3,750	$5,750	$9,000	$17,500
1849, Half Eagle, Reeded Edge	2,600	3,750	5,750	9,000	17,500
1850, HALF EAGLE, With STOCKTON Beneath Date *(unique)*					

MOFFAT & CO.
SAN FRANCISCO 1849–1853

The firm of Moffat & Company was perhaps the most important of the California private coiners. The assay office they conducted was semi-official in character, and successors to this firm later sold its facilities to the Treasury Department, which used them to create the San Francisco Mint.

In June or July, 1849, Moffat & Co. began to issue small rectangular pieces of gold in values from $9.43 to $264. The $9.43, $14.25, and $16.00 varieties are the only types known today.

	EF
$9.43 Ingot *(unique)*	—
$14.25 Ingot *(unique)*	—
$16.00 Ingot	$35,000

237

The dies for the $10 piece were cut by Albert Kuner. The words Moffat & Co. appear on Liberty's coronet instead of the word liberty as in regular United States issues.

	F	VF	EF	AU	Unc.
1849, FIVE DOL. *(all varieties)*	$900	$1,500	$2,000	$3,500	$7,200
1850, FIVE DOL. *(all varieties)*	900	1,500	2,000	3,500	7,500
1849, TEN DOL.	1,800	2,750	5,500	10,000	20,000
1849, TEN D.	1,900	2,900	6,000	11,000	22,000

UNITED STATES ASSAY OFFICE
Augustus Humbert
United States Assayer of Gold, 1851

When Augustus Humbert was appointed United States Assayer, he placed his name and the government imprint on the ingots of gold issued by Moffat & Co. The assay office, a provisional government mint, was a temporary expedient to accommodate the Californians until the establishment of a permanent branch mint. The $50 gold piece was accepted as legal tender on a par with standard U.S. gold coins.

Lettered Edge Varieties

	F	VF	EF	AU	Unc.
1851, 50 D C 880 THOUS., No 50 on Reverse. Sunk in Edge:					
AUGUSTUS HUMBERT UNITED STATES ASSAYER OF GOLD					
CALIFORNIA 1851	$9,500	$14,000	$19,000	$27,000	$57,000

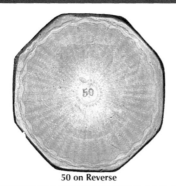

50 on Reverse

	F	VF	EF	AU	Unc.
1851, 50 D C, 880 THOUS., Similar to Last Variety, but 50 on Reverse	$10,500	$20,000	$26,000	$42,000	$77,000
1851, 50 D C, 887 THOUS., With 50 on Reverse	10,000	18,000	23,000	35,000	66,000

Reeded Edge Varieties

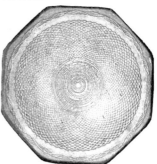

	F	VF	EF	AU	Unc.
1851, FIFTY DOLLS, 880 THOUS., "Target" Reverse	$7,000	$9,000	$13,000	$20,000	$35,000
1851, FIFTY DOLLS, 887 THOUS., "Target" Reverse	7,000	9,000	13,000	20,000	35,000
1852, FIFTY DOLLS, 887 THOUS., "Target" Reverse	7,000	9,000	13,000	20,000	37,500

Moffat & Co. proceeded in January, 1852 to issue a new ten-dollar piece bearing the stamp MOFFAT & CO.

	F	VF	EF	AU	Unc.
1852 TEN D. MOFFAT & CO. (Close Date)	$1,900	$3,200	$6,500	$16,500	$35,000

Entry continued on next page.　　　　　　　　　　　　　　　　　　　239

	F	VF	EF	AU	Unc.
1852, TEN DOLS., 1852, 2 Over 1	$1,650	$2,750	$4,200	$7,000	$14,500
1852, TEN DOLS.	1,350	2,000	2,750	5,000	12,500

	F	VF	EF	AU	Unc.
1852, TWENTY DOLS., 1852, 2 Over 1	$3,500	$5,200	$10,000	$19,500	$46,000

United States Assay Office of Gold – 1852

The firm of Moffat & Co. was reorganized as Curtis, Perry & Ward, which assumed the government contract to conduct the United States Assay Office of Gold.

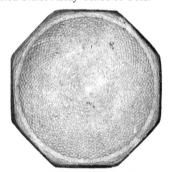

	F	VF	EF	AU	Unc.
1852, FIFTY DOLLS., 887 THOUS.	$7,200	$9,500	$15,000	$21,000	$38,000
1852, FIFTY DOLLS., 900 THOUS.	7,500	10,000	16,500	23,000	40,000

	F	VF	EF	AU	Unc.
1852, TEN DOLS., 884 THOUS.	$1,000	$1,650	$2,500	$4,000	$9,000
1853, TEN D., 884 THOUS.	3,500	7,000	13,500	18,000	35,000
1853, TEN D., 900 THOUS.	2,250	3,500	5,500	10,000	14,000
1853, TWENTY D., 884 THOUS.	4,250	7,000	10,000	16,000	25,000
1853, TWENTY D., 900 THOUS.	1,250	1,650	2,500	3,500	6,500

Moffat & Company Gold

The last Moffat issue was an 1853 $20 piece that is very similar to the U.S. double eagle of that period. It was struck after the retirement of John L. Moffat from Moffat & Company.

	F	VF	EF	AU	Unc.
1853, TWENTY D.	$2,000	$2,600	$3,900	$6,750	$16,000

CINCINNATI MINING & TRADING CO. (1849)

The origin and location of this company are unknown. It might have been organized in Ohio, and conducted business in California.

	EF	Unc.
1849, FIVE DOLLARS	—	—
1849, TEN DOLLARS	$350,000	—

MASSACHUSETTS AND CALIFORNIA COMPANY

This company was believed to have been organized in Northampton, Massachusetts, in May 1849.

	F	VF	EF
1849, FIVE D.	$60,000	$90,000	$150,000

MINERS' BANK
SAN FRANCISCO 1849

The institution of Wright & Co., exchange brokers located in Portsmouth Square, San Francisco, was known as the Miners' Bank.

A $10 piece was issued in the autumn of 1849, but the coins were not readily accepted because they were worth less than face value.

	VF	EF	AU	Unc.
(1849) TEN D.	$9,000	$16,500	$25,000	$45,000

J.S. ORMSBY
SACRAMENTO 1849

The initials J.S.O., which appear on certain issues of California privately coined gold pieces, represent the firm of J.S. Ormsby & Co. The firm struck both $5 and $10 denominations, all undated.

	VF
(1849) 5 DOLLS *(unique)*	—
(1849) 10 DOLLS *(4 known)*	$155,000

PACIFIC COMPANY, SAN FRANCISCO 1849

The origin of the Pacific Company is uncertain. All data regarding the firm are based on conjecture.

Edgar H. Adams wrote that he believed that the coins bearing the stamp of the Pacific Company were produced by the coining firm of Broderick and Kohler. The coins were probably hand struck with the aid of a sledgehammer.

	EF
1849, 1 DOLLAR *(2 known)*	—
1849, 5 DOLLARS	$165,000
1849, 10 DOLLARS	220,000

F.D. KOHLER
CALIFORNIA STATE ASSAYER 1850

The State Assay Office was authorized on April 12, 1850. That year, Governor Burnett appointed F.D. Kohler, who thereupon sold his assaying business to Baldwin & Co. Kohler served at both the San Francisco and Sacramento offices. The State Assay Offices were discontinued when the U.S. Assay Office was established, on February 1, 1851.

	EF
$36.55 Sacramento	—
$37.31 San Francisco	—
$40.07 San Francisco	—
$45.34 San Francisco	—
$50.00 San Francisco	—
$54.09 San Francisco	—

DUBOSQ & COMPANY
SAN FRANCISCO 1850

Theodore Dubosq, a Philadelphia jeweler, took melting and coining machinery to San Francisco in 1849.

	VF
1850, FIVE D.	$75,000
1850, TEN D.	75,000

BALDWIN & CO.
SAN FRANCISCO 1850

George C. Baldwin and Thomas S. Holman were in the jewelry business in San Francisco and were known as Baldwin & Co. They were the successors to F.D. Kohler & Co., taking over its machinery and other equipment in May 1850.

	F	VF	EF	AU	Unc.
1850, FIVE DOL.	$3,750	$6,200	$12,000	$18,000	$23,000
1850, TEN DOLLARS, Horseman Type	19,000	35,000	50,000	70,000	100,000

	F	VF	EF	AU	Unc.
1851, TEN D.	$5,000	$12,500	$19,000	$30,000	$70,000

	VF	EF	AU	Unc.
1851, TWENTY D.	$90,000	$150,000	—	—

SHULTZ & COMPANY
SAN FRANCISCO 1851

The firm, located in back of Baldwin's establishment, operated a brass foundry beginning in 1851. Judge G.W. Shultz and William T. Garratt were partners in the enterprise.

	F	VF
1851, FIVE D.	$16,000	$33,000

DUNBAR & COMPANY
SAN FRANCISCO 1851

Edward E. Dunbar operated the California Bank in San Francisco. Dunbar later returned to New York and organized the famous Continental Bank Note Co.

	EF
1851, FIVE D.	$140,000

WASS, MOLITOR & CO.
SAN FRANCISCO 1852–1855

The gold-smelting and assaying plant of Wass, Molitor & Co. was operated by two Hungarian patriots, Count S.C. Wass and A.P. Molitor. They maintained an excellent laboratory and complete apparatus for analysis and coinage of gold.

	F	VF	EF	AU	Unc.
1852, FIVE DOLLARS	$2,100	$4,100	$8,500	$14,000	$28,000

Large Head   **Small Head**

	F	VF	EF	AU	Unc.
1852, TEN D., Large Head	$1,400	$2,200	$3,750	$7,250	$12,500
1852, TEN D., Small Head	3,200	4,250	10,000	17,000	37,000
1855, TEN D.	6,100	9,100	12,500	16,000	30,000

Large Head   **Small Head**

	F	VF	EF	AU	Unc.
1855, TWENTY DOL., Large Head	—	—	$175,000	—	—
1855, TWENTY DOL., Small Head	$6,500	$16,000	20,000	$40,000	$75,000

	F	VF	EF	AU	Unc.
1855, 50 DOLLARS	$13,500	$18,000	$25,000	$47,500	$100,000

KELLOGG & CO.
SAN FRANCISCO 1854–1855

When the U.S. Assay Office ceased operations, a period ensued during which no private firm was striking gold. The new San Francisco branch mint did not produce coins for some months after Curtis & Perry took the government contract. The lack of coin was again keenly felt by businessmen, who petitioned Kellogg & Richter to "supply the vacuum" by issuing private coin. Their plea was soon answered, for on February 9, 1854, Kellogg & Co. placed their first $20 piece in circulation.

	F	VF	EF	AU	Unc.	PF
1854, TWENTY D.	$1,500	$2,000	$2,750	$4,500	$11,000	
1855, TWENTY D.	1,500	2,000	3,200	5,000	13,500	
1855, FIFTY DOLLS.						$190,000

OREGON EXCHANGE COMPANY
OREGON CITY 1849
The Beaver Coins of Oregon

On February 16, 1849, the legislature passed an act providing for a mint and specified $5 and $10 gold coins without alloy. Oregon City, the largest city in the territory
with a population of about 1,000, was designated as the location for the mint. At the
time this act was passed, Oregon had been brought into the United States as a territory by act of Congress. When the new governor arrived on March 2, he declared the
coinage act unconstitutional.

	F	VF	EF	AU	Unc.
1849, 5 D.	$15,000	$23,000	$31,000	$66,000	—
1849, TEN.D	36,000	67,500	120,000	175,000	—

MORMON GOLD PIECES
SALT LAKE CITY, UTAH, 1849–1860

Brigham Young was the instigator of the coinage system and personally supervised
the mint, which was housed in a little adobe building in Salt Lake City. The mint was
inaugurated in 1849 as a public convenience.

	F	VF	EF	AU	Unc.
1849, TWO.AND.HALF.DO.	$5,500	$9,000	$15,000	$27,000	$45,000
1849, FIVE.DOLLARS	4,000	8,000	14,000	16,500	31,000

	F	VF	EF
1849, TEN.DOLLARS	$85,000	$125,000	$160,000
1849, TWENTY.DOLLARS	35,000	70,000	90,000

	F	VF	EF	AU	Unc.
1850, FIVE DOLLARS	$4,750	$8,500	$13,000	$23,000	$45,000
1860, 5.D	9,000	16,500	22,000	32,500	45,000

COLORADO GOLD PIECES
Clark, Gruber & Co.
Denver 1860–1861

Clark, Gruber & Co. was a well-known private minting firm in Denver, Colorado, in the early 1860s.

	F	VF	EF	AU	Unc.
1860, 2 1/2 D.	$850	$1,250	$2,000	$3,200	$7,000
1860, FIVE D.	950	1,500	2,100	3,750	7,500

	F	VF	EF	AU	Unc.
1860, TEN D.	$4,000	$6,000	$9,000	$16,000	$27,000
1860, TWENTY D.	25,000	40,000	70,000	120,000	250,000

	F	VF	EF	AU	Unc.
1861, 2 1/2 D.	$900	$1,400	$2,100	$3,500	$8,500
1861, FIVE D.	1,200	1,700	2,600	4,700	17,000
1861, TEN D.	1,200	1,800	2,750	4,800	16,000

	F	VF	EF	AU
1861, TWENTY D.	$7,000	$15,000	$26,000	$50,000

John Parsons & Company
Tarryall Mines – Colorado, 1861

Very little is known regarding the mint of John Parsons and Co., although it is reasonably certain that it operated in the South Park section of Park County, Colorado, near the original town of Tarryall, in the summer of 1861.

	VF
(1861) Undated 2 1/2 D.	$110,000
(1861) Undated FIVE D	160,000

J.J. Conway & Co.
Georgia Gulch, Colorado, 1861

Records show that the Conway mint operated for a short while in 1861. As in all gold mining areas, the value of gold dust caused disagreement among the merchants and the miners. The firm of J.J. Conway & Co. solved this difficulty by bringing out its gold pieces in August 1861.

	VF
(1861) Undated 2 1/2 DOLL'S	$67,000
(1861) Undated FIVE DOLLARS	110,000
(1861) Undated TEN DOLLARS	—

CALIFORNIA SMALL-DENOMINATION GOLD

There was a scarcity of small coins during the California Gold Rush and, starting in 1852, quarter, half, and dollar pieces were privately minted from native gold to alleviate the shortage. The need and acceptability of these pieces declined after 1856 and they then became popular as souvenirs. Authentic pieces all have CENTS, DOLLAR, or an abbreviation thereof on the reverse. The tokens are much less valuable. Modern restrikes and replicas have no numismatic value.

The values in the following charts are only for coins made before 1883 with the denomination on the reverse expressed as CENTS, DOL., DOLL., or DOLLAR.

Quarter Dollar – Octagonal

	EF-40	AU-50	MS-60
Liberty Head	$75	$100	$160
Indian Head	90	125	170
Washington Head	350	550	750

Quarter Dollar – Round

	EF-40	AU-50	MS-60
Liberty Head	$75	$100	$160
Indian Head	80	110	180
Washington Head	350	550	750

Half Dollar – Octagonal

	EF-40	AU-50	MS-60
Liberty Head	$75	$100	$160
Liberty Head / Eagle	375	500	900
Indian Head	85	125	250

Half Dollar – Round

	EF-40	AU-50	MS-60
Liberty Head	$75	$100	$200
Indian Head	75	100	180

Dollar – Octagonal

	EF-40	AU-50	MS-60
Liberty Head	$200	$300	$550
Liberty Head / Eagle	750	1,200	1,850
Indian Head	200	350	500

Dollar – Round

	EF-40	AU-50	MS-60
Liberty Head	$900	$1,350	$2,000
Indian Head	900	1,350	2,150

HARD TIMES TOKENS (1832–1844)

During the financial crises of 1832 to 1844 many government coins were hoarded, and privately made tokens were used out of necessity. The so-called Hard Times tokens of this period were slightly smaller and lighter than normal large cents. They were made of copper or brass and are of two general groups: political tokens whose theme centered on President Jackson's fight against the United States Bank, and tradesmen's cards, issued by merchants. Many different designs and varieties exist.

	VF	EF
Hard Times Tokens, 1832–1844, most common pieces	$13	$25

CIVIL WAR TOKENS (1860S)

Civil War tokens are generally divided into two groups: tradesmen's tokens, and anonymously issued pieces with political or patriotic themes. They came into existence only because of the scarcity of government coins and disappeared as soon as the bronze coins of 1864 met the public demand for small copper change.

These tokens vary greatly in composition and design. A number were more or less faithful imitations of the copper-nickel cent. A few of this type have the word "not" in very small letters above the words ONE CENT.

	F	VF	EF	Unc.
Copper or Brass Tokens	$7	$11	$15	$26
Nickel or German Silver Tokens	18	25	50	90
White-Metal Tokens	20	30	50	75
Copper-Nickel Tokens	30	50	75	115
Silver Tokens	75	125	200	350

BULLION VALUES

Common-date silver coins are valued according to the price of silver bullion. In recent years the price of silver bullion has been subject to extreme fluctuation. Therefore, when you read this it is highly probable that the current bullion price may differ from the prevailing market price used in tabulating valuations of many 19th- and 20th-century silver coins (priced in italics) listed in this edition. The following chart will help to determine the approximate bullion value of these coins at various price levels. Or, the approximate value may be calculated by multiplying the current spot price of silver times the content for each coin as indicated below. Dealers generally purchase common silver coins at 15% below bullion value, and sell them at 15% above bullion value.

Bullion Values of Silver Coins

Silver Price Per Ounce	Wartime Nickel .05626 oz.	Dime .07234 oz.	Quarter .18084 oz.	Half Dollar .36169 oz.	Silver Clad Half Dollar .14792 oz.	Silver Dollar .77344 oz.
$9	$0.51	$0.65	$1.63	$3.26	$1.33	$6.96
10	0.56	0.72	1.81	3.62	1.48	7.73
11	0.62	0.80	1.99	3.98	1.63	8.51
12	0.68	0.87	2.17	4.34	1.78	9.28
13	0.73	0.94	2.35	4.70	1.92	10.05
14	0.79	1.01	2.53	5.06	2.07	10.83
15	0.84	1.09	2.71	5.43	2.22	11.60
16	0.90	1.16	2.89	5.79	2.37	12.38
17	0.96	1.23	3.07	6.15	2.51	13.15
18	1.01	1.30	3.26	6.51	2.66	13.92
19	1.07	1.37	3.44	6.87	2.81	14.70
20	1.13	1.45	3.62	7.23	2.96	15.47

The value of common-date gold coins listed in this book may be affected by the rise or fall in the price of gold bullion. Nearly all U.S. gold coins have an additional premium value beyond their bullion content, and thus are not subject to the minor variations described for silver coins. The premium amount is not necessarily tied to the bullion price of gold, but is usually determined by supply and demand levels for actual gold coins occurring in the numismatic marketplace. Because these factors can vary significantly, there is no reliable formula for calculating "percentage above bullion" prices that would remain accurate over time. For this reason the chart below lists bullion values based on gold content only. Consult your nearest coin dealer to ascertain current premium prices.

Bullion Values of Gold Coins

Gold Price Per Ounce	$5.00 Liberty Head 1839–1908 Indian Head 1908–1929 .24187 oz.	$10.00 Liberty Head 1838–1907 Indian Head 1907–1933 .48375 oz.	$20.00 1849–1933 .96750 oz.
$700	$169.31	$338.63	$677.25
750	181.40	362.81	725.63
800	193.50	387.00	774.00
850	205.59	411.19	822.38
900	217.68	435.38	870.75
950	229.78	459.56	919.13
1,000	241.87	483.75	967.50
1,050	253.96	507.94	1,015.88
1,100	266.06	532.13	1,064.25
1,150	278.15	556.31	1,112.63

Note: The U.S. bullion coins first issued in 1986 are unlike the older regular issues. They contain the following amounts of pure metal: silver $1, 1 oz.; gold $50, 1 oz.; gold $25, 1/2 oz.; gold $10, 1/4 oz.; gold $5, 1/10 oz.

INDEX

The PATH
to PERSONAL
POWER

NAPOLEON HILL

A TarcherPerigee Book

An imprint of Penguin Random House LLC
375 Hudson Street
New York, New York 10014

Copyright © 2017 by The Napoleon Hill Foundation
Penguin supports copyright. Copyright fuels creativity, encourages diverse voices,
promotes free speech, and creates a vibrant culture. Thank you for buying an authorized
edition of this book and for complying with copyright laws by not reproducing, scanning,
or distributing any part of it in any form without permission. You are supporting
writers and allowing Penguin to continue to publish books for every reader.

Tarcher and Perigee are registered trademarks, and the colophon
is a trademark of Penguin Random House LLC.

Most TarcherPerigee books are available at special quantity discounts
for bulk purchase for sales promotions, premiums, fund-raising, and educational needs.
Special books or book excerpts also can be created to fit specific needs.
For details, write: SpecialMarkets@penguinrandomhouse.com.

ISBN 9780143111535

Printed in the United States of America

1 3 5 7 9 10 8 6 4 2

Book design by Elke Sigal

CONTENTS

FOREWORD

By Don M. Green,
Executive Director, The Napoleon Hill Foundation

As a young reporter working for *Bob Taylor's Magazine* in 1908, Napoleon Hill conducted his first major interview at the home of steel magnate Andrew Carnegie. As many followers of Napoleon Hill's life and writings know, Carnegie asked young Napoleon to spend the next twenty years or so, without pay, conducting interviews so that he could write the first book in America on how its great men had achieved success.

Napoleon accepted the challenge, did the necessary research and interviews, and produced the first major treatise on the science of personal achievement. Published in 1928 as *Law of Success*, it was followed in 1937 by an abbreviated version, titled *Think and Grow Rich*, which is without a doubt the most read and most valued motivational book of the 20th Century, and thereafter.

The Napoleon Hill Foundation, founded by Mr. Hill in 1962, eight years before his death, continues to promote his philosophy. It has licensed his books in over fifty languages throughout the world. It is a non-profit charitable foundation which uses its revenues to endow scholarships, teach Hill's principles in correctional institutions, and conduct research into his life and work. It has recently unearthed three unpublished full-length books by Mr. Hill, one of which, *Outwitting the Devil*, was published in 2011 to critical acclaim.

The book you are about to read is excerpted from a series of lessons on success that Napoleon Hill wrote in 1941 at the urging of Dr. William Plumer Jacobs of Clinton, South Carolina. Dr. Jacobs was president of Presbyterian College, owner of Jacobs Press, and consultant to many textile mill owners. He had heard Mr. Hill lecture a year earlier, was impressed, and believed that a self-help course and lecture series by Mr. Hill would help South Carolina and its neighboring states emerge from the lingering effects of the Great Depression. Believing that many Americans were still beaten down by the hard times of the 1930s, and were depending too much on the government for economic support, Mr. Hill saw this opportunity to teach people how to succeed.

Napoleon accepted Dr. Jacobs' offer and moved to Clinton to write his lessons on success. He called the lessons "Mental Dynamite," taking the title from an observation Mr. Carnegie made when they first met: "The power with which we think is mental dynamite." He authored seventeen lessons, in booklet format, and each based on one of the principles of success he had discovered in his discussions with Mr. Carnegie and other men of achievement. Most of the lessons included lengthy excerpts from Napoleon's interviews with Mr. Carnegie, and then set forth specific examples of how Mr. Carnegie's principles had been applied by other successful people in America.

Mr. Hill's Mental Dynamite booklets and lecture series were well received, but everything changed on December 7 of the year of their publication, when Japan bombed Pearl Harbor and the United States entered World War II. These Mental Dynamite lessons were put aside during the War, and largely forgotten thereafter. In this book, the Foundation has put together three of the lessons, which focus on what many people think are the most important of all of Hill and Carnegie's principles.

The Mental Dynamite lessons chosen for this book are those that anyone can use to achieve personal power. More importantly, they must be used in order to achieve personal power. The principles are Definiteness of Purpose, the Mastermind Principle, and Going the Extra Mile. As these lessons from the Foundation's archives are read, and more importantly applied, you will begin your journey on the path to personal power.

THINK!

Croesus, a wise philosopher and confidential advisor to Cyrus, king of the Persians, said:

> "I am reminded, O king, that
> there is a Wheel on which
> the affairs of men revolve,
> and its mechanism is such
> that it prevents any man
> from being always fortunate."

There is a Wheel of Life that controls the destiny of men. It operates through the minds of men, through the power of thought. The Philosophy of Individual Achievement set forth in Mental Dynamite was designed for the purpose of aiding men in the mastery and control of this great wheel, to the end that it may yield them an abundance of all they desire or need and bring enduring happiness. Remember, you who are beginning the study of this philosophy, that this same wheel which "prevents any man from being always fortunate," provides, also, that no man shall be "always unfortunate," if he will take possession of his mind and use it.

THE AUTHOR

CHAPTER ONE

DEFINITENESS
of PURPOSE

Through the lessons of this book you will be provided with usable knowledge that would cost you a huge fortune if you acquired it, as it was originally organized, from the minds of Andrew Carnegie and more than five hundred other distinguished leaders in American business and industry. Among the persons whose successful experience is published here are Henry Ford, Thomas A. Edison, Stuart Austin Wier, Cyrus H. K. Curtis, Edward Bok, Dr. Alexander Graham Bell, Dr. Elmer R. Gates, John Wanamaker, James J. Hill, Edwin C. Barnes, William Howard Taft, Charles M. Schwab, Theodore Roosevelt, Elbert H. Gary, Charles P. Steinmetz, and Woodrow Wilson.

For all practical purposes you may assume that you are now entering a classroom in which your teachers will consist of more than five hundred of the men who have made America the "richest and freest" country known to civilization. Moreover, you will be privileged to acquire in this book the same knowledge that would have required over ten years of intense study had you procured it from its original source.

Through this book you will be schooled in an entire philosophy of success, complete and adequate in every respect for the needs of any person seeking the privilege of self-determination under the great American system of personal advancement. You will receive instruction that is not available at any price nor under any circumstances through any other source.

These lessons have been presented in a manner best suited to enable you to assimilate the knowledge they convey, with no effort on your part beyond a sincere desire to avail yourself of the secrets of achievement which are known to have been the foundation of almost all of the successful business leaders this country has produced.

In thus departing from the usual academic style of presenting knowledge, the author has kept in mind the fact that this book is for men and women in all walks of life, whose educational background, occupation, and family responsibilities make it necessary for them to acquire practical knowledge by the shortest and quickest method available. The author has had in mind, too, the fact that this book is intended as a "family" schooling and should therefore be presented in an easy, readable style that will be interesting to young men and young women who have not yet finished high school or college as well as to the adult members of the family. Every principle of individual achievement here presented has been tested and tried in the great crucible of practical experience.

You can read these lessons in a few hours, but more than thirty years of careful research made it possible for you to do this. Moreover, this research was carried on by practical business men who acquired their experience by the trial and error method, over a long period of years.

Read slowly and digest that which you read, as you go along. The most important part is not in these lessons but in your mind. The major purpose of this chapter is not that of suggesting to you what your definite goal in life should be but rather to bring to your attention the necessity of your choosing a major objective as a starting point toward individual achievement.

Mark the paragraphs which impress you most as you read and come back to these for a more detailed analysis when time permits. It will be helpful if two or more people form a study club for the purpose of reading and analyzing the lessons together. The benefits of this plan will become more obvious after you finish the lesson on the Master Mind in the next chapter.

Somewhere in this book, you will find yourself—that "other self," which will throw off all the chains of limitation that previously bound you and reveal to you a veritable giant of power asleep in your brain, needing only some outside force to awaken it. You will find this awakening force. It will come in the form of an idea that you will pick up as you read and think.

To begin with, there are 17 major principles of success and every person who attains the objective of his major goal, in any undertaking, must use some combination of these principles. I shall name first, the most important. It stands at the head of the list of the 17 principles of achievement because no one has ever been known to succeed without applying it. You may call it the principle of Definiteness of Purpose. Study any person who is known to be a permanent success and you will find that he has a Definite Major Goal; he has a plan for the attainment of this goal; he devotes the major portion of his thoughts and his efforts to the attainment of this purpose.

Everyone wishes for the better things of life, such as money, a good position, fame, and recognition; but most people never go far beyond the "wishing" stage. Men who know exactly what they want of life and are determined to get it do not stop with wishing. They intensify their wishes into a Burning Desire, and back that desire with continuous effort based on a sound plan.

The first step from poverty to riches is the most difficult.

All riches and all material things that anyone acquires through self-effort begin in the form of a clear, concise mental picture of the thing one seeks. When that picture grows, or has been forced to the proportions of an obsession, it is taken over by the sub-conscious mind through some hidden law of nature. From that point on one is drawn, attracted, or guided in the direction of the physical equivalent of the mental picture. I shall come back to this subject of the subconscious mind many times before we finish, as it is one of the vital factors in connection with all outstanding achievements.

It has long been a mystery to some people why men with little or no schooling often succeed, while men with extensive schooling often fail. Look carefully and you will discover that great successes are the result of understanding and the use of a positive mental attitude through which nature aids men in converting their aims and purposes into their physical and financial equivalent. Mental attitude is the quality of mind which gives power to one's thoughts and plans.

The length of time which it takes for one's mental attitude to begin attracting the physical and financial requisites of one's major purpose depends entirely upon the nature and extent of one's desires and the control one exercises over his mind in keeping it free from fear and doubt and self-imposed limitations. This sort of control comes through constant vigilance, wherein one keeps his mind free of all negative thoughts and leaves it open for the influx and the guidance of Infinite Intelligence. Definiteness of purpose involving a hundred dollars, for example, might be translated into its financial equivalent in a few days, or even a few hours, or a few minutes, whereas, desire for a million dollars might call for considerably more time, depending to some extent on what one had to give in return for the million dollars.

The best way to describe the time necessary for the translation of a definite purpose into its physical or financial equivalent can be accurately stated by determining the exact time necessary to deliver the service, or the equivalent in value one intends to give in return for the object of that purpose.

Before I finish describing the most important principles of achievement, I hope to be able to prove to you that there is a definite connection between giving and getting. Generally speaking, riches and material things that men get are the effect of some form of useful service they have rendered.

The only known way of insuring that a definite purpose will be carried out to a full realization, through the forces of natural law working through the minds of men, is by first establishing a cause for such realization, through useful service, rendered in a spirit of harmony.

A well-disciplined mind is capable of holding and acting upon a definite major purpose without any form of outside, or artificial aid. The undisciplined mind needs a crutch to lean upon while dealing with a definite major purpose. The best method to be followed, by one with an undisciplined mind, is that of writing down a complete description of one's major purpose and then adopting the habit of reading it aloud at least once every day. The act of writing down one's major purposes forces one to be specific as to its nature. The act of habitual reading fixes the nature of the purpose in the mind, where it can be picked up by the sub-conscious mind and acted upon.

The good there is in money consists of the use to which it is put and not in the mere possession of it. Generally speaking, the man who earns his own money acquires, along with it some of the necessary wisdom as to its constructive use.

If you want a practical illustration of this reasoning, look at what happens to the boy or girl who is brought up by rich parents and is made to feel from early childhood that individual effort in the accumulation of riches is unnecessary. I have never known of a single instance in which a boy brought up in this fashion came within sight of the business acumen and achievements of his father. The real joy of having money comes from earning it; not from receiving it as a gift.

We have more opportunities in America for the making of fortunes in return for useful service than in all other countries combined. This is a new country. Our resources have only been tapped. Every day brings on new endeavors to open hundreds of new roads of opportunity: Today it's the automobile and the aeroplane—industries in their infancy. Their development opens fields for thousands of young men with imagination, skill, and initiative.

Our only lack of opportunities is going to be a shortage of imagination, self-reliance and initiative which will be needed to man the future of this country. The whole world is turning to America for new ideas, new inventions, new opportunities for skill and imagination. Look around you everywhere and you will see that this is but the budding age of stupendous opportunity on every hand.

In the field of Life Insurance there will be great opportunities for men and women to render useful service and make themselves financially independent. The institution of Life Insurance is rapidly becoming the major medium for the development of the habit of saving for millions of our people. The Life Insurance agent of the future will become a teacher as well as a salesman; he will teach people to budget their time and their expenditures by systematic investment in insurance. Keep your eyes on this field, because it represents one of the major pillars of our great American economic system. It will give profitable employment to hundreds of thousands of men and women whose services to the people will be no less useful than the services of the clergymen, or the school teachers. The selling of Life Insurance will become one of the most recognized professions that will pay as well as or better than most of the learned professions. The sale of Life Insurance will be reduced to a science, and eventually it will be taught in the colleges.

A man's achievements correspond with unerring certainty to the philosophy with which he relates himself to others. If you follow through your willingness to give something in return for the knowledge you desire, you are certain to make yourself so useful to the world that it will be compelled to reward you in terms of your own choice. This is the spirit of true Americanism.

Every person who seeks personal success in America should both understand and respect the fundamentals of Americanism. Those who neglect or refuse to give loyal support to the institutions of Americanism may unconsciously contribute to the downfall of these supporting pillars, thereby cutting the very foundation from under their own opportunities for personal achievement. It is obvious that no individual may enjoy permanent success if he is out of step with the forces which have given him his opportunity to succeed.

THE SIX PILLARS OF AMERICANISM

You can best describe Americanism by analyzing the six major pillars which distinguish this country from all others, viz.:

1. Our American form of Government, as it was originally written into the Constitution of the United States, providing the fullest possible measure of right to individual liberty, freedom of thought, freedom of speech, freedom of worship, and above all, freedom of individual initiative that gives to every citizen the privilege of choosing his own occupation and setting his own price upon his knowledge, skill, and experience. No other country in the world offers its citizens such an abundant choice of opportunities for the marketing of his services as those provided under our form of government.

2. Our Industrial System, with its matchless natural resources of leadership and raw materials, coordinated, as it is, with our American spirit of Democracy, and supported by our American form of Government through which it is protected in every manner possible from the competition of other countries. So long as there is harmony and understanding and sympathetic cooperation between leaders of industry and the officials of our government, every citizen will benefit, directly or indirectly, by our expanding industrial system. If the time ever comes when the leaders of the government and the leaders of industry neglect or refuse to work in harmony toward a common end, the weight of their short-sightedness will fall heavily on the

economic life of every citizen. This is definitely becoming an industrial nation. Industry not only supplies a major portion of the income for men who work for wages, but it absorbs a major portion of the products of agriculture, and it is the major source of support for lawyers, doctors, dentists, engineers, educators, churches and others engaged in professional work. There is no way of separating "Americanism" from industry without destroying one of the strongest and most important of the six pillars.

3.   Our Banking System, providing, as it does, the life-blood which keeps our industrial system and our agriculture and our business and professional systems active and flexible at a cost that is not a burden to anyone. Understand the nature of the service being rendered by our banking system and you will be forever done with the ignorant few who cry out against the imaginary sins of "Wall Street." Every well-informed person knows that in this country we have a twin-system of government, with a political division operating in Washington and a financial division operating in New York. When these two branches of our form of national life operate harmoniously, we have prosperous times. Moreover, we have the resources of both political and financial economy to compete successfully with any other country in the world. When these two branches of our national life become antagonistic, as they have done from time to time in the past, we are cursed with "panics" and other ills that damage every citizen. The Banking Houses are just as essential to the successful operation of our system of living as are the merchandising stores and business

offices. As a matter of fact, no form of merchandising or business could be carried on successfully without access to a ready supply of cash or credit, which the banks supply.

4. Our Life Insurance System, serving, as it does, as the people's greatest national institution of individual savings, and providing our economic system with a form of flexibility that would not be available through the Banking System alone. No other American institution provides the people with a source of savings that gives the individual protection for his family and at the same time releases his mind from worry in connection with the possibility of approaching old age and its economic uncertainties. The institution of Life Insurance, which is definitely a part of the fundamentals of America, provides a system which makes it unnecessary for any physically sound person to humiliate himself in old age by the acceptance of charity.

5. Our National Spirit of Love for Liberty and our demand for the privilege of self-determination, as expressed by the pioneers in industry and government, and the national love of freedom of speech, thought and action, which were the distinguishing characteristics of the great leaders produced by America in the past.

6. Our National Sense of Justice, which inspires us to fight for the protection of the weak as well as the strong, and has never tolerated territorial annexation by conquest without adequate compensation.

Under these six headings you will find everything of major importance that distinguishes this country from all others. *Anything which weakens any of the six pillars* of Americanism, *undermines correspondingly the whole of our national life.* It is not enough for an individual to refrain from doing or saying anything that would weaken these pillars; but it is the duty of every loyal American to defend these fundamentals against all who endeavor to weaken or destroy any portion of them.

We Americans should think and talk less of our rights, and more of our duties and privileges as individuals in protecting the very foundation on which our rights and privileges are founded. It is plainly the duty of every citizen to make the defense of these fundamental pillars of Americanism a definite part of his *Major Purpose in life.*

There is a growing tendency in this country for men with a radical trend of mind to find fault with our form of government, our industrial system, our banking system, and about everything else that represents the basic pillars of our Americanism. Careful analysis of these men will disclose the truth that they are suffering with some form of inferiority complex which expresses itself in a desire to discredit all who succeed and who are accepted as leaders in business and industry.

Some of these radicals are men of great brilliancy of mind on most subjects except that of economic and social philosophy. Some are foreign born, some are American born. You will find them in politics, in some of the churches, in many public schools and colleges, in the labor unions, and in nearly every other calling. Their efforts to destroy our nation, whether based on sincere ignorance or out and out sinister motives, should be met blow for blow. They should not be permitted to destroy the world's greatest nation merely because we preach and practice the right of free speech in this country. The right of free speech does not carry with it a license to libel respectable men merely because they have been successful! Since the beginning of civilization wealth has found its way into the hands of men who think accurately; men with definiteness of purpose; men with keenness of imagination and the initiative to translate imagination into useful service. No amount of preachment by radicals can change this, and it is this very truth that has led me to the belief that the very best method of distributing wealth is that of distributing the principles of achievement by which wealth is procured.

In speaking of the great resources of this country it should be kept always in mind that the greatest of these is not the money in the banks, nor the minerals in the ground, nor the trees in the forest, nor the richness of our soil; but it is the mental attitude, and the imagination, and the pioneering spirit of the men who have mixed experience and education with these raw materials, thereby transforming them into various types of useful service for our own people and for the people of other nations.

The real wealth of this nation is not any material, tangible thing. Our real wealth consists of the intangible power of thought, as it is expressed by our leaders who understand and apply the philosophy of individual achievement. It reflects itself in broader visions, wider horizons, greater ambitions and initiative. Anyone who misses this truth will fail to understand why ours is the "richest and freest" country in the world.

The principle of *Definiteness of Purpose* obviously is a necessity to all who succeed, since no one may achieve success without first knowing precisely what he wants. It is interesting to know that approximately 98 out of 100 people are totally without a major goal, and it is significant that approximately the same percentage of people are regarded as failures.

The principle of definiteness of purpose, to be of enduring value, must be adopted and applied as a daily habit. Absence of this habit leads to another habit that is fatal to success, and that is the habit of drifting. We have found that salesmen sell more merchandise when they are given definite sales quotas than when they sell without quotas.

A good definition of success is *"The power with which to acquire whatever one demands of life, without violating the rights of others."* No person without definiteness of purpose can wield enough power to be sure of getting anything except that which no one else desires. You will observe that men with power are men who reach decisions quickly and change them slowly, if they change them at all. Decision is a twin brother of definiteness. These are two words with which to conjure—Definiteness and Decision. They represent a positive mental attitude without which no worthwhile success can be achieved in any calling. These qualities are an important part of the mental attitude of all great leaders.

If you will analyze my definition of success, you will see that there is no element of luck about it. A man may, and sometimes men do, fall into opportunities through mere chance, or luck, but they have a queer way of falling out of these opportunities the first time opposition overtakes them. You will find this theory substantiated by studying those who inherit money which they did not earn and those who are lifted into high positions through what is commonly called "pull." A man may come into possession of opportunity by inheritance or pull, but he can stay in possession of it only by push, and that calls for Definiteness of Purpose. The person who tries to go through life on "pull" and luck finds Old Man Fate standing just around the comer with a stuffed club, and it is not stuffed with cotton. When the blow falls on his head, he can't take it.

Personal power is acquired through a combination of individual traits and habits. Briefly, the ten qualities of personal power (which I call the ten-point rule of personal power) are these:

(a) The habit of definiteness of purpose

(b) Promptness of decision

(c) Soundness of character (intentional honesty)

(d) Strict discipline over one's emotions

(e) Obsessional desire to render useful service

(f) Thorough knowledge of one's occupation

(g) Tolerance on all subjects

(h) Loyalty to one's personal associates and faith in a Supreme Being

(i) Enduring thirst for knowledge

(j) Alertness of imagination

You will observe that this ten-point rule embraces only the traits which anyone may develop. You will observe, also, that these traits lead to the development of a form of personal power which can be used without "violating the rights of others." That is the only form of personal power anyone can afford to wield.

The old adage, "knowledge is power," is not quite true. Knowledge never is power until it has been expressed in some term of useful service. The space a man occupies in life corresponds, in minute exactness, to the quality and the quantity of service he renders, plus the mental attitude in which he renders the service. Men who wield great personal power, if they remain powerful, must understand and apply the Q + Q + C formula. That is, the quality of their service must be right, the quantity must be right, and their conduct must be agreeable. You might state this truth in another way, viz.: Quality of service, plus quantity of service, plus mode of conduct, equals the degree of success one will command.

Again observe that the QQC formula represents only qualities which anyone may develop. The formula has nothing whatever to do with luck, unless it may be said that those who apply this formula seem to have luck on their side in a great majority of their experiences. The fellow who is always complaining about not getting the "breaks," or that luck is against him, is merely using this excuse as an alibi with which to apologize for laziness, indifference, or lack of ambition. The fellow who wants something for nothing will be quick enough to complain of "bad luck" when failure overtakes him. The successful man says little or nothing about luck, because he has a more dependable philosophy on which to lean. He makes or largely influences his own "breaks."

John Wanamaker served the people through one of the greatest retail stores in America. When asked, he replied quickly enough, that his success as a merchant was due entirely to definite principles of achievement, and not to luck.

James J. Hill built the Great Northern Railroad system with definiteness of purpose, and he made of it a huge success. His rise from the lowly position of telegraph operator to the position of directing head of a great railroad system was systematically planned. At no time did he rely upon luck for the acquisition of personal power.

Thomas A. Edison gave the world the incandescent electric lightbulb, the talking machine, the moving picture, and a score or more of other aids to mankind; but no part of his success was achieved through luck. The very fact that Edison met with more than ten thousand failures before he found a method by which to harness electricity and make it serve to light a lamp, proves that he had no faith in luck. Measure these men, and all others of their type, by the ten-point rule (already described) for the development of personal power, and you will be forced to the conclusion that they succeeded because they developed and used these ten qualities. Success is the result of mind power properly organized, controlled and directed with definiteness of purpose.

Let me caution you, however, against jumping to the conclusion that DEFINITENESS OF PURPOSE, by itself, is sufficient for the achievement of success. There are sixteen other major principles of individual achievement, with some or all of which definiteness of purpose must be combined. The choice of a definite major purpose is but the starting point toward success. The personal power with which to translate definiteness of purpose into its physical or financial equivalent comes through understanding and use of other principles of achievement.

Another important characteristic connected with personal power is the necessity of understanding the difference between power that is acquired with the full consent and approval of all who are affected by it and power that is forced upon others without their consent. Lack of understanding of this difference has brought failure to many who would, otherwise, have been great successes. Study the ten-point rule carefully and you will be convinced that it leads only to that form of power which is acquired with the consent and the co-operation of other people.

In the city of Detroit there is a man by the name of Henry Ford whose philosophy of human relationship promises to lift him into a dominating position in the industrial world. I want you to go to Detroit and meet Mr. Ford, for the time is coming when he is sure to dominate the automobile industry. Study this man carefully, weigh his philosophy accurately, and observe how definitely he is acquiring personal power by applying the ten-point rule. DEFINITENESS OF PURPOSE is his obsession. He knows enough to put all his eggs in one basket and then guard that basket carefully, through definiteness of purpose.

Simply stated, his purpose has been that of making a low priced, dependable automobile. His was a "one track" mind, but it led him precisely where he wished to go. His philosophy has brought him great wealth and a nation of friends and patrons. It will, perhaps, enable him to occupy more space in the world than any other industrialist of his time.

Look what F. W. Woolworth accomplished through his understanding of the ten-point rule for the development of personal power. His philosophy was the same as that of Henry Ford. He built one of the tallest buildings in America; built it on nickels and dimes that other people had spent carelessly. He, too, had a "one-track" mind. He took one simple, unique idea of merchandising and made it yield him a huge fortune. The strangest thing about his success is the simplicity of his business policy. He had no patent rights on his merchandising plan, yet he has but few imitators, and it is for that reason that he moves with definiteness of purpose while most of the other merchants lack such a purpose. They have a different policy for every item of merchandise they sell. Woolworth has but one policy for the sale of all his merchandise. Study this man, and all others whose efforts are based on definiteness of purpose, and you will be forever cured of the notion that success and luck have anything in common.

These ten qualities of personal power must become habits. Occasional application of the qualities will be of little value. The man who only applies them when they serve his immediate purpose, but ignores them when they appear to be unprofitable, will never have enduring power. The qualities of personal power must become so definitely a part of a man's character that they take on a spiritual nature. This cannot be accomplished in a day, or a week, or perhaps in a year. It will be helpful if an individual writes out a list of these ten qualities and carefully grades himself on each of them once every day. By this procedure they will be taken over by the sub-conscious mind and made a part of his character. But one must not stop by merely rating himself daily; he must put these qualities into practice in all his relationships with others. An ounce of practice is worth a million tons of theory.

After the individual blends the ten qualities into his own character through habit, he must make it his business to endeavor by every practical means at his command to induce his associates to appropriate and use them; especially his more intimate associates, such as the members of his family, his personal friends, and those with whom he works. It has been said that "The best way to acquire the virtues of sound character is by helping others, through example, to acquire them."

Successful men of the past, generally speaking, acquired their knowledge of the principles of successful achievement by the trial and error system. But that is a long and costly method. That is why so many men have failed, although their aims and purposes were worthy enough. Good intentions and high resolves are not sufficient for the achievement of permanent success. One must know the rules by which personal power may be acquired, a form of knowledge that is available only to those who understand and apply all the principles of achievement.

We are here concerned only with that form of success which is achieved through deliberate planning and which remains permanently. The man who achieves success through the application of the success principles may, through some mistake of judgment, or for some cause over which he has no control, temporarily lose the fruits of his success; but he will know how to recoup his losses. He will understand how to build a new success out of an old defeat. Moreover, the man who is master of the principles of success quickly learns how to convert stumbling blocks into stepping stones; he learns how to extract useful knowledge from temporary defeat, and above all, he learns the difference between temporary defeat and failure. If he meets with temporary defeat, he stages a quick come-back and profits by the experience. He supplants the spirit of defeatism with the spirit of faith. He knows how to remove the self-imposed limitations that hold most men back, because he realizes that most limitations are nothing but states of mind.

To the master of the principles of achievement, the experience of temporary defeat is nothing but a signal to rebuild his plans and increase his determination to win. In brief, these principles provide one with a philosophy that recognizes no such circumstance as failure. Accurate understanding of the philosophy of achievement makes one success-conscious; it converts one's mind into a powerful magnet that attracts to him an exact equivalent of his own mental attitude, as it is reflected in his plans, aims and purposes.

The master of this philosophy finds an abundance of opportunity placed in his path as if by some queer stroke of magic. He finds people going out of their way to lend him cooperation, and this without any apparent efforts or requests on his part. You might say that the individual first masters the philosophy of achievement; then it masters everything that gets in his way; and all this happens through some strange mixture of mind chemistry which science does not understand, nor does science undertake to explain the source of its power.

It is not likely that anyone who understands the principles of achievement will ever become a "quitter" because all who understand the philosophy know that it provides sufficient power to meet any ordinary human emergency! It will put sounder legs under a man's religion, no matter what may be his religious beliefs. It will give the salesman more ability, regardless of the commodity he is selling. It will make of one a more loyal American because the philosophy is literally the very foundation on which this nation was developed. Mastery of the principles will bring one riches in terms of enduring friendships, peace of mind, harmony in family relationships, financial security, and that state of mind known as happiness. The philosophy is complete in that it helps all who master it to negotiate their way through life with a minimum amount of friction, resistance and opposition from their fellow men. Once you get this conception you will know that it brings one very close to an understanding of Infinite Intelligence through which the individual recognizes his proper relationship to himself, to all others, and to his Maker.

Any dominating idea, plan, thought, or purpose that is held in the mind through a strong desire for its realization, is picked up by the sub-conscious mind and translated into its physical or financial equivalent by whatever practical means are available. Let us here stress the fact that any desire, plan, or purpose which is backed by faith in its fulfillment and emotionalized by a strong desire for its fulfillment takes precedence in the magical operations of the sub-conscious mind and is acted upon more quickly than any plan or purpose placed in the mind with nothing but cold reason as its motivating force. This applies with equal certainty to both negative and positive states of mind. A mind that is dominated by thoughts which dwell continuously upon fear and poverty will lead to misery and failure, just as definitely as thoughts which dwell upon faith and opulence will lead to success.

It is highly important that you understand the truth that your "mental attitude" is a two-way entrance into your mind, the mental attitude of faith leading into a reservoir of power that automatically translates your desires, plans and purposes into their exact physical equivalent, and the mental attitudes of fear and doubt leading into an equally definite reservoir of power which converts your desires, plans and purposes into certain nothingness.

With definite knowledge of what I am saying I can tell you that this is the way the mind works. Neither me nor any other person has ever been able to tell how or why the mind works in this manner. It is no mere phrase of speech, nor is it any exaggeration to say that "Whatever man can believe, man can do." It is a well-known fact that man's only limitations are those which he sets up in his own mind. If this were not true, how could we account for the achievements of a man like Thomas A. Edison, who, with but three months of schooling, controlled and made such practical use of the powers of his mind that he became the world's most distinguished inventor?

If this were not true, how shall we account for the achievements of Henry Ford, who, starting at scratch, with but little of that form of education known as a common-school education, belted the earth with the physical products of his mind and accumulated a huge fortune in return for his service?

Careful analysis of the achievements of such men as Ford and Edison is sufficient to convince any thinking person that men who move with Definiteness of Purpose, backed by faith in their ability to achieve the object of their purpose, project the powers of their minds into the very reservoir of Infinite Intelligence, wherein may be found the answer to all human problems, the fulfillment of all human desires.

It is not the purpose of this book to undertake to lead the reader into an intricate or abstract study of all the working principles of the mind, or to present an intricate and abstract discourse in psychology, but it is the purpose to show by convincing evidence that in a country such as ours, with its super-abundance of everything people need or desire, there is no legitimate reason for anyone remaining in want. Acquisition of the material things we need and desire begins, always, in a clear concept of what we want, plus a burning desire for its attainment. In a country such as ours the only thing in which the people are lacking is sufficient faith to take possession of their own minds and to make the fullest use of those minds. It has been proved too many times for its soundness to be doubted, that "mental attitude," and not mere knowledge or education, is the real source of all achievements.

I have said that the sub-conscious mind accepts and carries out the dominating thoughts of the mind which have been mixed with emotion, whether the emotion be positive or negative; that it translates thoughts of limitation, fear and doubt into certain failure, just as surely as it translates thoughts of faith into success. Let us take inventory of some well-known experiences which prove the soundness of this statement.

Take, for example, the experiences of 1929, the beginning of the most extended and devastating depression this country has ever known. When millions of people throughout the country started to gamble in the stock market, and their frenzied trading caused a crash in the market through which they lost their money, their highly emotionalized minds began to broadcast vibrations of fear, and those vibrations extended themselves in every direction until they reached the minds of other millions of people who were not gambling, resulting, finally, in a state of mass fear that paralyzed all banking, caused runs on banks, tied up the machinery of industry, and closed down normal business activities on a scale without precedent.

Here we were, jumping, almost overnight, from opulence and plenty into panic and poverty, despite the fact that there was exactly the same amount of all forms of riches in this country during the panic as before it started. The affairs of the people of the world change with their change of "mental attitude" as definitely and as regularly as the rise and flow of the tides of the oceans. Out of this truth came that old saying that "Success attracts success and failure attracts failure."

Accurate analysis of more than 25,000 men and women who were classed as "failures" established positive evidence of the working principles of the mind through which these unfortunate people brought about their own misfortunes. Listed without any attempt to classify these causes of failure as to their relative effects, these are some of the major causes:

(a) The widespread habit of accepting the limitation of poverty, as reflected by a willingness to be contented with the three bare necessities of life: food, shelter and clothing. I am not here going into the causes of lack of ambition which result in people not aiming above a desire for more than the necessities of life; I am merely analyzing a well-known fact to show that in spite of the vast riches of our great country a majority of the people have no definite purpose beyond the procuring of a mere living.

(b) Failure to recognize that which every psychologist knows: that neither external matters nor circumstances have any influence over the "mental attitude" of anyone, save only those who, through refusal to take possession of their own minds and use them, impose limitations upon their minds. It has been proved, times too numerous to mention, that any normal mind can break these poverty limitations any time the individual takes possession of his mind and becomes determined to use it for the acquisition of riches. Andrew Carnegie proved that his mind had the power to remove self-limitations when he became determined to quit the work of common labor and begin the more profitable work of organizing and operating a great steel industry. Thomas A. Edison made a similar demonstration of the powers of his mind when he became determined to leave his lowly work as a tramp telegraph operator and become the world's greatest inventor. Strange as it may seem, the very mind-power with which he made the switch from the life of a tramp to that of a highly successful inventor, became the power with which he penetrated the secrets of Infinite Intelligence and uncovered Nature's secrets.

(c) Failure to recognize the important difference between wishing for a thing and being determined to get it. Everyone wishes for the better things of life, and many make the fatal mistake of believing that a wish is the same as a clearly defined definite purpose, backed by a burning desire for its possession. The difference is precisely the difference between success and failure.

(d) The habit of allowing the mind to become limited through some form of fear, and an accepted inferiority. Many people who are born in an environment of poverty, and those who are temporarily cast into association with those who have accepted poverty as their lot, set up in their own minds insurmountable barriers by such a phobia. Every year millions of children are born in poverty and never learn that they can make themselves financially independent. From early childhood until death they use their mind-power in reverse gear, condemning themselves to poverty as surely as if their prayers were for misfortune.

(e) Failure to develop the habit of initiative, a failure which usually may be traced to its prototype, the belief in the individual's inferiority. Very obviously those who suffer with lack of initiative never will take possession of their own minds or anything else.

(f) Shortness of vision, the habit of setting up, voluntarily or by neglect, limitations upon the use of their mind-power by not aiming for any station in life above mediocrity. Man's achievements end where his limitations of mind-power begin, no matter what may be the cause of the limitations. Those who seek little usually attain just what they seek.

(g) Lack of attention to the importance of the development of an attractive personality by learning traits, habits and skills which unselfishly serve others. The failure to forget self. Those who love themselves will have few rivals.

(h) Development of the habit of procrastination, which leads to the habit of perpetual drifting through life and taking the line of least resistance at every turn. Lethargy and political expediency never built an empire.

(i) Choosing as their closest associates people who suffer with a well-defined poverty-consciousness and others of limited vision. Mental attitudes are contagious. That is why men who are known as successes make it a part of their personal responsibility to associate with men of ambition, who refuse to accept the limitations of life.

(j) Lack of faith and an inadequate understanding of the principle of prayer, through which the sub-conscious mind transfers to Infinite Intelligence a definite picture of one's mental attitude.

Here you have a brief but accurate description of the major sources through which men condemn themselves to misery, poverty and failure. As a starting-point toward success, take inventory of yourself by determining how many of these causes of failure you are sheltering in your own mind.

Ideas are the only assets which have no fixed value. They are the beginning of all achievements; they form the foundation of all fortunes; they are the starting-point of all inventions; ideas have mastered the air above us, and they have enabled us to harness and use the energy known as ether, through which any brain may communicate with any other brain.

Ideas begin as the result of Definiteness of Purpose. The talking machine was nothing but an abstract idea until Edison submitted it to the sub-conscious portion of his brain where it was projected into the great reservoir of Infinite Intelligence and flashed back to his mind in the form of a definite plan for its mechanical perfection.

The Anti-Saloon League was nothing but a rather vague sort of an idea that existed nowhere except in the minds of the two people who gave birth to it, in the village of Westerville, Ohio, over forty years ago; but there came a time when that idea, backed by Definiteness of Purpose, wiped out the saloons. I am not here trying to present the merits of the idea. I am only calling attention to the power of ideas when they are persistently backed by the human mind.

Al Capone gave birth to an idea, as the direct result of the changed social conditions brought about by the work of the Anti-Saloon League, and despite the unsavory nature of his idea, he placed definiteness of purpose back of it and thereby gave it such momentum that the entire forces of the law enforcement agencies of the powerful United States Government were required to stop the damage his idea was doing. Thus it will be recognized that ideas, backed by definiteness of purpose, work just as definitely for harm as for good, but above all they work.

The Rotary Club movement began as an idea, originally created in the mind of a lawyer for the purpose of extending his personal acquaintanceship and thereby building up his law practice without violating the ethics of the legal profession. The Rotary Club idea was humble enough at the start; but it was backed by definiteness of purpose until it now belts the entire earth and serves as a medium by which men come together in a spirit of friendly fellowship in nearly every country of the world.

The New World was discovered and brought under the influence of civilization as the result of an idea backed by definiteness of purpose expressed in the single mind of a humble sailor. The time may come, soon, when this newly discovered world may become the last frontier of civilization, thereby lifting the idea back of its discovery to first position in the important things which affect mankind.

Christianity, the greatest single power for good known to the world, began as an idea in the mind of one humble carpenter. Through persistent application of the principle of definiteness of purpose this idea has gone marching onward for nearly two thousand years, and it may well be expected to save the present trend toward destruction of civilization, if men will practice its tenets.

That which men believe, talk about, and expect has a queer way of making its appearance in one form or another. Let those of us who are struggling to free ourselves from the limitations of poverty and misery not forget this great truth, as it applies to an individual as well as to a nation of people.

Let us now turn our attention to the working principle through which thoughts, ideas, plans and purposes placed in the conscious mind find their way into the sub-conscious section of the brain, where they are picked up and carried out to their logical conclusion by Infinite Intelligence.

Transfer of thought from the conscious to the sub-conscious mind may be hastened by the simple process of stepping up or stimulating the vibrations of thought through faith, fear, or any other intensified emotion, such as enthusiasm, a burning desire based on definiteness of purpose, or hatred and jealousy. Thoughts based upon faith appear to have precedence over all others in the matter of definiteness and speed with which they are handed over to the subconscious mind. The speed with which the power of faith works has given rise to the belief that certain phenomena are the result of "miracles." Psychologists recognize no such phenomenon as a miracle today, claiming that everything that is and everything that happens is the result of a definite cause. Be this as it may, it is a well-known fact that the person who is capable of freeing his mind of all self-imposed limitations, through the mental attitude known as faith, generally finds the solution to all his problems, regardless of their nature.

Infinite Intelligence, while it is not an automatic solver of riddles, carries out to a logical conclusion any clearly defined idea, aim, purpose or desire that is submitted to the sub-conscious mind in a mental attitude of perfect faith. However, Infinite Intelligence never attempts to modify, change or otherwise alter any thought that is submitted to it, and it has never been known to act upon a mere wish or indefinite idea, thought or purpose. Get this truth well-grounded in your mind, and you will find yourself in possession of sufficient

THE PATH TO PERSONAL POWER

power to solve your daily problems with much less effort than most people put into worrying over their problems.

So-called "hunches" often are signals indicating that Infinite Intelligence is trying to reach and influence the conscious mind. They usually come in response to some idea, plan, purpose or desire, or some fear that has been handed over to Infinite Intelligence through the sub-conscious mind. Hunches should be treated civilly and examined carefully since they often convey, either in whole or in part, information of the greatest value to an individual. These hunches often make their appearance many hours, days or weeks after the thought that inspires them has reached the reservoir of Infinite Intelligence; meanwhile, the individual often has forgotten the original thought that inspired them.

This is a deep, profound subject about which even the wisest of people know but little. It becomes a self-revealing subject only upon deep meditation. Many believe that it is in the manner described that the power of prayer operates. Many believe, also, that Definiteness of Purpose, backed by faith, is of itself the finest of prayers. Understand the principle of the mind here described and you will have a dependable clue as to why prayer sometimes brings that which one desires, while at times it brings that which one does not wish. Consider the fact that most people turn to prayer only after everything else has failed them, generally in the hour of emergency when their minds are saturated with fear and doubt, and you may have the answer as to why prayer often brings that which one least desires. If you go to prayer with your mind wholly or partly filled with fear or doubt, Infinite Intelligence seems to accommodate by carrying out to its logical conclusion the precise mental attitude in which you pray.

The sort of faith that brings results, without exception, is that mental attitude in which one sees the object of one's desires already in hand, even before going to prayer. This sort of mental attitude comes only through preparation and discipline of the mind. Sometimes the discipline may be the result of deliberate effort on the part of an individual; at other times it may be the result of some great sorrow or deeply seated disappointment that forces one to turn to the "inner self" for consolation, wherein consists the truth that failure sometimes is a blessing in disguise.

A careful analysis of civilization will impress you with the profound way in which the human race is chastised every so often, through some great calamity such as a world depression, thus giving logic to the theory that failure and disappointment are weapons of discipline with which human beings are forced to turn to their spiritual natures for aid. The ten-year depression which spread over the entire world from 1929 to 1939 might easily be conceived to have been Nature's own way of forcing the people of the world to reclaim the spiritual values they so prodigiously wasted during the First World War.

No great leader has ever been known to achieve noteworthy success without drawing upon spiritual forces. There is a power greater than man himself, and it is often incomprehensible to the finite mind of man. An acceptance of this truth is essential to the successful culmination of any definite purpose. The great philosophers of all ages, from Plato and Socrates on down to Emerson and the moderns, and the great Statesmen of our times, from George Washington down to Abraham Lincoln, have been known to have turned to the inner self in times of emergency. No great and enduring success has ever been achieved, and none will ever be achieved, except by those who recognize and use the spiritual powers of the infinite as sensed in their inner selves. Failure to recognize this profound truth may be the major reason why the world is now so nearly bankrupt spiritually! No matter who you are, or what may be your calling, you will never come into possession of great power if you neglect or refuse to recognize and make use of your spiritual forces.

There was a man who was said to be the greatest life insurance salesman in America. For fifteen consecutive years he has been a member of the Million Dollar a Year Club, an organization of Life Insurance salesmen who sell a minimum of one million dollars of insurance annually. As "cool-headed and calculating" as he is said to be in connection with his business affairs, he never makes a call on a prospective purchaser of insurance without preparing his mind by at least an hour of introspective communion with his "inner self" during which he does away with his "coolheadedness" and substitutes in its place all the spiritual force he can command. It is another way of saying that he communed with God in prayer. He has discovered that Infinite Intelligence acts on his desire to serve his fellow men through the medium of Life Insurance, just as quickly and definitely as it acts on any other purpose.

This man makes no dramatic outward gestures in connection with his sales methods, nor does he feature his religious beliefs. His method of drawing upon the spiritual forces of his being for aid in his daily profession is something between himself and his Maker. It becomes manifest in a sincere desire to serve his fellow men. Somehow we cannot escape the belief that perhaps the quiet, unpretentious way in which this man goes about seeking the source of spiritual power within himself brings him much nearer to the source of all power than the methods of some men who advertise their religion in more dramatic ways. People who judged the late Thomas A. Edison, without knowing very much, if anything, about his personal beliefs, made the mistake of assuming that he became the world's most distinguished inventor because of his great reasoning power. The exact opposite to this belief is the real truth. The author was in the close confidence of Mr. Edison, over a long period of years, and he is in a position, therefore, to say that Mr. Edison's success was due largely to his habit of turning to the "inner man" for the solution of his most baffling problems. Mr. Edison understood, and used to the fullest, his spiritual estate. He was much more profoundly spiritual in nature than many people who proclaim deep-seated spiritual beliefs.

To many people it may also be something of a surprise to learn that Henry Ford's stupendous industrial and financial wisdom has its seat in his habit of drawing upon and using his spiritual forces. Mr. Ford never features, or advertises his spiritual belief, but be assured he knows that he owes his riches and his great achievements to his knowledge and use of the spiritual. Unlike the Dictators of Europe, who blatantly cry from the housetops that they are bound to win because God is on their side of the battle, Mr. Ford goes quietly about his business, and silently submits his every aim and purpose to the spiritual reservoirs of his soul. If one may judge him by his achievements, his system has the advantage of carrying him continuously forward, despite the opposition of powerful groups of men who, times without number, have tried to defeat him.

Andrew Carnegie once said, "Look out for the fellow who strengthens his aims and purposes with spiritual forces, for he is apt to challenge you at the post and pass you at the grand stand." When

Mr. Carnegie looked into the future more than thirty years ago, and prophesied that Henry Ford would become the dominating factor in the automobile industry, he based his prophecy upon his knowledge of Mr. Ford's recognition and use of his spiritual estate.

A little while ago the publisher of THINK AND GROW RICH (a one volume interpretation of a portion of the philosophy of individual achievement) began to receive telegraphic orders for that book from the stores in and near Des Moines, Iowa. The orders called for immediate shipments of the book, by express. Neither the author of this volume nor the publisher knew what had caused this sudden stimulation of sales of the book in the vicinity of Des Moines until several weeks afterward, when the author received a letter from Mr. Edward P. Chase, of Des Moines, a life insurance salesman representing the Sun Life Assurance Company, in which he said:

> *"I am writing to express my grateful appreciation of your book, THINK and GROW RICH. I followed its advice to the letter. As a result I received an idea which resulted in the sale of a two million dollar policy. The above is the largest single sale of its kind ever to be made in Des Moines."*

The key sentence in Mr. Chase's letter is the second sentence: "I followed its advice to the letter." I wish to tell you briefly why Mr. Chase so easily converted the contents of a book into a sale of life insurance greater in amount than the average insurance agent sells in four years of hard effort. First of all, the book, which inspired this large business transaction, literally abounds in spiritual stimuli, a fact to which many of its quarter of a million readers could testify.

In one sentence Mr. Chase testifies that he read the book with an open mind and "followed its advice to the letter." When he went out to sell a two million dollar insurance policy, he took with him a DEFINITENESS OF PURPOSE that was supported by the irresistible power of faith. He didn't merely read the book, as some perhaps have done. He did not lay it aside in an attitude of cynicism with the thought that the principles it described might work, and then again they might not. He read it with an open mind, recognized the stimulating spiritual forces it described, appropriated those forces, and immediately put them to work in his business of selling life insurance.

Somewhere in the reading of the book Mr. Chase's mind established contact with the mind of the author, and that contact quickened his own mind so definitely and intensely that an idea was born. The idea was to sell a large insurance policy, perhaps the largest he had ever sold. The sale of that policy became his immediate DEFINITE MAJOR PURPOSE. He moved on that purpose without delay and, behold! the objective was reached. No more time or effort was required to sell the two million dollar policy than might have been needed to sell a thousand dollar policy. As Mr. Carnegie so well stated, the man who is motivated by the spiritual "may challenge at the post and pass you at the grand stand," whether he is selling life insurance or digging ditches. There is simply no such reality as failure for the man who becomes acquainted with spiritual power and has faith in this power to use it as a means of mastering his problems.

As Mr. Carnegie once said, "A great weakness in some men is that they know too much! They know too many things which will not work." What he meant was this: Some people are so unfamiliar with the power of spiritual force that they neglect to use the power, depending on what they believe to be their own reasoning wisdom to get them through life. The truly great men are always open-minded and humble. The arrogant egotist never comes within arm's reach of Infinite Intelligence, without the aid of which man's accomplishments are small.

The mere casual reading of this book will not give its students the fullest benefits of the knowledge it conveys. There is more to the book than that which appears in its printed pages. There is "that something" hidden back of the lines of the printed page which can be uncovered only by the reader who reads with an open mind with a DEFINITE PURPOSE, and with a determination to tune in and catch the spirit of the great steel master and the other distinguished men whose philosophy of achievement will be found throughout these lessons.

Vision is an asset of priceless value. But passive vision leads only to impractical day-dreaming. Mr. Carnegie described the principle of definiteness of Purpose in plain English that any school boy or school girl can understand, but definiteness of purpose means nothing more than passive vision until and unless it is given life and action through the application of one's spiritual powers. Definiteness of Purpose is but the starting point toward success.

One's purpose must be lifted out of the passive category and clothed with the spiritual forces of action! One's major purpose, to insure its re-alization to the fullest, must be given obsessional proportion. There is a definite formula through which this desirable end can be attained, and I come, now, to the presentation of this formula, viz.:

THE FORMULA FOR TRANSLATION OF DEFINITENESS OF PURPOSE INTO ITS PHYSICAL EQUIVALENT

(a) Write out a full, clear statement of your Definite Major Purpose in life, sign it, commit it to memory and repeat it orally at least once daily. As you do this you should proceed as if your major purpose were a prayer, and your faith in your ability to acquire the object of your major purpose should be so definite that you can see yourself already in possession of it.

(b) On another page write out a clear statement of the plan or the plans by which you hope to attain the objective of your major purpose. It is important that you leave all plans sufficiently flexible so that you can alter, modify, change or supplant them with better plans at any time you may feel the "inner urge" to do so. Remember, the object of repeating your major purpose daily is to impress it upon your sub-conscious mind after which it will be picked up and acted upon by Infinite Intelligence. Remember, too, that Infinite Intelligence may find its own plans for the translation of your purpose into its physical equivalent. Be always on the alert, therefore, for the signal to change your plans. The signal will come in the form of a sudden idea or "hunch" that will present itself to your mind, perhaps at a moment when you are least expecting it. When the call comes do not hesitate but respond immediately and make whatever change of plans it inspires.

(c)   When you write out a statement of your major purpose, include in your statement a definite time limit within which you desire its fulfillment. With the laws of nature, as with the laws of man, time is of vital importance. Legal contracts, to be enforceable, must have a reasonable time limit within which the terms of the contract must be carried out. The same is true in connection with a compact with Infinite Intelligence. If no time limit is mentioned in connection with the acquisition of the object of one's major purpose, Infinite Intelligence may establish its own time. Infinite Intelligence has an abundance of time and, unless you establish your own time within which to achieve the object of your major purpose, Infinite Intelligence may not get around to its fulfillment in time to do you any good.

(d)   Control your "mental attitude" during the period when you are repeating orally the written statement of your major purpose. Never begin this profound ceremony until you are completely alone, and do not begin it until you clear your mind of fear, doubt and worry. Infinite Intelligence acts upon and carries out the "mental attitude" in which you present your desires and demands. If you catch the full significance of this instruction, and form the habit of carrying it out faithfully, you will soon find yourself in possession of the key which will open the door to the reservoir of your spiritual estate at will.

WHAT THE WRITTEN STATEMENT
OF YOUR DEFINITE MAJOR PURPOSE
SHOULD CONTAIN

In order that no reader may be confused as to what subjects one's Definite Major Purpose should cover, the author presents the following skeleton outline as a guide:

(a) The first paragraph should state precisely the achievement one desires within the time-limit chosen for the realization of one's major purpose.

(b) The second paragraph should describe clearly and definitely the exact quality and quantity of service one intends to give in return for the reward demanded. Let there be no illusions on this point. Infinite Intelligence never rewards people with something for nothing, nor does Infinite Intelligence favor the person who expects or demands pay out of proportion to the value of that which is given in return. Men can, and sometimes they do, cheat one another; *but no one has ever been known to cheat Infinite Intelligence.*

(c) The third paragraph should describe the "mental attitude" in which you intend to deliver the service you are to give in return for the money you demand. Your description should clearly state that you will relate yourself in a spirit of harmony toward every person who is in any manner affected by the service you render. Remember, as you carry out this instruction, that the people to whom you render service are affected by your "mental attitude" and your mode of personal conduct; that they respond in kind to your "frame of mind" the same as Infinite Intelligence takes notice of it. Here again, do not lose the profound significance of this instruction. If you do, your mistake may cost you the full results of your efforts.

(d) In the fourth paragraph write out a clear description of the part you intend to take in fulfilling your duty as an American citizen, remembering, as you write, that no one has a right to enjoy the far-flung privileges of Americanism without definitely contributing something of value to perpetuate and support the American system of living. Your commitment in this paragraph will be an accurate measure of your character; therefore, be generous in your assumption of responsibility to your country. Remember, too, that your "mental attitude" toward your country will reflect, to a surprising degree, the "mental attitude" you will display in connection with your closest associates and those to whom you render the service you expect to give in return for the material riches or other type of achievement which you expect. To be respected and well liked by others is the equivalent of removing most of the obstacles that you will find between you and the object of your definite major purpose. You have, therefore, a very sound self-interest reason for improving your relationship with all with whom you become closely associated.

(e) In the fifth paragraph write out a clear statement of the ways and means you intend to adopt to develop and use the spiritual forces at your command. This commitment on your part may assume any method you desire, but it surely obligates you to follow definite religious habits aimed at a broader and more positive use of your spiritual estate. If you belong to a church, you should intensify and improve your relationship with your spiritual advisers. If you do not belong to a church, and follow no religious learning, you should make such an affiliation. The church provides an atmosphere of spiritual stimulation which every person needs. But here, as in all other human relationships, one can get only in proportion as one gives. The best portion of any church benefit comes from the part one takes in connection with the church activities. Get into harness.

(f) In the sixth paragraph commit yourself to exercise your right and your duty to vote in all elections in which you are eligible to vote. You cannot be a good citizen without doing your part in choosing dependable and honest public officials. If the spirit of Americanism of which we boast is to remain a free and democratic power for the good of all its citizens, every citizen must assume his full duty in the matter of helping to keep honest men in office, through the power of the ballot.

(g) In the seventh paragraph write out a clear, definite description of the "mental attitude" in which you intend to improve your relationship with the members of your family. This instruction is of especial importance to men who are the heads of families. A man's wife is, if he relates himself to her properly, of great benefit in helping him to maintain and use his courage. She should be the most important member of his Master-Mind group, but she will do more harm than good if she is not in full sympathy with his aims and purposes. The fact that a majority of the great leaders, all back through the ages, have had back of them the harmonious cooperation of a woman is profoundly significant. When the minds of a man and his wife are blended in a spirit of continuous harmony, sympathy and oneness of purpose, they can surmount almost any obstacle that may get in their way.

(h) In the eighth paragraph commit yourself, definitely and irrevocably, never to slander or to speak disparagingly of another person, no matter what may be your impulses to do so. Nothing is more fatal to the development of one's spiritual state than the habit of gossip, small talk, and the slandering of other people. Successful people do not engage in this vulgar habit. It is an insult to one's own soul, a thrust at Infinite Intelligence.

SOME MEN WHO HELPED TO MAKE AMERICA, THROUGH THE PRINCIPLE OF DEFINITENESS OF PURPOSE

As a fitting climax for this chapter, I here present a few brief sketches of some of the well-known men who have contributed to the spirit of Americanism, as we, of this generation, understand that spirit. The records of the achievements of these men show clearly that they understood and applied the principle of Definiteness of Purpose without which, doubtlessly, they could not have been included in this list of distinguished successes.

Henry Ford, America's number one industrialist, although he rates very high on most principles of the philosophy of achievement, has as his greatest distinguishing feature the habit of moving with Definiteness of Purpose. To his application of this principle can be traced, more than to any of the other principles of success, his industrial supremacy and his fortune. Mr. Ford has permitted engineers to streamline his automobiles, but not so with his business policy. From the very beginning of his industrial career he adopted as his Definite Major Purpose the manufacture and the sale of a dependable, low-priced automobile. That still is his major purpose, and no one will question its soundness, in view of the forty year record of success back of it.

More than two hundred other men, whose names are not now remembered by most people, have come and gone in the business of making automobiles since Henry Ford started in that business. Many of these men had better educations than Mr. Ford, and nearly all of them had more working capital than he, with which to begin their industrial careers. What they did not have, and what they needed more than working capital, was a clear, well-defined spirit of *DEFINITENESS OF PURPOSE*.

Thomas A. Edison was great because he had a mind that worked with Definiteness of Purpose. Any man who sticks to one task through ten thousand failures, as Edison did in his search for a workable principle for the incandescent electric lamp, could be described with no other adjective than "great." People who are not great generally give up the ghost and quit after but one or two failures, and some even anticipate failure before it arrives and run to cover rather than face it.

When **Walter Chrysler**, as a young man, spent his last dollars for an automobile he took the machine home to take it apart. He removed every nut, bolt and screw. He lifted out the pistons and the crankshaft. He removed the valves and the timing gears. Then he went to work and put it all back together again. Over and over again he repeated this performance, until at last his relatives began to think he had lost his mind. But Chrysler knew what he was about! He had chosen, as his Definite Major Purpose, the making of automobiles. Before going into the business he wanted to learn all he could about the mechanical construction of automobiles. But, more important than this, he wanted to make his own mind automobile-conscious. When he finally swung into action and began to build automobiles, his sudden rise to fame and fortune became the talk of the industrial world.

It has been said that a man can have anything he wants if he knows exactly what he wants and desires it badly enough. This seems like a broad claim, but observation of the powers of the mind appear to back it up. A great many years ago **Russell Conwell** wanted a large sum of money with which to found a college in Philadelphia. Having no money of his own, and not knowing where to turn to acquire it from others through the orthodox commercial channels, he finally was forced to turn to his "inner self," where he influenced his mind to produce an idea that he exchanged for the money he needed. The idea was handed over to him, through a "hunch" that struck his brain with such force that it awakened him from sleep. The idea was simple. It consisted of a lecture he was inspired to write, which he delivered under the title of "Acres of Diamonds." The lecture was delivered by Dr. Conwell many thousands of times, and yielded, during his life-time, an income of over four million dollars. It was later published in book form and it became a best seller for many years. It is still published.

The lecture seems elementary and simple enough, when it is read from the printed pages of a book, but it has in it the full spiritual force of the great enthusiast who wrote it, and it was this spiritual element which caused it to penetrate the hearts of all who heard the lecture. Whether a man writes a book, preaches a sermon, or builds a motor car, if he draws freely upon the forces of his spiritual estate while he is at work, and knows precisely what he wishes to accomplish through his work, he will be more than apt to turn out a masterpiece. Half-hearted efforts produce nothing but half-finished products. The "mental attitude" in which a man does his work is the determining factor as to its quality. That is why a man does best that which he likes best to do.

Frank Gunsaulus, a young preacher, longed to found a college in Chicago. Being without funds and without influential friends through whom he might procure money, he turned like Dr. Russell Conwell to the "inner self" for his needs. The amount he required was the huge sum of one million dollars, quite a tidy sum for a young, unknown clergyman to procure, single-handed. But, "God works in a mysterious way, His wonders to perform."

The Reverend Gunsaulus wanted the million dollars badly enough to cause him to become determined to get it. Starting with nothing but an idea based on a Definite Major Purpose, he sat down in his study and began to concentrate his thoughts upon ways and means of acquiring the fortune he needed. For more than three hours he never took his mind off that subject. He demanded from his subconscious mind that it project itself into the great reservoir of Infinite

Intelligence, where he knew there was no shortage of power to produce money or anything else human beings desire or need, and that it bring him the plan by which he might acquire the money. His disciplined mind went to work for him with speed and accuracy. Disciplined minds always work in this manner.

Within a few hours the answer came. It flashed into his mind out of thin air, as he expressed it. The idea consisted of a sermon he was inspired to prepare, entitled "What I Would Do with a Million Dollars." Through the Chicago newspapers he announced he would preach the following Sunday morning on this subject. The announcement came to the attention of the packing house king, the late Philip D. Armour, who, perhaps out of curiosity (the Reverend Gunsaulus attributed the strange phenomenon to another and providential cause), went to hear the sermon.

After the Reverend Gunsaulus had delivered his sermon, Mr. Armour arose from his seat, walked slowly down the aisle to the pulpit, and to the astonishment of the congregation, reached up and shook hands with the young preacher, and said, "I was greatly impressed by your sermon. If you will come to my office tomorrow morning, I will give you my check for the million dollars you desire." He provided the money and Gunsaulus used it to found the Armour Institute of Technology, one of the well-known colleges of the Middle West.

Gunsaulus told how he went about drawing on his spiritual estate for the answer to his needs. "Before I went into the pulpit to preach that sermon," he explained, "I went into my bath-room, turned out the lights, got on my knees and prayed, for one whole hour, that my sermon would bring the million dollars I needed. I didn't undertake to tell God where to get the money. I only asked that He guide me to the right source. As I walked into the pulpit, a great feeling of assurance came over me. I felt, then, that I already had the money."

A subsequent comparison of notes between the Reverend Gunsaulus and Mr. Armour revealed the astounding fact that at almost the very minute Gunsaulus entered the bath-room to pray Mr. Armour was reading the newspaper announcement of his sermon, and it was while he was praying that Mr. Armour decided to hear the sermon. "There came over me," said Mr. Armour, "a queer feeling that impelled me to get up and go to hear that sermon."

There is something profoundly impressive about such experiences as these—especially when one knows the principals and has every reason to believe their testimony. Is it not strange, indeed, that men seek their needs hither and yon, only to discover at long last that the real method of approach to the source of supply consists of the only thing over which human beings have full control and that is the power of their own minds? Here is the source of all riches, the answer to all desires, the solution to all problems, yet we often turn to this source only as a last resort, after we have all but killed our spiritual powers through disappointments growing out of our efforts in seeking our needs in other directions.

Knut Hamsun, a young Norwegian, spent twenty years of his life trying to find his place in the world. He had a desire to become successful in some calling, but everything he tried turned out to be a "flop." He accepted such menial jobs as he could find, and was kicked around from place to place. Finally, he secured a job as a street-car conductor in Chicago. The job lasted but a few weeks after which he was summarily discharged. The man who discharged him told him he did not have brains enough to accept nickels from people when they handed the money to him. This challenge aroused Hamsun and caused him to reach a decision to do something which brought about his emancipation from poverty. He sat down on the side walk and meditated for several hours, and began, unconsciously at first, to apply the principle of Definiteness of Purpose. He reasoned that whereas he had been the world's most pronounced failure, he would write a book in which he would describe the feelings of a man who enjoyed such "distinction." He called the book *Hunger*, quickly followed by the epic book *Growth of the Soil*. He was awarded the Nobel prize of $25,000 for literary achievement, and thereafter retired to his beloved Norway, where the publishers of the world made a beaten pathway to his door. He, too, turned to the "inner self," after every other source had failed him and found there a rich gold-mine he did not know he possessed.

Milo C. Jones, of Wisconsin, was stricken with double paralysis, and could not move a muscle in his body. Before being afflicted, he was a farmer who made a bare living. When his "misfortune" overtook him, he could no longer work on his farm. Accordingly, out of sheer necessity he turned to the "inner self," discovered his own mind, and started to use it. Lying flat on his back in bed he directed his family in carrying out an idea that came to him as a "hunch" after he became paralyzed. The idea was simple enough. It consisted of raising corn and hogs and converting them into sausage. He called his product "Little Pig Sausage." Before he died, several years afterward, he had amassed a fortune of more than a million dollars, and had established a business that served people throughout the United States.

How strange it is that men do not discover the power of their own minds before they are forced, through affliction or failure, to do so. In his hour of greatest despair Milo C. Jones discovered his spiritual estate. He drew upon that estate because he had nothing else on which to draw. He told the author that it had never occurred to him, prior to his affliction, to depend upon his mind for his needs. He had been depending upon his hands and legs, a source of supply worth but a few dollars a day at best, overlooking, entirely, the riches of his spiritual estate.

James J. Hill built the Great Northern Railroad system with Definiteness of Purpose and made of it a great success. His rise from the lowly position of telegraph operator to the position of directing head of this system was systematically planned. At no time did he rely upon luck for the acquisition of personal power.

How long will it be until we will learn that people move to one side and make room for the man who knows exactly where he is going and shows by his actions he is determined to get there? But this is true. Test it for yourself and be convinced. Start down the street through a crowd, walking slowly as if you do not know where you are going, with indecision clearly written on your face, and observe how rudely people will push you to one side. Reverse your tactics, quicken your step, look straight ahead and carry a look of determination in your face; then observe how quickly people move out of your way and let you go by. Any crowd will make room for the man who is definitely going somewhere and whose actions indicate definitely he expects people to get out of his way.

The crowded street is not the only place where people will step aside when a man with Definiteness of Purpose showing in his face and actions passes. Any person engaged in the business of selling knows that his own "mental attitude" is a strong deciding factor in making sales. The salesman who approaches his prospective buyer in a doubtful frame of mind somehow projects his frame of mind to the buyer, who picks it up, acts upon it, and refuses to buy. It is a well-known fact that salesmen who know exactly what they want, and are determined to get it, take millions of dollars away from the public annually in return for worthless pieces of paper. It is an equally well known fact that other salesmen, with less determination and self-assurance, come home empty-handed, although they offer commodities of unquestionable merit and value.

Definiteness of Purpose is a resistless force, no matter how or for what purpose it is used.

In reading the works of **Thomas Paine**, I came upon this very significant statement: "By far the better part of such useful knowledge as I have acquired flashed into my mind following deep meditation and thought." This is the testimony of the man who was credited with being a strong factor in starting the American Revolution.

While organizing the philosophy of individual achievement, in collaboration with **Andrew Carnegie**, the author had the good fortune to be privileged to study, for three and a half years, under the distinguished scientist, **Dr. Elmer R. Gates**, of Chevy Chase, Maryland. I learned from close association with Dr. Gates that the majority of patents which he procured on useful inventions were uncovered through the principle of Definiteness of Purpose.

The method by which these discoveries (some of them basic) were made is as follows: Dr. Gates seated himself at a table in a dark, sound-proof room, concentrated his mind upon such known facts as he possessed in connection with the inventions on which he worked, waited until his mind began to send over new information to him; then he switched on the lights and wrote whatever came into his mind. He earned his living by "sitting" for ideas in this manner, for some of the largest corporations in America, who paid him a fat sum per hour, whether he got desired results or not.

This is an authentic description of the methods of a great scientist. The basis of his procedure was Definiteness of Purpose, through concentration of his mind.

How tragic (but it is true!) that most of us spend the major portion of our lives searching for some idea or plan by which we hope to achieve success, without recognizing that the secret of all success is in our own minds. To draw upon this endless source of power, we have but to take possession of our minds and use them. We of America need nothing of a material nature that we do not already possess in great abundance. We have liberty and freedom such as exists nowhere else. We have undeveloped riches of every conceivable nature. We have great educational institutions and libraries wherein may be had, for the asking, all the worthwhile knowledge that mankind has acquired throughout the history of civilization. We have the greatest industrial system available anywhere. We have the right to use our own initiative in whatever occupation or calling we choose. We have a religious background which offers powers unlimited and full freedom of worship. In brief, we have everything except a well-defined under-standing of the power of our own minds; this, unfortunately for those who lack it, is the thing we need most, and paradoxically as it may seem, the thing that costs nothing but the effort to appropriate and use it.

The responsibility of benefiting by this chapter is now yours! Your success or failure in appropriating and benefiting by the principles described in this lesson is inseparably bound up in nine words—positive, dynamic, inspiring words. They are Definiteness, Decision, Determination, Persistence, Courage, Hope, Faith, Initiative, and Repetition. Repeat the words in which you state your Definite Major Purpose over and over again. Make the object of your major purpose in life your obsession. Think about it during every idle moment throughout the day, and never let a day pass without doing something, no matter how little, that will lead you nearer the realization of your goal. Mere repetition of your Definite Major Purpose is not enough. You may repeat it the remainder of your life and avail yourself nothing unless you back your words with action, action, action, and still more action. It is the doing, not the knowing, that counts in life.

If you do not have the proper tools, or the working capital, or the personal associates needed in the full realization of your major purpose, go to work anyway, right where you stand, and you will be surprised when you learn how, in some mysterious manner you may not understand, better tools will be placed in your hands.

Remember, no one is ever thoroughly ready to undertake anything. Always there is something missing, or the time seems to be not quite right. Successful men do not wait for the time to begin a task to be entirely right. They start wherever they happen to be; they take the curves of their course when they reach them, never minding the obstacles they may encounter around the curve, beyond their immediate range of vision. Those who wait for all the equipment needed before making a start never experience success, because complete equipment is seldom available in the beginning of any person's plan.

When asked for the secret of his success, after his triumph over powerful enemies who were trying to destroy him, Disraeli, who was perhaps the greatest Prime Minister Great Britain ever had, replied, "The secret of success is constancy of purpose." This is a fitting thought with which to end this chapter on Definiteness of Purpose.

CHAPTER TWO

The MASTER MIND
PRINCIPLE

Before you read this chapter you should know that the Master Mind principle is the basis of all personal power that attains noteworthy proportions, in every calling. Throughout the analysis of more than 500 distinguished Americans, whose achievements covered many fields of business and industry, this principle was found to be the very foundation of their successes.

The Master Mind principle probably is the most essential of the principles of this philosophy, for the reason, as Mr. Carnegie has so adequately stated, that it is the medium by which one may borrow the education, experience and influence of others. Through the application of this principle Thomas A. Edison, handicapped as he was by lack of even an elementary schooling, became America's greatest inventor. Henry Ford used it to develop his industrial empire throughout America and many other parts of the world.

Andrew Carnegie said that if he were compelled to choose but one of the principles of achievement, and risk his entire chances of success or failure on that one principle, he would choose the Master Mind. A careful analysis of the records of many successful men shows clearly that their achievements were based mainly upon two of the success principles, the Master Mind and Definiteness of Purpose. It would be difficult for anyone to rise above mediocrity without having established a definite goal, through the principle covered by chapter one; but, having chosen an objective one might attain it only with the aid of the Master Mind principle, by using the intelligence of others.

Before turning this lesson over to Mr. Carnegie, it may help you to follow his analysis of the Master Mind principle if we define this principle as, "An alliance of two or more minds, coordinated and working together in a spirit of perfect harmony, for the attainment of a definite purpose."

From this definition it is obvious that a Master Mind alliance may consist of two people, working in harmony for the achievement of some special purpose; or it may consist of any number that may be required, according to the nature of the purpose to be accomplished.

Observe, with profit, the emphasis on the word "harmony," the reason for which will become clear as you read what Mr. Carnegie has to say on this subject. I take you now, to the private study of the great steel-master, where you may sit in while he describes the principle to which he gives credit for the major portion of his astounding achievements.

CARNEGIE: Definiteness of Purpose is the first of the Principles of Achievement. The second of these principles is the Master Mind. No one can hope to become successful without having first decided what he wants; but the mere choice of a major purpose in life is not, of itself, enough to insure success. To achieve the object of one's major goal, if it be of proportions above mediocrity, one must have the help and the education and the experience of others.

Moreover, one must so relate himself to the members of his Master Mind alliance that he will procure the full benefit of their brains, in a spirit of harmony! Failure to understand the importance of harmony and sympathy of purpose in the mind of every member of a Master Mind alliance has cost many men their chances of success in business.

A man may bring together a group of men whose cooperation he appears to have, and perhaps on the surface he will have it; but, the thing that counts is not surface appearances; it is the "mental attitude" of each member of the group. Before any alliance of men can constitute a Master Mind every man in the group must have his heart as well as his head in full sympathy with the object of the alliance, and he must be in perfect harmony with his leader and every other member of the alliance.

HILL: I believe I understand your point, Mr. Carnegie, but I do not see how a man can ever be sure of inducing his associates, in a Master Mind alliance, to work with him in complete harmony. Will you explain how this is accomplished?

CARNEGIE: Yes, I can tell you exactly how harmonious relations are established and maintained. To begin with, remember that everything a man does has back of his action a definite motive. We are all creatures of habit and motive. We begin doing things because of a motive; we continue doing them because of both motive and habit, but there may come a time when motive is forgotten and we continue on because of established habit.

There are but nine major motives to which people respond. I will describe these, then you will see for yourself how men are influenced to work with others in a spirit of harmony. At the very outset, in the organization of a Master Mind group, the leader must select, as individual members of his alliance, first: men who have the ability to do what is required of them; and secondly, men who will respond in a spirit of harmony to the particular motive held out to them in return for their aid.

THE NINE MAJOR MOTIVES

Here are the nine motives, some combination of which creates the "moving spirit" back of everything we do:

1. The emotion of LOVE (The gateway to one's spiritual power)
2. The emotion of SEX (Purely biological, but may serve as a powerful stimulant to action, when transmuted)
3. Desire for FINANCIAL GAIN
4. Desire for SELF-PRESERVATION
5. Desire for FREEDOM OF BODY AND MIND
6. Desire for SELF-EXPRESSION leading to fame, recognition
7. Desire for perpetuation of LIFE AFTER DEATH
8. The emotion of ANGER, often expressed as envy or jealousy
9. The emotion of FEAR
   (The last two motives are negative, but very powerful as stimulants to action)

Here you have the nine major approaches to all minds!

In the successful maintenance of a Master Mind alliance the leader around whom the alliance is formed must depend upon one or more of these basic motives to induce each member of his group to give the harmonious cooperation required for success.

The two motives to which men respond most generously in business alliances are the emotion of sex and the desire for financial gain. Most men want money more than any other thing; but they often want it mainly to please the woman of their choice. Here, then, the motivating force is three-fold: LOVE, SEX and FINANCIAL GAIN.

There is a type of man, however, who will work harder for recognition than he will for material or financial gain. This type of ego may become very powerful, in the attainment of highly constructive objectives, where sufficient self-control is used to insure harmony.

HILL: From what you say, Mr. Carnegie, it appears that the man who successfully builds an organization of men into a Master Mind alliance must know men quite well. Will you explain how you managed to choose, so successfully, the men in your Master Mind group? Did you pick your men at sight, or did you select them by the trial and error method, replacing those that proved unsuited for the purpose for which they were chosen?

CARNEGIE: No man is smart enough to judge other men accurately by sight. There are certain surface indications which may be suggestive of a man's ability, but there is one quality which is more important than all others, as the deciding factor of a man's value as a member of a Master Mind alliance, and that, unfortunately, is not a mere surface quality; it is his "mental attitude" toward himself and his associates. If his attitude happens to be negative, and he is inclined to be selfish, egotistical or adversely provocative in his relationship with others, he will not fit into a Master Mind alliance.

Moreover, if such a man is allowed to remain as a member of a Master Mind group he may become so obstructive in his influence with the other members that he will destroy their usefulness as well as his own.

An experience we had in our own Master Mind group, some years ago, will illustrate my meaning. Our Chief Chemist died and we had to find a man to fill his place. We tried out the assistant in the job, but he lacked the experience the job required, so we had to search for an older and more experienced man. We finally located a man in Europe whose record made him appear to be the very man we wanted, but when we came to negotiate with him we discovered that he did not wish to leave Europe. To procure the services of this man it became necessary to offer him, as the motive to which he was willing to respond, a much larger salary than we had been paying our Chief Chemist. In addition to this, he demanded a five-year contract. He got what he asked for and we installed him in the job, only to learn very quickly that he was a stubborn, temperamental fellow who could not or would not work harmoniously with the other members of our staff. We tried, without success, to induce him to change his mental attitude. Accordingly, at the end of the first six months of his association with us it became evident that we had to rid ourselves of him, so we paid him off for the full five years and he went back home. The experience was costly, but nothing to compare with what he would have cost us if we had kept him, as a disrupting force, in our Master Mind group.

Our next Chief Chemist was employed on a year's probationary period, with full notice in advance of his employment that harmony was the watch-word of our organization.

It is a well-known fact that one man, whose mental attitude is negative, if he is in a position of authority, will project his influence down into the rank and file of an entire organization of men, so changing their mental attitude as to make them dissatisfied and therefore inefficient in their work.

Emerson knew what he was saying when he wrote, "Every institution is the lengthened shadow of one man." Successful men make it their business to watch carefully the sort of "extended shadow" they project. I would change Emerson's statement slightly, by saying that every business is the extended shadow of the men who manage it, for in this day of large organizations it is impossible for one man to become the entire guiding influence of a great industrial enterprise such as the United States Steel Corporation. It would be more correct if we said that this corporation is the extended shadow of the Master Mind that guides it. In this instance the Master Mind consists of more than a score of individual minds, working together in a spirit of harmony, for the achievement of a definite purpose.

Some of the members of our Master Mind group came up from the rank and file of our workers, after having demonstrated their ability. Some of them were chosen from the outside, through the trial and error method. In most instances, those who came from the outside had established their ability in some other field or occupation, where their records of achievement were sufficiently outstanding to bring them to our attention. Some of the ablest men in our Master Mind group started at the very bottom and worked their way up through many different departments of our industry. These men know the value of harmony and cooperative effort. That is one of the secrets of their ability to promote themselves into high positions. The man who has ability in any line, plus the right mental attitude toward his associates, usually is found at the top of the ladder, no matter what his occupation may be. There is a great premium on efficiency plus the right mental attitude. I wish you would stress this fact in your presentation of the philosophy of individual achievement.

HILL: What about the man who organizes a group of men into a Master Mind alliance? Is it not necessary for him to be a master in the field of endeavor in which he is engaged, before he can successfully manage others in that field?

CARNEGIE: I can best answer that question by telling you that I, personally, know but little of the technical requirements in manufacturing and marketing of steel; nor is it essential that I have this knowledge. Here is where the Master Mind principle comes to one's aid. I have surrounded myself with more than a score of men whose combined education, experience and ability give me the full benefit of all that is known, up to the present time, about the making and marketing of steel. My job is to keep these men inspired with a desire to do the finest possible job. My method of inspiration can be easily traced right back to the nine basic motives, and especially to the motive of desire for financial gain. I have a system of compensation which permits every member of my Master Mind group to name his own financial reward, but the system is so arranged that beyond a certain maximum salary which each man is allowed, an individual must establish definite proof that he has earned more than this amount before he receives it.

This system encourages individual initiative, imagination and enthusiasm, and leads to continuous personal development and growth. Under the system I have paid such men as Charlie Schwab as much as a million dollars in one year, over and above the maximum salary scale. It was this system which inspired Schwab to develop his own individual initiative to the point at which he was the major moving spirit in the organization of the great United States Steel Corporation. Along with his initiative he developed great ability as a leader.

Remember, my major purpose in life is the development of men—not merely the accumulation of money. The money I possess came as a natural reward for the efforts I have put into developing men.

I know that some people accuse me of being money-mad, but those who do so know nothing of my major purpose. The best evidence of the true nature of my purpose is the fact that I am giving my money away as rapidly as I can do so without damaging other people, and the better portion of my riches, consisting of the knowledge I have gained in the art of developing men, I am presenting to the world, through your efforts, in the form of a practical philosophy of individual achievement. This is the only way wealth can be fairly and permanently distributed, because true wealth is the product of the mind, a form of riches toward which every material thing gravitates.

HILL: You say that all success, of noteworthy proportions, is the result of understanding and application of the Master Mind principle. Are there not some exceptions to this rule, Mr. Carnegie? Couldn't a man become a great artist, or a great preacher, or a successful salesman, without the use of the Master Mind principle?

CARNEGIE: The answer to your question, the way you have stated it, is no! A man might become an artist, or a preacher, or a salesman without direct application of the Master Mind principle, but he could not become great in these fields of endeavor without the aid of this principle. An all-wise Providence has so arranged the mechanism of the mind that no single mind is complete. Richness of the mind, in its fullest sense, comes from the harmonious alliance of two or more minds, working toward the achievement of some definite purpose.

For example, the Master Mind that gave this nation its birth of liberty and freedom consisted of a composite mind that grew out of the harmonious alliance of the 56 men who signed the Declaration of Independence. Back of that Master Mind was the Definiteness of Purpose which we, of today, know as the American Spirit of Self-determination, a portion of which has served as the motivating power in the development of our great American industry.

No one mind, no matter how great it might have been, could have given this nation the vision, the initiative, the self-reliance by which its leaders in every walk of life have been inspired.

There are one-man industries, and one-man businesses, but they are not great; and there are individuals who go all the way through life without allying themselves, in a spirit of harmony, with other minds, but they are not great, and their achievements are meager.

Remember you have been assigned the responsibility of giving to the world a complete philosophy of individual achievement; therefore, you must include in the philosophy those factors which enable an individual to rise above mediocrity. The most important of these factors is an understanding of the power that is available to the person who blends his mind-power with that of other people, thereby giving himself the full benefit of an intangible force which no single mind can ever experience.

We live in a great nation. It is great because of the power and the vision of the combined forces of the minds of many people who, working in harmony under our form of government, enable industry and banking and agriculture and private enterprise in every walk of life to put up a solid front. Our form of government is an excellent example of the principle of the Master Mind, combining as it does, the harmonious cooperative effort of both the State and Federal units of government. Under this friendly alliance, we have grown and prospered as no other nation known to civilization has done. Successful businesses become successful because their leaders adopt and use this same principle of friendly alliance between those who manage the businesses.

Come over here to the window and I will show you, out there in the railroad yards, a fine example of the Master Mind in action in transportation. Out there you see a freight train being made ready for its run. The train will be in the charge of a crew of men who coordinate their efforts in a spirit of harmony. The Conductor is the leader of the crew. He can take the train to its destination only because all the other members of the crew recognize and respect his authority and carry out his instructions in a spirit of harmony. What do you suppose would happen to that train if the Engineer neglected or refused to obey the Conductor's signals?

HILL: Why, there might be a wreck that would cost the entire crew their lives.

CARNEGIE: Exactly so! Well, running a business successfully calls for the application of the same Master Mind principle that is so essential in the operation of a railroad train. When there is lack of harmony between those engaged in running a business, the bankruptcy court is not far away. Are you following me in this description? I want you to understand it, because it deals with the very heart of all successful achievement, in every field of human endeavor.

HILL: I understand the Master Mind principle, Mr. Carnegie, although I never thought of it as being the sole source of your stupendous achievements in the steel industry, and the basis of your huge fortune.

CARNEGIE: Oh no! It is not the sole source of my accomplishments. Other principles have entered into the accumulation of my money, and the building of a great steel industry, but they have been of less importance than the Master Mind. The principle of second importance to the Master Mind is Definiteness of Purpose. These two principles, combined, have produced what the world calls a successful industry. Neither of these, by itself, could have brought success.

Look at those hoboes down there in that freight yard, and you'll see a perfect example of a group of men without either Definiteness of Purpose or a Master Mind. There is also an example of lack of purpose and coordination of effort. If those men would put their heads together and choose a definite purpose, and adopt a definite plan for carrying out their purpose, they might well be the crew that runs that freight train, instead of an unfortunate, poverty-stricken group of homeless men. Do you see what I mean?

HILL: I see well enough, sir; but how is it that these men were never taught the principles of achievement as you are describing them to me? Why have they not discovered the power of the Master Mind, as you have done?

CARNEGIE: I did not discover the Master Mind principle. I appropriated it; took it literally from the Bible.

HILL: From the Bible, sir? Why, I never knew the Bible taught the practical philosophy of achievement. In what portion of the Bible did you find the Master Mind principle?

CARNEGIE: I found it in the New Testament, in the story of Christ and His Twelve Disciples. You remember the story, of course.

As far as I have been able to learn, Christ was the first person in history who made definite use of the Master Mind principle. You recall Christ's unusual power and the power of His disciples after He was crucified. It is my theory that Christ's power grew out of His relationship with God and that the power of His disciples grew out of their harmonious alliance with Him. I believe that He stated a great truth when He said to His followers that they could perform even greater things, for He had discovered that the blending of two or more minds in a spirit of harmony with a definite end in view, gives one contact with the Universal Mind which is of God. I call your attention to what happened when Judas Iscariot broke faith with Christ. The breaking of the bond of harmony brought the Master the supreme catastrophe of His life, and for the sake of practical paraphrasing may I suggest that when the bond of harmony is broken, for any cause whatsoever, between the members of a Master Mind group that operates a business, or a home, *ruination is just around the corner!*

> If called upon to state your major purpose in life, in one sentence, what would your answer be?

HILL: Can the Master Mind principle be of practical benefit in other than business relationships, Mr. Carnegie?

CARNEGIE: Oh yes! it can be of practical use in connection with any form of human relationship where cooperation is necessary. Take the home, for example, and observe what happens when a man and his wife and other members of the family put their hearts and heads together and work for the common good of the entire family.

Here you will find happiness, contentment, and financial security. Poverty and misery are attracted by those who neglect to work together in harmony.

You have often heard it said that a man's wife can make or break him!

Well, it is true, and I'll tell you why. The alliance of a man and a woman in marriage creates the most perfect known form of Master Mind, providing the alliance is blended with love, sympathy of understanding, oneness of purpose, and complete harmony. Evidence of this may be found in the fact that one may find the influence of a woman as the major motivating force in the life of practically all the distinguished men of achievement down through the ages. But let misunderstanding and disagreement enter into such an alliance between a man and his wife, and he will become practically helpless in the use of his will-power. A man's wife may make or break him because her mind and his become so closely blended in marriage that her virtues become his virtues and her faults become his faults.

Fortunate indeed is the man who is married to a woman who devotes her life to strengthening his own mind power by blending with it her own, in a spirit of sympathetic understanding and harmony. That type of wife will never "break" any man, but she will be most likely to help him rise to greater heights of achievement than any he would have known without her help.

HILL: If I understand you correctly, Mr. Carnegie, a proper application and use of the Master Mind principle gives an individual the benefit of the education and experience of other people, but it goes much beyond this and aids the individual in contacting and using the spiritual forces available to him. Is that your understanding of the principle?

CARNEGIE: That is precisely my understanding of it. A great psychologist once said that no two minds ever come into contact without there being born, of that association, a third and intangible mind, of greater power than either of the two minds. Whether this third mind becomes a help or a hindrance to one or both of the two contacting minds depends entirely upon the mental attitude of each. If the attitude of both minds is harmonious, sympathetic and cooperative, then the third mind born of the contact may be beneficial to both. If the attitude of one or both of the contacting minds is antagonistic or controversial, unfriendly, the third mind born of the contact will be harmful to both.

The Master Mind principle is no man-made principle, you know. It is a part of the great system of natural law, and it is as immutable as the law of gravitation which holds the stars and planets in their places, and as definite in every phase of its operation. We may not be able to influence this law, but we can understand it and adapt ourselves to it in ways that will bring us great benefits, no matter who we are or what our calling may be.

Two very humble men of my acquaintance found a practical use for the Master Mind. One of them is blind and the other is crippled so that he has lost the use of his legs. One day these two men met and began to tell of their handicaps. The blind man said he was having a very hard time getting along, with people stepping on his toes, and automobiles whizzing by. "You have nothing on me," said the crippled man. "I can see the automobiles, but I can't get out of the way fast enough." Straightening himself up, with a broad grin on his face, the blind man exclaimed that he had an idea which might be of help to both men. "I have a sound pair of legs," said he, "while you have a sound pair of eyes. Now, you climb on my back and use your eyes, while I will supply the legs, and between us we will get along lots faster and much safer."

Everyone, figuratively speaking, is a bit blind or lame in that he needs some form of cooperation from others. The blind man needed only the use of another man's eyes. In the operation of my business I needed the education and experience of a large corps of men who understood the technical requirements in making and marketing steel. In your work of organizing all of the causes of success and all of the major causes of failure into a new practical philosophy of individual achievement you will need the cooperation of hundreds of men who have succeeded in their chosen fields of endeavor, and the help of many thousands who have tried and failed. Because of the nature of your undertaking you will need to understand and apply the Master Mind principle over a long period of years. Without the aid of this principle you cannot complete the work you are beginning, for there is no one person living *who could supply you with all the major causes of both success and failure.*

HILL: From your analysis of the Master Mind Principle I gather the impression, Mr. Carnegie, that men who have been deprived of an early education need not limit their ambition on that account since it is both possible and practical for them to use the education of others. I also get the impression, from what you have said, that no man ever acquires so much education that he can achieve noteworthy success without the aid of other minds. Is this your understanding?

CARNEGIE: Both of your statements are correct. Lack of schooling is no valid excuse for failure; neither is an exhaustive schooling a guarantee of success. Someone once said that knowledge is power, but he told only a half truth, for knowledge is only potential power. *It may become a power only when it is organized and expressed in terms of definite action!* Many young men have done themselves great damage by assuming, upon graduation from college, that their knowledge of academic subjects is sufficient to guarantee them good jobs. There is a big difference between having an abundant stock of knowledge and being educated. The difference will become apparent if you look up the Latin root from which the word educate is derived. The word *educate* comes from the Latin word *educare*, which means to draw out, to develop from within, to grow through use. *It does not mean to acquire and store knowledge!*

Success is the power to get whatever one desires in life, without violating the rights of others. Observe that I used the word POWER! Knowledge is not power, *but the appropriation and use of other men's knowledge and experience, for the attainment of some definite purpose, is power*; moreover, it is power of the most beneficial order.

The man who applies the Master Mind principle for the purpose of availing himself of the minds of other men, usually begins by taking complete charge of the power of his own mind! I wish to emphasize the importance of an individual's removing self-imposed limitations which most people set up in their own minds.

In a country like America, where there is an abundance of every form of riches; where every man is free to choose his own occupation and live his own life in his own way; there is no reason why any man should set low limitations on his achievements, nor be satisfied with less than all the material possessions his personal desires need or demand.

In our country there is a high premium on individual initiative, imagination, and definiteness of purpose, and they are aided by the easy accessibility of the material things each man requires to fulfill his idea of success. Here a man may be born in poverty, but he does not have to go through life in poverty. He may be illiterate, but he does not have to remain so. But here, as in every other part of the world, *no amount of opportunity will benefit the man who neglects or refuses to take possession of his own mind power* and use it to his own personal advancement.

For the sake of emphasis, I repeat that no man can take the fullest possession of his own mind power without combining it, through the Master Mind principle, with the minds of others, for the attainment of a definite purpose.

HILL: Inasmuch as you have commissioned me to give the world a practical philosophy of individual achievement, will you outline for me step by step a complete plan which one should follow in the organization of a Master Mind group? This procedure is not quite clear to me; it may be less so to the person who has had no experience in the use of the Master Mind principle.

CARNEGIE: The procedure in every individual case would be slightly different, depending on the education, experience, personality, and mental attitude of the person starting to organize a Master Mind group, and the purpose for which he is organizing it; but in every instance there are certain fundamentals to be observed, some of the most important of which are as follows:

(a) DEFINITENESS OF PURPOSE. The starting point in all achievement is definite knowledge of what one wants. Under this classification one should follow the formula laid down in chapter one, carrying out every detail of those instructions to the letter.

(b) CHOOSING MEMBERS FOR A MASTER MIND GROUP. Every person with whom an individual allies himself, under the Master Mind principle, *should be in complete sympathy with the object of the alliance, and must be able to contribute something definite toward the attainment of that object.* The contribution may consist of the member's education, experience, or, as is so often the case, it may consist of the use of the good-will he has established in his relationship with the public, commonly known as "contacts." Many banks and other corporations add to their Master Mind groups many high-priced men who serve no purpose other than to provide the corporation with the use of the *good-will and public influence they carry.*

(c) MOTIVE. No one has the right, and seldom does anyone have the ability, to induce others to serve as members of their Master Mind group, without giving something in return for the service they receive. The motive may be financial reward, or it may consist of some form of return favors, but it must be something which is of equal value to or greater than the service expected. In my own Master Mind alliance, as I have stated, the motive used to induce full and harmonious cooperation from some of the members of my group was financial reward. I helped some of the members of my alliance—those who had the ability to earn it—to earn more money by far than they could have made through any sort of effort independent of me. I believe it is no exaggeration to say that every member of my Master Mind group made a more practical and profitable use of his individual ability, in alliance with me, than he would have done if he had worked independently. I cannot over-emphasize the fact that the man who tries to build a Master Mind alliance without determining that every member of his alliance *profits in proportion to his value in the alliance is doomed to certain failure.*

(d) HARMONY. Complete harmony must prevail among all members of a Master Mind alliance, if success is to be insured. There can be no "behind the back" disloyalties on the part of any member of the group. Every member of the alliance must subordinate his own personal opinions, his own desires for personal advancement for the fullest benefit of the group as a whole, *by thinking only in terms of the successful achievement of the object of the alliance.* In the choice of individuals to serve as allies in a Master Mind group, first consideration should be given to the question as to whether or not the individual can and will work for the good of the group. Any member who is unable to do this must, upon discovery of his deficiency, be replaced by someone who can and will do so. *There can be no compromise on this point,* a fact which often will automatically exclude one's relatives and closest personal friends who, unfortunately, cannot subordinate their personal ego for any purpose.

(e) ACTION. Once formed, a Master Mind group must become and remain active to be effective. The group must move on a definite plan, at a definite time, toward a definite end. Indecision, inaction or delay will destroy the usefulness of the entire group. Moreover, there is an old saying that the best way to keep a mule from kicking is to keep him so busy pulling he will have neither the time nor the inclination to kick. The same may be said about men. I have seen sales organizations die of dry-rot because the man in charge of the organization allowed his men to come and go as they pleased, without giving them definite quotas to attain. Lack of a definite plan for budgeting and using time is the greatest evil of all salesmen who work on a commission basis, such as Life Insurance salesmen. Success in any undertaking calls for definite, well-organized, and continuous WORK! Nothing has yet been invented to take the place of WORK! Not all the brains of the world are sufficient to enable a man to achieve outstanding success without WORK.

(f) LEADERSHIP. Do not imagine that the mere selection of a group of men who agree to work together in a spirit of harmony, for the achievement of a definite purpose, is sufficient to insure the success of their efforts. The leader who organizes the group must actually lead. As far as work is concerned he should be the first to arrive at the place of work, and the last to leave; moreover, he should set his associates a good example by doing as much or more work than they. The greatest of all "bosses" is the man who makes himself the most nearly indispensable, and not the man who happens to have the last word when decisions are to be made and plans are to be chosen. Every leader's motto should be "The Greatest Among You Shall Be the Servant of All!"

(g) MENTAL ATTITUDE. In a Master Mind alliance, as in all other human relationships, the factor which, more than all others, determines the extent and nature of the cooperation one gets from others is his own MENTAL ATTITUDE. I can say truthfully that in my relationship with my own Master Mind group there never was a time when I did not hope that every man in the alliance would get from the alliance the fullest possible measure of personal benefit; and there never was a time when I did not try, with all the resources of what ability I possessed, to develop in every member of my alliance the fullest potentialities of his own ability. I believe this attitude on my part was the strongest factor in the development of men like Charlie Schwab, who earned as much as a million dollars a year over and above their regular salaries. I could have had the services of such men as Schwab, without being compelled to pay such high bonuses for extraordinary achievements; but I would have deprived myself of the benefits of that sort of service, because *I would have destroyed the motive which prompted them to render it.*

One of the most beautiful sights on earth, and one of the most inspiring, is that of a group of men who work together in a spirit of perfect harmony, each man thinking only in terms of what he can do for the benefit of the group. It was this spirit that gave almost superhuman power to the ragged, underfed, underclothed armies of George Washington, in their fight against the overwhelming odds of better equipped soldiers. These men were fighting for a common cause, and not for personal *aggrandizement* alone. Wherever one finds an employer and his employees working together in this spirit of mutual helpfulness, one finds a successful organization.

One of the major benefits of athletic training is that it tends to teach men to do team work in a spirit of harmony! What a pity that after leaving school men do not always carry with them into their jobs this same spirit of team work. I have often wished I might organize all the workers in my steel plants into a gigantic two-team group of men who would devote an hour each day to friendly opposition, through some form of athletics that would inspire them with the spirit of team work. It would help them overcome intolerance, envy, and selfishness, and improve them in other ways that would make them worth more to the business and more to themselves inside and outside of their jobs. Life is less burdensome to the man who has the spirit of good sportsmanship in his make-up. Therefore, let the spirit of sportsmanship become an important factor in every undertaking based on the Master Mind principle, *and let it begin with the man who organizes the group.* The others will get the spirit from his example.

(h) CONFIDENTIAL RELATIONSHIP. The relationship existing between men, under the Master Mind principle, should be a confidential one. The purpose of the alliance should never be discussed outside of the ranks of the members unless the object of the alliance is that of performing some public service. There are people who take keen delight in placing obstacles in the way of those who are working for personal achievement. Such people can do little harm if they do not understand what is the purpose of one's Master Mind alliance. The best of all possible ways of telling the world what one is going to do is by showing the world what one has already done. Publicity, press notices and the like have great value at times, but they may do great harm if they disclose the nature of one's unachieved plans.

> Be careful what you set your heart upon, for you may live to see yourself in possession of it

I have heard it said that every very great man—and there are a few such men during every generation—always has some aims and purposes in his mind which are known to no one except himself and his God. Perhaps you may not aspire to be great, but you may profit greatly if you bear this statement in mind and refrain from announcing your aims and plans prior to their fulfillment. It is always more satisfying to say "I have accomplished my aim" than it is to say "I am going to do thus and so, if and when I get around to it." The personal pronoun goes much better with the past tense than it does with the future tense.

It is astounding to learn to what extent some men will go to give away the vital trade secrets of their business, to whomsoever will listen, because of their love of idle self-expression. In this manner employees often disclose important business and trade secrets of their employers. The desire for self-expression is one of the nine basic motives which move men to action, but it can become a dangerous habit if not used with discretion. The smartest people who indulge their desire for self-expression usually do so by asking questions instead of answering questions for others. This is one way to give full play to the desire for self-expression without self-injury.

HILL: Mr. Carnegie, will you describe what you believe to be the most important Master Mind alliance in the United States, and give some idea of how it operates?

CARNEGIE: The most important Master Mind alliance in America, or for that matter in the entire world, is the alliance between the states of our country. From this alliance comes the freedom and liberty of which we in America feel so proud. *The strength of the alliance lies in the fact that it is voluntary and that in a spirit of harmony it is supported by the people.* The alliance between the States has created a greater variety of opportunities for the exercise of individual initiative than exists anywhere else in the whole world. Moreover, it has created the necessary power to defend its people and the system under which it operates, against all who may envy us or desire to interfere with our privileges.

Our entire system (including our form of government, our industrial plan, our banking institution, and our life insurance system) was designed and is maintained as a favorable medium for the support of private enterprise and as an encouragement to personal initiative. It is the greatest system in the world because it is so designed and maintained that it provides the simplest and best of all possible media for the free and undisturbed expression of individual effort based on the nine basic motives.

The Master Mind principle under which our country is operated is so flexible and democratic that it can be modified, changed, or improved at will to meet the needs of changing times. It serves as a dependable pattern by which individuals or corporations desiring to adopt the Master Mind principle can be safely guided. When our Master Mind alliance becomes inadequate for our needs, in any respect whatsoever, the people who formed it can improve it by the simple process of voting an amendment to our Constitution.

If all employers and employees related themselves to one another under a Master Mind plan similar to the one under which our country is operated, there would be no occasion for serious misunderstanding between them. Moreover, both the employer and the employees would receive more benefits from their joint efforts. There could be, and there should be, a pure democracy as the basis of all relationships between employers and employees, the same as there is a pure democracy on which the relationship between the States of America is based.

The operating principle of the Master Mind alliance under which our country is managed is simple. It consists of a triumvirate known as the executive, the judiciary, and the legislative bodies, all working in a spirit of harmony, in direct response to the will of the people. This system is used in the management of the individual States, as well as in the management of the entire alliance of States known as the Federal Government. The system can be changed by the will of the people, and the public officials who administer the system can, with very few rare exceptions, be retired on short notice. So far no better system of human relationship has been found, and no better system is in the prospect of being found within the near future. Perhaps no better system than ours will ever be found and none will be necessary as long as our present system is managed as its founders intended it should be managed for the greatest possible benefits to all, with special privileges for none.

HILL: Can you think of any improvements the people of America could make in their present form of government, Mr. Carnegie?

CARNEGIE: I can think of no improvements they might make in their form of government, but I can name one very great improvement they might make in their method of administering their government, and that would be the passing of a law requiring all qualified voters to vote in all local and national elections, under the penalty of heavy fines for failure to vote. If our form of government ever ceases to serve us adequately, it will be because of the negligence of the people in not voting. Already I can see great abuses of public office due to the failure of people to concern themselves about the election of dependable men. This form of neglect is an open bid to dishonest men to grab the reins of government, as some have done in such cities as New York and Chicago, where individual interest and civic pride are lacking.

I can think of one other improvement that might be made in connection with our method of choosing public office-holders, and that would be a system through which the personal records of all candidates for public office would have to be adequately published so all voters could judge a candidate's fitness for office. Under our present system the only publicity the voters see, in connection with a candidate's personal record, is that which the candidates themselves publish concerning themselves or their opponents, and this is *none too reassuring in most instances*. A third improvement which might be made that would aid the people in a wise choice of candidates for public office, would consist of a course of training through which the people would be taught, in the public schools, how to choose candidates best fitted to serve them.

Successful business men do not employ men to fill responsible positions without enquiring into the applicant's personal record. They look into the ability of the man whom they employ to do the job for which he is chosen, and they also investigate his character. The same procedure should be followed in selecting men to fill public office.

HILL: You made some brief reference to application of the Master Mind principle as a medium for the successful operation of the home, Mr. Carnegie. Will you go further into this subject and explain just how this principle can be applied in the management of the home?

CARNEGIE: I am glad you thought of this, because my experience has taught me that a man's home relationship has an important bearing on his business or professional achievements. Now I want you to remember that my remarks on this subject will be general, and not intended as a guide in all cases.

The alliance between a man and a woman in marriage creates a relationship which reaches deeply into the spiritual nature of both parties. For this reason marriage provides the most favorable of all human alliances for the effective use of the Master Mind principle.

In marriage, as in all other relationships, there are certain precautions one can take to insure the successful operation of the Master Mind principle. The more important of these safe-guards is:

(a) THE CHOICE OF A MATE. A successful marriage begins with an intelligent choice of a partner. Let me explain what I mean by an intelligent choice. In the first place, inasmuch as a man usually does the choosing (or at least thinks he does), he should test his prospective partner in marriage through a series of very frank and intimate talks with her, covering at least the fundamentals of a marriage relationship.

He should tell her how he intends to make a living and be very sure she is in full accord with him, both as to his chosen occupation and his methods of following it. It is all very well to talk of love, and romance, and the aesthetic side of life, when a man is selling himself to the woman of his choice; but he should not forget that there is a very practical, and a somewhat prosaic side to marriage, and this side of marriage begins to make its appearance at about the time the honeymoon begins to cool down. So, the sensible thing for a man to do is to anticipate the practical realities of marriage and reach an understanding with his prospective wife concerning them, well in advance of their arrival.

It will be of priceless help to a man if his wife becomes so thoroughly sold on his occupation, and his method of earning his living, that her interest may be described as intensely enthusiastic; but her minimum interest in this very important fundamental of the partnership of marriage should be an unreserved approval of his occupation. Failure to have an understanding on this important subject has destroyed the possibility of application of the Master Mind principle in many marriages. If a man's wife is more interested in a game of bridge than she is in her husband's source of income, he may as well look in some other direction for his Master Mind cooperation. Sometimes this is exactly what a man does. *Let the wives of men remember this!* If a woman is really very smart, she will take this suggestion and carry it through to its logical climax, through the aid of her own imagination.

I have observed several instances where a man and his wife were engaged in the same occupation, or the same business, and worked together for the attainment of a common purpose. In every such circumstance I was impressed by the fact that their close association in occupation led also to a close relationship in their social affairs, which left very little surplus time for either of them to become interested in anything or anyone that did not concern both.

There is another advantage of vital importance to both a man and his wife in their having a mutual interest in the source of their income, and that is the fact that this leads to a mutual understanding regarding their household and personal expenditures. If a man's wife knows precisely how he makes his money, and how much he makes, she will, if she is a faithful partner, adjust her household and personal expenditures to fit his income; moreover, she will do it cheerfully. I have known of more than one marriage to go on the rocks because the wife made financial demands upon her husband which he could not meet, and I have known of more than one husband who was driven to dishonesty in his struggle to satisfy his spendthrift wife.

So far I have been speaking for the benefit of the man who has not chosen a life partner in marriage. "But what about the man who is already married?" some will ask. "What can he do if he has chosen a wife who has no interest in his occupation, or perhaps no common interest with him on any subject? Have you no remedy to offer this man?"

Yes, there is a remedy for most cases of this sort, and it consists of a reselling job on the husband's part, with the object of inducing the wife to begin all over again, under a plan that will insure closer co-operation between them. There are but few marriages which do not need a new and improved plan of relationship at frequent intervals, to insure the fullest measure of benefits to both parties to the marriage and to their children where there are children.

Success in marriage calls for continuous vigilance on the part of both parties, with the object of avoiding misunderstandings through a carefully planned relationship affecting all members of the family. The time would be well spent if married people set aside a regular hour for a confidential Master Mind meeting at least once every week, during which they would come to an understanding concerning every vital factor of their relationship, both in and outside of the home association. Continuous contact between men engaged in the management of a business is an essential for harmony and cooperative effort. It is no less essential between a man and his wife.

The United States Navy follows a rule which might well be adopted in every home. It is a requirement that every ship of a Naval Fleet communicate with the Flagship hourly, whether there is anything to report or not. Contact is all important! It is just as important in the management of a home as it is in the operation of the United States Navy. Taking things for granted, without mutual agreement between a man and his wife, is the beginning of loss of interest in one another. The Master Mind principle cannot be successfully applied in marriage without a deliberate, carefully planned program for its application. An occasional discussion of the mutual affairs of marriage is not enough. There must be an established period set aside for Master Mind relationships, and this portion of the marriage program should be respected and carried out with the same courtesy, the same definiteness of purpose, and the same formality that is observed by business men who use the Master Mind principle for the management of their affairs.

Fortunate, indeed, will be the mates in marriage who heed this counsel and make the fullest possible use of it in the management of their alliance, for they are sure to discover in it an approach to perfection in marriage which can never be attained through mere physical attraction or sex emotion.

A sound partnership in marriage must include understanding and harmony of purpose in connection with the source of the income that supports the home. The income should be budgeted so that both a man and his wife may have equal access to it. The man who forces his wife to go through his pockets after he goes to sleep at night for the purpose of stealing spending money she wishes to use for her own private purposes, will never hold her respect nor will she be of much help to him as a Master Mind ally.

A partnership in marriage should include a joint interest and joint ownership in every material thing owned by both partners! The man who believes he can keep his business affairs to himself, without taking his wife into his full confidence, may as well recognize that if he follows this policy there can be no application of the Master Mind principle in his home affairs. Of course, there are instances where a man's wife, through lack of interest in her husband's affairs, or an irritable disposition, forces him to keep his own counsel. In a case of this nature, the only remedy is that of the renaissance of the mutual interests of the two which brought them together and led to their marriage. Here one should take warning that if this revival of mutual interest is delayed or neglected for very long, the job may prove difficult.

HILL: Your impression, then, seems to indicate that you believe the future of America holds as many opportunities as any that were available to you in the past. Is that correct?

CARNEGIE: You have understated my belief! The future of America holds opportunities far greater than any the world has ever known. Ours is destined to become the industrial center of the world. The development of the steel industry will give birth to scores of other related industries. Furniture and household equipment will be made of steel, and it will serve in the place of lumber in a thousand other ways. It will give us sky-scrapers taller than anything man has ever constructed in the entire history of the world. It will supplant lumber in the building of houses. It will span the widest rivers with bridges that are safe and indestructible. It will enable us to supplant the horse and buggy with speedy automobiles; and remember, the automobile industry alone is going to create opportunities for thousands of men of vision.

And do not forget that all this advancement of the American way of life will take place through the Master Mind alliance of the men who are the leaders of American Industry and American Finance. Billions of dollars of organized capital will be required. The money will come from the savings of the American people, and it can be truthfully said that the great Master Mind of America will, therefore, be a composite mind consisting of the individual assets of the minds and the money of millions of people. This is Democracy in its purest form! Such a democracy is one in which the brains, the spirit, and the finances of the people will be coordinated and used for the development of American opportunity in a thousand different directions.

Let this truth become the common property of all the people of America and we will hear less complaint against the "capitalists of Wall Street" and the "predatory interests." The real capitalists of America are the people whose savings are invested in the great industrial enterprises.

> Definiteness of Purpose, if backed by the will to win, is a road map to success

HILL: Your description of the sources of American Opportunity is both dramatic and thrilling, Mr. Carnegie. I have never previously heard Americanism analyzed in terms of its Five Foundation Stones, nor had I ever understood these fundamentals to be the real source of all American Opportunity. But I see that they are. Will you now go back to the analysis of the Master Mind principle as it applies to the individual efforts of the American people? Describe, if you will, the various uses an individual may make of this great principle, in his daily endeavor to appropriate his portion of American Opportunity.

CARNEGIE: I was coming back to that, as a climax for this chapter on the Master Mind. But, as I have stated, it is essential for an individual to know where we get our right to speak of this country as the richest and the freest country in the world, before he can appropriate and use his portion of this freedom and riches. The privileges available to the American people, like all other rights and privileges, have back of them a source of power. Privileges do not spring, mushroom-like, from the earth. They must be created and maintained! The founders of our American form of government, through their foresight and wisdom, laid the foundation for all American freedom and riches. But, they only laid the foundation. It is the responsibility and the duty of every person who claims any portion of this freedom and riches, to contribute his share in the maintenance of these privileges.

I have already described the most important relationship in which an individual can make use of the Master Mind principle: the relationship of marriage. I will now analyze some of the other individual uses of this great universal principle, as it may be applied in the development of various human relationships contributory *to the attainment of one's Major Purpose in life*. I want every reader to recognize the fact that the attainment of his Major Purpose (his highest aim in life) can be reached only by a series of steps, and that every thought he thinks, every transaction in which he engages in his relationship with others, every plan he creates, and every mistake he makes, has a vital bearing on his ability to attain his chosen goal. The mere choice of a Definite Major Purpose in life, even though it be written out and fully fixed in one's mind, will not insure the successful realization of that purpose. One's Major Purpose must be backed up and followed through by continuous effort, the most important part of which consists of the sort of effort that is applied in relationship with other people. With this truth well fixed in the mind it is not difficult to understand how necessary it is for an individual to be careful in his choice of associates, especially those with whom he comes into close daily contact.

Here, then, are some of the sources of human relationship which the man with a Definite Major Purpose in life must cultivate, organize, and use in his progress toward his chosen goal:

OCCUPATIONAL: Outside of the relationship of marriage there is no other form of relationship as important as that which exists between a man and those with whom he works, in the pursuit of his daily occupation. There is a tendency, and it is one that is common to all men, for an individual to take on the mannerism, the mental attitude, the philosophy of life, the political viewpoint, the economic leaning, and the other general traits of the most outspoken of the men with whom he associates in his daily work. The tragedy of this tendency is the fact that not always is the most outspoken man among one's daily associates the soundest thinker; and very often he is a man with the poorest character!

Also, the most outspoken man usually is an individual who has no Definite Major Purpose of his own; therefore, he devotes his time and his efforts to endeavoring to belittle the man who has such a purpose. Men with sound character, who know exactly what they want from life, usually have the wisdom to keep their own counsel, and seldom if ever do they waste any of their time trying to discourage other men. They are so busily engaged in promoting their own purpose that they have no time to waste with anything or anyone that does not contribute, in one way or another, to their benefit.

Realizing that one may find in almost every group with which a man comes into contact in his daily work, some persons whose influence and cooperation may be helpful, the discriminating man with a Definite Major Purpose in life will prove his wisdom if he forms close friendships only with those who can be, and are willing to be, mutually beneficial to him. The others he will tactfully avoid! Naturally, he will seek his closest alliances with men whom he recognizes to possess traits of character and knowledge and experience greater than his own, and of course he will not overlook those holding positions higher in rank than his own, with his eye on the day when *he can excel them!*, remembering the words of Abraham Lincoln, who said, "I will study and prepare myself, and some day my chance will come."

The man with a constructive Definite Major Purpose in life will never envy his superiors: he will study their methods and appropriate their knowledge instead. You may put it down as a sound prophecy that the man who spends his time finding fault with his boss will never be a successful boss on his own account.

The greatest soldiers are those who can take and carry out the orders of their superiors in rank. Those who cannot or will not do this never will become successful leaders in military operations. The same is true of the man in a private job. If he fails to emulate the man above him, in a spirit of harmony, he will never benefit greatly from his association with that man. No fewer than twenty men have risen from the ranks of labor, in my organization, and have made themselves richer than they needed to be. They did not get there by finding fault with me, although they well knew that I have many faults; but they *promoted themselves by appropriating and using the experience of everyone with whom they came into daily contact, including myself.*

The man with a Definite Major Purpose will take careful inventory of every person with whom he is associated in his daily work, and he will look upon every such person as a possible source of knowledge or influence that he can borrow and use in his own promotion. If he looks around him intelligently he will discover that his daily place of labor is literally a school room in which he can acquire the greatest of all educations, that which comes from experience.

"How can one make the greatest use of this sort of schooling?" some will ask. *No one ever does anything without a motive.* Men lend their experience and their knowledge and their aid to other men because they have been given a sufficient motive for doing so. The man who relates himself to his daily associates in a friendly, cooperative mental attitude stands a better chance of learning from them than the man who is belligerent, irritable, discourteous or neglectful in the little amenities of courtesy that exist between all cultured people. The old saying that a man can catch more flies with honey than he can with salt might well be remembered by the man who wishes to learn from his daily associates who know more than he does, and whose cooperation he needs and seeks.

EDUCATIONAL: No man's education ever is finished. The man whose Definite Major Purpose in life is of noteworthy proportions must continue to be a student, and he must learn from every possible source—especially those sources from which he can gather specialized knowledge and experience related to his major purpose.

The public libraries are free. They offer a great array of organized knowledge on every subject known to civilization. They carry, in every language, the sum total of all of man's knowledge. The successful man makes it his business to read books, and to learn important facts concerning his chosen work which have come from the experience of other men who have gone before him. It has been said that a man cannot consider himself even an elementary student of any subject until he has availed himself, as far as possible, of all knowledge on that subject that has been preserved for him through the experience of others.

A man's reading program should be as carefully chosen as his daily diet, for it, too, is food without which he cannot grow mentally. The man who spends all his reading time on the funny papers and the sex magazines is not headed toward great achievement; you may put that down as definite and accurate. The same may be said of the man who does not include in his daily reading program some form of reading which definitely provides him with knowledge which he can use in one way or another in the attainment of his major purpose. Random reading may be pleasing, but it seldom is helpful in connection with a man's occupation.

Reading, however, is not the only source of education available to a man. By a careful choice among his daily associates in his work, and his social relationships, a man may ally himself with men from whom he can acquire a very liberal education, through ordinary conversation. Business and professional clubs offer an opportunity for one to form alliances of great educational benefit, provided a man chooses his clubs and his individual associations in those clubs, with a definite objective in mind. Through this sort of association many men have formed both business and social acquaintances of great value to them in carrying out the object of their major purpose.

No man can go through life successfully without the habit of cultivating friends. The word "contact," as it is used in connection with personal acquaintanceship, is an important word. If a man makes it a part of his duty to extend his list of personal "contacts," he will find the habit of use to him in ways that cannot be foreseen while he is cultivating his acquaintances, but the time will come when they will be ready and willing to aid him if he has done a good job of selling himself to them.

CHURCH ACTIVITY: No philosophy of individual achievement would be complete without at least a brief reference to the benefits of a church alliance. It is not my intention to advocate any particular religion, as I believe a man's religion is something that is so intimate and definitely a part of himself that he should be left alone to form his own ideas of religion. But it does come within the scope of my privileges, as an analyst of the causes of success and failure, to call attention to the many benefits a man may gain from a church alliance; and I have reference to purely economic advantages, as well as to spiritual benefits available through a church relationship.

The church is among the most desirable of sources through which to meet and cultivate people, because it brings people together at a time and under circumstances which inspire the spirit of fellowship among men. Every man needs some source through which he can associate with his neighbors under circumstances which will enable him to exchange thoughts with them for the sake of mutual understanding and friendship, quite aside from all thoughts connected with pecuniary gain. The man who shuts himself up in his own shell, and engages in but little or no outside form of intercourse with his neighbors, soon becomes selfish and narrow in his views.

Aside from this viewpoint, the habit of church attendance enables a man to form acquaintances with people who may, and often do, become of great help to him in the promotion of his business, or the sale of his personal services. People who attend church together soon establish between themselves a bond of mutual confidence which may serve them in both business and social relationships outside of the church.

POLITICAL ALLIANCE: It is both the duty and the privilege of every American citizen to interest himself in politics and exercise his right to help, through the ballot, to place worthy men and women in public office. The political party to which a man belongs, if any, is of much less importance than the question of his exercising his privilege of voting. If politics becomes smeared with dishonest practices, there is no one to blame but the people who have it in their power to keep dishonest, unworthy, and inefficient people out of office. In addition to the privilege of voting and the duty it carries with it, one should not overlook the benefits to be gained from an active interest in politics, through "contacts" and alliances with people who may become helpful in the attainment of one's major purpose.

In some occupations political influence becomes a definite and important factor in the promotion of one's personal interests. Business and professional people certainly should not neglect the possibility of promoting their interests through active political alliances. While one may not care to become a politician, or become a candidate for public office, the possibilities in connection with the obligations to voters that public office-holders incur may be converted into an asset of great benefit to every voter, in the promotion of his own private occupation. The alert individual, who understands the necessity of reaching out in every possible direction for friendly allies he can use in achieving the object of his major purpose in life, will make the fullest use of his privilege of voting.

SOCIAL ALLIANCES: Here is an almost unlimited, fertile field for the cultivation of friendly "contacts." It is particularly available to the married man whose wife understands the art of making friends through social activities. Such a wife can convert her home and her social activities into a priceless asset for her husband, if his occupation is one that requires him to make friends with people on a sizable scale.

Most professional men, whose professional ethics forbid direct advertising or self-promotion, may make telling use of their social privileges—especially if they have wives with a bent for social activities. One successful life insurance agent sells more than a million dollars' worth of insurance every year, with the aid of his wife who is a member of a prominent Business Woman's Club. His wife's part is simple. She entertains her fellow club members in her home, along with their husbands, where her husband becomes acquainted with them under friendly circumstances.

A lawyer's wife is credited with helping him build the most lucrative law practice in a Middle Western city, by the simple process of entertaining, through her social activities, the wives of wealthy business men. The possibilities in this direction are endless.

One of the major advantages of friendly alliances with people in a variety of walks of life is the opportunity such contacts provide for "round-table" discussions. If one's acquaintances are sufficiently numerous and varied, they may become a valuable source of information on a wide range of subjects, thus leading to a form of intercourse which is essential for the development of versatility of thought.

I have observed, on many occasions, when groups of men get

together and enter into round-table discussions on any subject, that this sort of free and spontaneous expression of thought enriches the minds of all who participate in it. Every man needs to reinforce his own ideas and plans with new food for thought which he can acquire only through frank and honest discussion with people whose ideas differ from his own.

The preacher who preaches the same sermon over and over again, without injecting into it new ideas appropriated from the thoughts of other men, will soon find himself preaching to empty pews. The writer who becomes a top-notcher and remains in that exalted position must add continuously to his own stock of knowledge by appropriating the thoughts and the ideas of others, through personal contacts and by reading.

A mind that remains brilliant, alert, receptive, and flexible must be fed continuously from the storehouse of other minds. If this renewal is neglected the mind atrophies, the same as an arm that is taken out of use. This is in accordance with nature's laws. Study nature's plan and you will discover that every living thing, from the smallest insect to the complicated machinery of a human being, grows and remains healthy only through constant use. Only dead objects wear from use. Round-table discussions not only add to one's store of usable knowledge, but they develop and expand the power of the mind.

The person who stops studying the day he finishes school will never become an educated person, no matter how much knowledge he may have accumulated while he was going to school. Life itself is a great school and everything that inspires thought is a teacher. The wise man knows this; moreover, he makes it a part of his daily routine to contact other minds with the object of developing his own mind through exchange of thoughts.

We see, therefore, that the Master Mind principle has an un-limited scope of practical use. It is the medium by which an individual may supplement the power of his own mind with the knowledge and the experience and the mental attitude of other minds. As one man aptly expressed the idea: "If I give you one of my dollars in return for one of your dollars, each of us has no more than he had to start with; but if I give you a thought in return for one of your thoughts, each of us has gained a hundred percent dividend on our investment." No form of human relationship is as profitable as that through which men exchange thoughts, and it is surprising but true that one may pick up from the mind of the humblest person an idea of the first magnitude.

Let me illustrate what I mean through the story of a preacher who picked from the mind of the janitor of his church an idea that led to the attainment of his major purpose in life. The preacher's name was Russell Conwell, and his major purpose was the founding of a college he had long desired to establish. The fly in the ointment was lack of the necessary money, a tidy sum of more than a million dollars.

One day the Reverend Russell Conwell stopped to chat with the janitor who was busily at work, cutting the grass on the church lawn. The janitor had a philosophical trend of the mind. As they stood there, talking of the odds and ends of light conversation, Conwell casually remarked that the grass on the lawn adjoining the church yard was much greener and better kept than that on their own yard. He intended his remark, of course, as a mild reprimand to the old caretaker.

With a broad grin on his face the man said, "The grass looks green on the other side of the fence because we are used to the grass on this side." That remark planted in the fertile mind of Russell Conwell the seed of an idea—just a bare tiny seed, mind you—which led to the solution of his major purpose in life. From that humble remark was born an idea for a lecture which Conwell composed, and delivered more than four thousand times. He called it "Acres of Diamonds." The central idea of the lecture was this: A man need not seek his opportunity in the distance, but he can find it right where he stands, by recognizing the fact that the grass on the other side of the fence is not greener than it is where one stands: it only appears to be so.

The lecture yielded an income, during the life of Russell Conwell, of more than four million dollars. It was published in book form and became a best seller throughout the country for many years after he passed on. The money was used to found and maintain Temple University, one of the great schools of America. The idea around which the lecture was built did more than found a university. It enriched the minds of thousands of people, by influencing them to look for opportunity right where they stood. The philosophy of the lecture is as sound today as it was the day it came from the mind of a philosophical yard worker.

Remember this: Every active brain is a potential source of inspiration from which one may procure an idea, or the mere seed of an idea, of priceless value in the solution of one's personal problems. Sometimes great ideas spring from humble minds, but generally they come from the minds of those closest to one, where the Master Mind relationship has been deliberately established and maintained. The most profitable idea of my own career came to me one afternoon when Charlie Schwab and I were on the golf course. As we finished our shots on the thirteenth hole, Charlie looked up at me with a sheepish grin on his face, and said, "I'm three points up on you at this hole, Chief; but I have just thought of an idea that should give you a lot of time to play golf."

My curiosity prompted me to inquire into the nature of his idea. He gave it to me, in one brief sentence, every word of which was worth, roughly speaking, a million dollars. "Consolidate all your plants into one big corporation," he exclaimed, "and sell out to Wall Street."

Nothing more was said about the matter during the game, but that evening I began to turn the suggestion over in my mind and think about it. Before I went to sleep I had converted the seed of his idea into a definite plan. The following week I sent Charlie Schwab to New York to deliver a speech before a group of Wall Street bankers, among them J. Pierpont Morgan. The substance of the speech was a plan for the organization of the United States Steel Corporation, through which I consolidated all my steel interests and retired from active business, with more money than any one person needs. Now, let me emphasize one point. Charlie Schwab's idea might never have been born, and I probably never would have received the benefit of it, if I had not made it my business to encourage the creation of ideas. This encouragement was provided through a close and continuous Master Mind relationship with the members of my Master Mind group, among them Schwab.

"Contact," let me repeat, is an important word! It is much more important if we add to it the word "harmonious!" Through harmonious relationships with the minds of other men, an individual may have the full use of his capacity to create ideas. The man who overlooks this great truth thereby condemns himself eternally to mediocrity. No man is smart enough to project his influence very far into the world without the friendly cooperation of other people. Drive this thought home in every way you can, in your presentation of the Philosophy of American Achievement, for it is sufficient unto itself to open the road of success to thousands of men and women who might otherwise go through life without coming within sight of their major purpose in life, let alone the attainment of that purpose.

Too many people look for success in the distance, afar from where they are; and altogether too often they search for it through complicated plans based upon a belief in "miracles" and luck. As Russell Conwell so aptly stated the matter in his famous lecture, some people seem to think the grass is greener on the other side of the fence from where they stand, and they pass up the "Acres of Diamonds" in the form of ideas and opportunities available to them through the minds of their daily associates.

I found my "Acres of Diamonds" right where I stood, while looking into the glow of a blast furnace that was so hot I could penetrate it only with my thoughts. I remember well the first day I began to sell myself the idea of becoming the leader of a great steel industry instead of remaining an unimportant puddler in another man's "Acre of Diamonds."

At first the thought was not very definite; it was more a wish than a definite purpose. Soon I began bringing it back into my mind and encouraging it to take up its regular residence there, until came the day, finally, when the idea began to drive me instead of my driving it.

That day I began with earnestness to work my "diamond mine," and it was surprising to learn how quickly a definite purpose finds a way of translating itself into its physical equivalent. The main thing is to know what one wants. The next thing of greatest importance is to begin digging for diamonds right where one stands, using whatever tools may be at hand, even if they be nothing but the tools of thought. In proportion to the faithful use of tools at hand will one receive other and better tools. The man who understands the Master Mind principle and makes use of it, will find the necessary tools much more quickly than the fellow who knows nothing of this principle.

No doubt it will interest some of the readers to learn how and where I first acquired an understanding of the Master Mind principle to which I owe, more than to all else, the financial success with which my work has been rewarded.

Well, I'll tell you the story, and in doing so you will have a better understanding of my reason for including church attendance as one of the important sources for profitable use of the Master Mind principle. Of course all who know me know that I have never emphasized my religious views, or my church attendance, in the sense of holding myself out as an example to be emulated; but I have made it a part of my regular life program to lay aside all thoughts of material things, at least one day out of every seven, by reading a book or listening to a lecture or a sermon.

One Sunday morning I heard a clergyman preach a sermon in which he gave a vivid description of what he believed Christ would do if He lived in a world where business and industry were the dominating interests of the people. In a very dramatic manner he drew a picture of Christ and His Twelve Disciples, living in our modern world, transformed into modern-day life, and described them seated around a table as a board of directors of a great industry. He placed modern words in the mouths of Christ and the Disciples and painted an impressive picture of how he believed they would manage a business, if they lived and moved in an industrial age such as ours.

I was only a young, unknown laborer, but that sermon planted in my mind the seed of the Master Mind principle. I began to think about it. I began to talk about it with my fellow laborers, and very soon two of my closest associates began to catch a vision of its stupendous possibilities. We clothed the idea with our practical understanding of the steel industry. Very soon, almost before we fully realized the power of the principle we had stumbled upon, we had crystalized our conversation into a Definite Major Purpose which led to the source from which we procured the necessary working capital for my first industrial venture.

This is a world of cynicism and doubt, and you will find plenty of men who will tell you that they do not attend church because preachers talk only of a world of which they know not; that their ideas are impractical and unsuited for use in a work-a-day world where a man must attend to the needs of his stomach before he can do much about the salvation of his soul. No wise man will be misled by this sort of philosophy. The church is a place where one may find fuel for the fire of thought. It may be true that preachers sometimes talk too much about a future life, and too little about the life we are living in this world. The fact remains, nevertheless, that I found the way out of poverty into riches through an idea planted in my mind by a preacher in a church.

Do not misunderstand me to say that the church is the only place where one may become inspired with sound ideas that help in the solution of material problems; nor do I intend to convey the impression that the church is always the best place for such inspiration. I do wish to emphasize the fact, however, that friendly human intercourse through the operation of the Master Mind principle, whatever may be its source, *is essential for mind development and growth*, and the church often offers a favorable environment for the development of this principle.

Every mind needs contact with other minds for the food of expansion and growth. The discriminating person chooses, with the greatest of care, the types of minds with which he associates most intimately, recognizing that he takes on a definite part of the personality of every person with whom he associates regularly. I wouldn't give a fig for a man who does not make it his business to seek the company of people who know more and have more influence than he himself has, for it is true that as day follows night, so a man rises to the level of his superiors or falls to the level of his inferiors, according to which class he emulates through his choice of close associates.

It is a well-known fact that I surrounded myself with a Master Mind group of men who knew more than I about the making and the marketing of steel. If I had not done so I would never have been recognized as the leading manufacturer of steel.

HILL: I follow your explanation clearly enough, Mr. Carnegie, but there is one thing you have not explained, and it is bothering me quite definitely. What I would like to know is the rule by which one is governed in choosing, as his Master Mind allies, men who have superior ability and knowledge. It occurs to me that men of superior ability will not be easily influenced to ally themselves with a man of inferior ability. How may one overcome this obstacle in the building of a Master Mind alliance?

CARNEGIE: I am very glad you asked that question, for it gives me an opportunity to set you right on this point. Let us begin by calling attention to the nine basic motives which serve as the moving spirit in all that people do or refrain from doing. Men go into alliance with other men because of some benefits they expect to get from the alliance.

> The man who controls his own mind may control practically everything else he desires

It often happens that a man with very little ability in connection with many subjects, has experience and knowledge of great practical value along some one particular line. If he can show that his ideas are sound, that they can be made to yield profits, he will have no difficulty in inducing others to join forces with him in the promotion and development of his ideas, although his associates may be his superiors in many respects outside of his own specialized knowledge.

Take my own case, for example: I was only a common laborer, but I conceived certain ideas in connection with the making and marketing of steel which were in advance of the accustomed methods in use in that industry. The novelty of my ideas, plus my ability to sell them to others, gave me the dominating position in an alliance with men who willingly supplied the necessary working capital to develop the ideas.

In most respects these men were my superiors. In the making of steel, under my plan, I was their superior, and they acknowledged me as such. Their specialty was the manipulation and use of capital for a profit. My specialty was making steel by improved methods. We needed each other. The men who supplied the capital could not make steel, but I could show them how to make it more economically than it had ever been made before. With the necessary working capital at my disposal, it was a simple matter for me to surround myself with men who had the technical ability needed in the making of steel. They were motivated, in their alliance with me, by their desire for financial gain. *They needed me as badly as I needed them*, because their specialties did not include the promotional ability necessary to convert their talents into money. Since I possessed that ability, they willingly joined forces with me.

I'll give you another typical example of how men with practical ideas induce men with superior ability to join them, through the Master Mind principle. In the city of Detroit there is a man by the name of Henry Ford. He had but little schooling, and his personality is nothing of which to boast; but he created an idea that attracted to him the technical ability and the working capital necessary to give his idea great commercial value.

His idea, as everyone knows, is a self-propelled vehicle of transportation known as an automobile. He devoted a lot of time and thought to his idea, and experimented with it until he proved it was of commercial value. His next step was to induce one of his acquaintances to provide a small amount of working capital with which to begin manufacturing his automobile. With the aid of his newly formed ally he induced the Dodge brothers, and other men with technical and mechanical ability, to become a part of his Master Mind alliance. Perhaps his allies had more ability, in many respects, than Henry Ford had; but the idea was his and they accorded him the privilege of becoming the dominating factor in the alliance.

This is the usual method of procedure through which men surround themselves with allies who have greater ability than they themselves possess. Always there is a motive back of such alliances. The most common motive is that of a desire for financial gain. I want you to watch this man Ford, because he will one day dominate the automobile industry of America. Watch him very closely, for he is a philosopher as well as a man with a sound mechanical idea, and you may see how a man can begin at scratch here in America, with nothing to go on but a sound idea, and climb to great heights of achievement.

While we are on the subject of ideas I wish to call attention to the fact that *ideas rule the world*! They are the seed from which all human achievements germinate. A man who can create a sound idea can always find both the brains and the ability, as well as the necessary capital, for its development and promotion.

Speaking of capital, it should be remembered that money, without the ability of men who are skilled in its use, is of little value in any business. The real capital back of any business consists of both the physical assets measurable in terms of money, and the brains necessary in the management of *those assets, with strong emphasis on the latter.*

Get this picture of the nature of capital well fixed in mind and you will have a better understanding of the procedure by which men with sound ideas manage to surround themselves with men who are their superiors, in many ways, for the profitable promotion of their ideas. An idea, no matter how sound, may be and it generally is worth but little or nothing until it is backed with money and commercially exploited. Very seldom does one man have the ability to create commercially sound ideas and possess, also, the necessary money with which to promote his ideas. Here is the factual circumstance which makes it comparatively easy for a man with a sound commercial idea to ally himself with a Master Mind group made up of men of superior ability but lacking the creative ability to originate sound ideas.

Sometimes the man with a sound idea has considerable difficulty in convincing men with money of the commercial possibilities of his idea; especially is he likely to meet indifference and opposition if the idea be basically new and untried. A recent example of this nature will serve to illustrate what I mean. The Wright brothers created a very sound, but new and untried idea, when they made a machine that would fly. The world had never seen a machine that could be flown through the air, with a man at the controls. Without a precedent to follow, the Wrights built such a machine, and they proved to their own satisfaction that it was practical.

At first the newspaper men were so skeptical that they would not take the time to investigate this flying machine. They believed that a flying machine was not practical because they had never seen such a machine, and they had never heard of one. If the Wright brothers had been just average men, they would have become discouraged and would have given up their idea before it was accepted by the world. But they are not average men; they are potential successes. They have a Definite Major Purpose and the courage to stand by their purpose until they achieve its object. With the aid of the Master Mind principle they will attract to them men with the necessary capital and other men with the necessary technical ability to perfect and promote their idea until they force the world to accept it. The flying machine industry is in the offing; but the time will come, and very soon at that, when travel by air will be as common as travel by train or automobile at the present.

This is the way of all human progress, and it has been so from the dawn of civilization to this very day. *Men accept new ideas slowly and unwillingly!* To be forewarned is to be forearmed; therefore, be sure to caution the students of the philosophy of Achievement against the common habit of quitting the moment the going becomes difficult.

Thomas A. Edison had hard going at first. Well do I remember how the world hooted and howled its contempt for Edison when he first announced that he had perfected a practical incandescent lamp that could be lighted with electricity. Edison went through the same experience that every man with a new or an improved idea goes through; but Edison was a man with a definite purpose and he stood by his purpose through more than ten thousand failures and disappointments, to see, at last, the triumph of courage over fear and doubt.

HILL: I am glad to have your counsel on the subject of persistence, Mr. Carnegie, for I shall probably need to follow it for a long time before I get the world to accept a new philosophy of individual achievement.

CARNEGIE: Yes, you will need a lot of persistence—more than is required in most undertakings, because you will need persistence to carry you through the long years of work you will have to do before you organize the philosophy, and you will need it before you get the world to accept the results of your labor. That is why I am stressing the importance of your taking notice of the experience of the men before you who, without a single exception, met with skepticism and doubt before they got their ideas accepted.

Your success or failure will hinge largely, if not entirely, upon your capacity to carry on without the approval of the world, until your work gains recognition. Nevertheless, you do have a combination of motives to supply you with the courage and the moving spirit to keep on until you get to where you have started.

In the first place, your gift to the world of its first practical philosophy of individual achievement will bring you more fame and public recognition than any man needs to satisfy his thirst for recognition.

In the second place, your triumph will bring you more financial reward than you will need.

In the third place, the service you will render the world, through your work, will bring you happiness of an enduring nature, of a quality and a quantity that you could find in no other way. Keep these thoughts in mind when discouragement overtakes you, and they will help you to remove every obstacle that gets in your way.

If you do your work well, you will live to see the day when you will have projected your influence into every part of the civilized world. Your name will become a byword in every village, town, and city in America. Your works will be translated into every language, and your contribution to the world will have been of a more practical and enduring nature than that of all the teachers of abstract philosophy known to civilization, from Plato and his school of thought, on down to Emerson and the recent philosophers. Get this viewpoint and hold fast to it, but don't let it get you! If you ever reach the point at which you begin to take yourself too seriously, or feel that you are indispensable to the world, you will have outlived your usefulness. Approach your job with humility of the heart, keeping ever in the uppermost part of your mind the thought that you are only a student searching the lives of men for knowledge about life and about living that will be helpful to those who have neither the ability nor the inclination to spend twenty or thirty years looking for the principles of human achievement.

You will become great only in proportion to the help which you extend to others in finding themselves, but never by feeling your own greatness!

Before I pass on I will open many doors to you and give you free access to the minds of many men of distinguished achievement. If you impress these men as one who takes himself or his work too seriously, or lead them to believe from your slightest deed or word that you are working only for your own personal aggrandizement, they will close up on you like clams and you'll get no co-operation from them. Approach them with sincerity of purpose written in your face and on your heart, and they will drop their own work and give you the full benefit of the richness of their own lives.

I will send you to Dr. Alexander Graham Bell, the inventor of the long-distance telephone; and Dr. Elmer R. Gates, the great American scientist who has spent his life in research in connection with the operation of the human mind; and I will send you to no fewer than a score of other distinguished men whose entire life-work will become an open book for you to appropriate and use, but you will get nothing from any of these men unless you approach them with evidence that you are laboring to give the world a better philosophy of individual achievement than any it has at present.

Remember, a man can get almost anything he asks for, within reason, if he seeks it on behalf of the yet unborn and the world at large; but, let him show by his acts and words that he is seeking co-operation for purely personal benefits and he will find the world cold and indifferent. If I seem to emphasize this truth to the point of personal effrontery, I do so because you and every person embarking on a task such as the one you have undertaken needs to understand this trait of mankind. I give it to you, not only for your own guidance, but I ask that you pass it on, through the Philosophy of Achievement, to others who also need it.

If you wish a practical illustration of what happens when this principle is put into operation by a man who proves to the community that he is working for the interests of the people and not for his own self-promotion alone, study the experience of the candidate for public office who rises up with righteous indignation because of the political evils of his day, and goes before the people as a reform candidate, promising them that he will sacrifice his own personal interests and his time for their welfare. I have known of more than one instance in which such men were swept into office by overwhelming majorities.

Just a little while ago a certain district in a large American city became so badly abused, through the sins of a mayor who had allied himself with the underworld, that it was unsafe for young people to enter that section of the city. The politicians were appealed to in vain. Finally, a clergyman made up his mind to do something about it. Despite his lack of experience in the ways of politics he selected a well-known business man as his choice for mayor, and went into the offending district, with his coat off and his fighting blood boiling to a white heat, and told the people in no uncertain terms that he was going to stay there until they helped him put a decent man in office. Night after night he stumped the district, speaking from a platform he had mounted on a wagon, winding up his speech each time with these words: "I am asking your co-operation, not for any benefit to myself, but for the sake of your children and your neighbor's children who are entitled to an example of decency on the part of all you older people."

His candidate was swept into office with the biggest majority that city ever gave any mayor! So the story goes, in all human relationships. The whole world wants to help the man who forgets himself and gives his services for the benefit of others. If I am not mistaken, this was the idea of a lowly carpenter who, nearly two thousand years ago, gave His services and His life for the betterment of others. His influence has spread until it is now the greatest single influence for good that the world has ever known, and His philosophy is as sound today as it was when He preached it.

> There are three sides to all disputes: your side, the other fellow's side, and the right side

I do not wish to make a preacher of you, but I do wish to bring to your attention a simple rule of human relationship that was given to the world by the greatest philosopher of all times; and I sincerely hope you will not neglect to pass on to the world the suggestion I have given you of His philosophy. If the time ever comes in this country, or in any other, when people become so cold and ultra-practical that they look with contempt upon the philosophy of the Nazarene, the world will be in a bad way indeed. Besides, I want you to remember that it was this same humble carpenter who gave the world its first demonstration of the soundness of the Master Mind principle. Some theologies may have drifted far afield from the original teachings of the Nazarene, and the business world may, therefore, sometimes have just reasons for looking upon modern applications of religion as being impractical in the management of industry, but let the world remember that the theology of some fallible interpreter and the simple teachings of the Master are two separate and distinct things. I have never held myself out as a model follower of any one modern interpretation of religion, but I do know what the Master said about human relationships, and I do know, from practical experience and observation of the methods of business men, good and bad, that His philosophy is as sound and applicable today as it was when He taught it.

ANALYSIS OF CHAPTER TWO: THE MASTER MIND PRINCIPLE

by Napoleon Hill

As Mr. Carnegie has so convincingly stated, the Master Mind principle is a practical medium through which one may appropriate and use the education, intelligence, and personal experience of other people; therefore it is the medium with which one may overcome practically every obstacle that has to be dealt with in the attainment of the object of one's major purpose.

Through the aid of the Master Mind principle one may examine the stars of the heavens without being an astronomer.

With the aid of this principle one may see and understand the structure of this earth on which we live, without being a geologist.

One may watch Nature as she produces a butterfly from a grub worm, without being a biologist.

Through this principle one may know the nature and the use of drugs and chemicals without being a chemist.

One may know about the history of mankind without having lived through it.

All these possibilities, and more, are available to the person who understands how to apply this universal principle; therefore it takes a position of the first magnitude in the philosophy of individual achievement.

No liberties have been taken with the foregoing recitation of Mr. Carnegie's interpretation of the Master Mind principle and its role in the philosophy of achievement. At his request the philosophy has been presented, as nearly as possible, in his exact words. The following are my additional observations about the Master Mind principle.

SUGGESTIONS FOR BEGINNERS IN THE USE OF THE MASTER MIND PRINCIPLE

Here is an outline of the directions for the practical use of the Master Mind principle which I give to all beginners:

(a) For all practical purposes the student may assume that there are two types of Master Mind alliances. First, the purely personal type, consisting of relatives, close personal friends, religious advisers and social acquaintances, with whom one may become allied for social enjoyment or educational purposes, without any intention of converting the alliance into material or financial gain. Second, occupational, business or professional alliances, consisting of those chosen entirely for financial, economic or professional advancement for profit. Harmony is the watchword for success in both of these groups. Remember that in both groups one of the major considerations which one must give to one's allies in return for their sympathy, loyalty, knowledge, experience, creative ability, harmony and cooperation, is a return, in full measure, of these same qualities.

(b) Select, as members of your Master Mind alliance, in both groups, men and women who are best suited to your needs. Choose those who are most likely to remain in complete sympathy with your Definite Major Purpose. Keep the object of your major purpose closely confined to your own mind and to the minds of those you have chosen to aid you in achieving that purpose. If you find you have chosen any unsuitable member of your alliance, dismiss the unwise choice and make a new selection.

(c) Six or seven people usually constitute the most favorable number for harmonious cooperation. A larger number sometimes becomes unwieldy. For purely social alliances (exclusive of business undertakings where technical ability is essential) a smaller number will suffice, the number depending, of course, upon the nature and purpose of the alliance.

(d) Members of a Master Mind alliance should remain, at all times, in close communication with one another. They should have a regular meeting time, just as the Board of Directors of a well-managed business meets at regular periods. It is not essential, however, for all members to be present at every meeting.

(e) At formal meetings of a Master Mind group, ways and means for the attainment of the object of one's Definite Major Purpose or the attainment of any minor object leading toward the achievement of one's major purpose, should be thoroughly analyzed through a discussion in which all members participate, so that final plans will represent the combined experience, knowledge, ingenuity, strategy and imagination of all the individuals in the alliance. However, the actual act of carrying out any plans created by the group is the sole responsibility of the leader. Do not expect others to tell you what to do, when to do it, where to do it and how to do it, and then go ahead and do it for you!

(f) Remember, always, that a BURNING DESIRE, DEFINITELY STATED, BACKED BY FAITH, is the beginning of all achievement, and the very core around which the Master Mind principle operates successfully. Desire—deeply seated, definitely defined desire—is the starting point from which the Master Mind can be applied. There is nothing available to an individual through his own efforts except that which is obtainable through definite desire. Therefore, let the object of your major purpose in life become an obsessional desire!

(g) Remember, also, that one's mental attitude is a contagious form of energy which extends to and influences every member of one's Master Mind group; therefore, go into your Master Mind sessions in a spirit of self-reliance based upon absolute faith in the attainment of the object of your major purpose. There can be no compromise with one's self concerning this state of mind called faith. It is the unseen power that unites the minds of a Master Mind group into one mind, once it becomes the dominating factor of each individual mind of the group. Faith and fear are the two opposite ends of the pole of energy created by a Master Mind alliance; one representing the positive end of the pole, the other representing the negative end.

Faith permits one to approach within communicating distance of God. Fear holds one at arm's length and makes communication impossible.

Faith evolves a great leader whose vision knows no bounds; Fear creates a cringing follower.

Faith makes men courageous and honorable at trade; Fear makes men dishonest, undependable and stealthy-minded.

Faith causes one to look for and to expect to find the best there is in man; Fear discovers only man's short-comings and deficiencies.

Faith unmistakably identifies itself through the look in one's eyes, in the expression on one's face, in the tone of one's voice, and in one's every act. Fear identifies itself through the same avenues, where all who will, may recognize its presence.

Faith attracts people in a spirit of willingness to co-operate; Fear repels people and causes them to become uncommunicative and unresponsive to one's overtures.

Faith attracts only that which is constructive and creative; Fear attracts only that which is destructive. Test this principle wherever you will, and be convinced of its soundness.

Right works through Faith; Wrong works through Fear. Pitted, one against the other, the man with abundant Faith will win over the man who is motivated by Fear, ninety-nine times out of every hundred; and this because Fear causes a man to plunge ahead without plan or purpose, while Faith moves only on well-defined plans, toward definite ends.

Both Faith and Fear begin, at once, to clothe their objectives in physical realities, through the most practical and natural media available.

Faith constructs; Fear tears down. This order never is reversed.

Faith can construct an Empire State Building, build a Panama Canal, or give security to a nation. Fear negates all enterprise, both large and small.

Faith and fear never fraternize. Both cannot and will not occupy the mind at the same time. One or the other must, and always does, dominate.

Fear ushers in the devastating wars and depressions; Faith drives them out again.

Faith can lift the humblest person to heights of great achievement in any calling. Fear can and does make achievement impossible.

Even a horse or a dog knows when its master is afraid, and definitely reflects that Fear in its conduct, thus proving that Fear is contagious.

Faith is a mysterious, irresistible power which the scientists have not been able to isolate or understand. It is Nature's own secret alchemy with which the mind of man is given Spiritual powers.

Fear will no more mix with Spiritual power than will oil mix with water.

Faith is a state of mind, and it is every man's privilege to use it. Significant is the fact that the only thing over which any individual has complete control is his state of mind.

When used, Faith removes most of the real and all of the imaginary limitations with which man binds himself in his own mind. No man has ever yet discovered any limitations to the power of Faith.

Faith begins to take possession of the mind when one crystallizes one's hopes, desires, aims, and purposes into a burning determination to succeed.

Faith forms a natural affinity with justice; Fear fraternizes with injustice.

Faith is a normal state of mind; Fear is unnatural and abnormal.

Whether large or small, to be successful every business must have a leader who can and does inspire Faith in all who serve and are served through that business.

When you no longer have Faith in your aims and hopes, you may as well write "finis" across your record, because you will be through, no matter who you are or what may be your calling.

"For verily I say unto you, if ye have faith as a grain of mustard seed, ye shall say unto this mountain, Remove hence to yonder place; and it shall remove; and nothing shall be impossible unto you."

. . .

I am here stressing an important factor of the Master Mind principle which Mr. Carnegie did not emphasize, namely, the state of mind known as Faith. I have done this because experience has proved, times without number, that the habit of friendly discussion of any subject, through what is popularly known as the round-table conference, has a decided tendency to drive away fear and encourage Faith. Most of the men of distinguished achievements have discovered this fact and they have made effective use of it.

It is common knowledge that four distinguished American leaders of industry made use of this principle, over a period of years. Their names are Henry Ford, Thomas A. Edison, Harvey Firestone, and John Burroughs, the naturalist. Once a year they laid down their respective business responsibilities and went away together, to some secluded mountain spot, where they entered into a Master Mind alliance for the purpose of exchanging thoughts. When they returned each man of the group brought back all the knowledge he took with him, plus something additional which he acquired from each of the other three. It has been said, by those in a position to know the facts, that every man in the group came back from these yearly pilgrimages with a new and more alert mind.

As Mr. Carnegie has so ably stated, no single mind is complete by itself. All truly great minds have been reinforced through contacts with other minds. Sometimes this reinforcement takes place through sheer chance, without the individual's full knowledge of what is happening or how it is happening, but the truly great minds are the result of deliberate understanding and use of the Master Mind principle. That is why there are but few truly great minds! The Master Mind principle is not a matter of common knowledge to all people, and it was his understanding of this fact that prompted Andrew Carnegie to say that he was presenting to the people of America the better portion of his real riches, by helping to organize all of the principles of success into a philosophy of individual achievement.

Take the successful men wherever you find them and you will observe, if you have the records of their lives available, that their success was due to the application, in one form or another, of the Master Mind principle.

Arthur Brisbane was a newspaper man with no outstanding record of achievement back of him. He formed an alliance with William Randolph Hearst, through which he became Mr. Hearst's confidential adviser. The relationship between the two men brought into operation that silent, unseen power known as Faith, and very soon Mr. Brisbane had lifted himself into a position of prominence, with his name at the head of a column called "Today" on the front page daily of every newspaper owned by Mr. Hearst. Brisbane's popularity grew until his name appeared on the front pages of hundreds of other newspapers throughout the country. His fortune also grew! And so did William Randolph Hearst grow, both in mind power and in material riches. The alliance brought great benefits to both men.

A little while ago Arthur Brisbane died, and immediately following his death the great Hearst newspaper empire crumbled and fell to pieces as if it had been built on a foundation of sand. The composite Master Mind that developed the Hearst papers and kept them operating profitably had died with Brisbane. Such circumstances of fact cannot be explained away as being mere coincidences or chance. The understanding mind knows better. Search wherever you will, among the men and women engaged in the more humble pursuits of life, as well as those engaged in the management of empires of business and industry, and you will find the Master Mind principle in evidence wherever an individual is succeeding.

Kate Smith adopted singing as her major purpose in life, but she got off to a bad start. Some people were willing to listen to her sing, but few were willing to pay for the privilege. Through long discouraging months she sang whenever and wherever she could get an audience, with or without pay. But nothing happened until she formed a Master Mind alliance with an agent, Ted Collins. Then her fortune took a new lease on life. She now sings regularly, on a national radio network, and her singing brings her more money for each performance than most singers earn in a whole year, despite the fact that America has a host of unemployed singers, many of whom probably sing better or at least as well as Kate Smith.

Edgar Bergen and "Charlie McCarthy," his irrepressible "stooge," worked up and down Broadway, New York, for many years, for whatever small compensation they could pick up. Most of the time they were gentlemen "at liberty," as theatrical folk say when they are out of employment. Through chance or otherwise, this now nationally famous pair were discovered by Rudy Vallee. Promptly he introduced them over his radio program to the largest audience to which they had ever played. That was their turning point! The temporary application of the Master Mind principle, operating through the mind of Vallee and Bergen, gave the necessary impetus to a man whom the whole of America now recognizes as a genius in his profession, and his stock sailed skyward! He was a genius before the world discovered him, but that was not enough. It never is. A man may make a better mouse-trap than that of his neighbor, but do not be deceived by believing the world will make a beaten path to his door unless and until his superiority is given impetus through the Master Mind principle.

Jack Dempsey was a young, unknown lad who sometimes engaged in boxing matches. He was unskilled in this art and unknown to most of America. Through a stroke of good fortune he formed a Master Mind alliance with Jack Kearns, and soon thereafter he was on the road to the World's Championship and a fortune. Came a time when the Master Mind arrangement between the two men was broken, and with it went the Dempsey popularity as a fighter and the loss of his technique. The story is too well known among men in the world of sportsmanship to justify a description of the details here. The fact of major importance to be remembered is that when the Master Mind principle is discarded, there goes with it one's chances of permanent success.

The Reverend Frank Crane was an itinerant preacher whose sermons, as he often complained, "hardly yielded enough to keep body and soul together." At the suggestion of a man who understood the Master Mind principle, Frank Crane stopped preaching sermons to small personal congregations and started to write sermonettes to huge unseen audiences, through the medium of a newspaper column that appeared in hundreds of newspapers. The man who helped him market his sermonettes, through the application of the Master Mind principle, is authority for the acknowledgment that Crane's annual income, at the time of his death several years back, was well above $75,000, being more in fact than the President of the United States receives.

No matter what may be one's Definite Major Purpose in life, whether it is managing a great industrial empire, or preaching sermons, he will achieve outstanding success only by applying the Master Mind. Let this truth sink in and you will be very near the starting point of success such as you, perhaps, have never known before.

The man who sells more life insurance in the State of Ohio than any other life insurance agent was formerly a street car conductor, with little schooling but an insatiable desire to be recognized as a famous man. His method of applying the Master Mind principle in the sale of life insurance is both interesting and educational. While he was still working as a street car conductor, he became a student of the Philosophy of American Achievement. Before he had actually completed his training, he resigned his job with the street car company and went into the business of selling insurance.

Having caught the full spirit and meaning of the Master Mind principle, he began his new occupation by a unique application of this principle. First, he made permanent alliances with several retail stores that sold furniture on the installment plan, through which he arranged for these stores to present a life insurance policy, with the first year's premium fully paid, to every newly married couple who purchased their complete household furnishings from one of these stores.

He then made similar alliances with the sales agents of several different brands of automobiles. Spurred on by his success in these fields, he entered into alliances with several investment firms through which they insured the lives of all who purchased homes from them. Next, he made similar alliances with three savings banks, through which the banks insured the lives of all new depositors who maintained a certain minimum balance to their credit. The first year of his operations this young man earned considerably more than the street car company had paid him during the entire ten years he had worked for the company. He now has several other life insurance agents working for him in other parts of the country, and his income is said to be much greater than the entire annual earnings of the street car company for which he formerly worked.

A few facts about this man will serve to explain his success. His schooling and his personal appearance were decidedly against him. He is a small, thin man, who looks as if the thing he needs most is a good square meal. In most respects he is inferior to the average man, and he knows it; but here is the secret of his success: His inferiority has been transmuted into a BURNING DESIRE for recognition and fame, the major motive that drives him to work hard, with a spirit of persistence that knows no such word as "impossible."

He is totally without fear! That, too, is the result of a build-up of himself in his own mind, to offset his lack of personality and his recognized inferiority in other ways. He works with a definite goal for every day in the year, and holds himself to a rigid adherence to his self-established sales quota. Of course he makes the fullest possible use of the Master Mind principle. Otherwise, he has no distinguishing features and no hidden ability. His achievement might be duplicated, with ease, by no fewer than six thousand other life insurance agents who had the same training that this young man received, but neglected or failed to grasp the full meaning and the possibilities of the Master Mind principle.

Reverend Paul Welshimer, of Canton, Ohio, made such effective application of the Master Mind principle that he organized the largest Sunday School in America, with a total membership of more than 5,000. His method of applying this principle was both simple and interesting. Briefly described, it consisted of a plan under which he made every member of his church and every member of his Sunday School an active member of his Master Mind. He gave each a part to perform, and with it a motive for the faithful performance of the part. He organized both the members of his church and the members of his Sunday School into a series of committees, each of which was given some definite task to perform in connection with the extension of the church influence. The secret of Mr. Welshimer's success might be explained in one brief sentence: "We keep everyone so busy pulling," said he, "that no one has any time or desire to kick."

And the motive which prompted all this harmonious co-operation was nothing more than each member's desire for personal recognition, for work well and faithfully performed. That recognition was given in abundance. The church published its own weekly newspaper, on its own printing press. The paper was devoted entirely to news concerning the members of the church and Sunday School, their work and their social and family activities. That was motive enough to insure hearty co-operation. Everyone had the thrill of seeing his or her name in the church paper. Those who performed the greatest measure of service had the thrill of seeing their pictures along with their names, occasionally.

"A great preacher!" some will say of Mr. Welshimer. Now, the irony of the whole story is the fact that he can hardly be called a preacher. He is not an able speaker. His sermons usually are dry and uninteresting. He explains his background by saying that prior to his going into the preaching business, he was engaged in the grocery business. But he is a great organizer. There is the real secret of his achievements. He understands the Master Mind principle and works it for all it is worth. His flock does the rest. They do it willingly and have a lot of fun in the bargain. Moreover, they have extended the original, small, one-room church building until it now covers the better portion of a whole city block, including the large public auditorium and the Sunday School rooms it now embraces.

Mr. Welshimer's fame as a churchman has spread far and near, and church and Sunday School leaders have visited his church from nearly every city in America, endeavoring to learn the secret of his success. Well, the "secret" is now the property of any other church leader who wishes to use it. It consists of intelligent application of the Master Mind principle. Nothing else.

Edwin C. Barnes, a business associate of the late Thomas A. Edison, owes much of his success to the unique way in which he applied the Master Mind principle in marketing the Ediphone, the trade name for the Edison dictating machine.

At the time he began the unusual application of this principle, his sales force consisted of about twenty men. He entered into a Master Mind alliance with several firms that were engaged in marketing office furniture and supplies, office labor-saving devices such as adding machines, and typewriters, through which the salesmen representing these firms practically became salesmen of the Ediphone.

The arrangement provided that the salesmen selling the Ediphone and the salesmen representing the office equipment and typewriter firms would exchange favors by supplying one another with the names of prospective purchasers of their respective wares, without expense to anyone.

The plan for carrying out the arrangement was simple, but effective. It consisted of a clearing house carried on by the Barnes organization's telephone switchboard operator, to whom the names of prospective buyers were telephoned daily. In their daily rounds, the salesmen of the office equipment and the typewriter firms kept a close lookout for business firms that might be in need of Ediphones—especially new firms just entering business. These salesmen promptly telephoned the information in to the clearing house.

The salesmen selling Ediphones likewise kept on the lookout for firms that might be in need of any sort of office equipment, or typewriters, and telephoned the information in. Under this plan all the firms participating in the Master Mind alliance had the services of a group of sales people who were not on their payrolls, but whose services were nevertheless very profitable.

Ten years of operation under this plan proved to be so successful that Mr. Barnes was able to retire from business, with much more money than he needed, and of course the other firms with which he was allied fared equally as well.

Just after the end of World War I, a young woman who had previously been employed as a highly paid private secretary lost her position, because of the failure of the firm for which she worked. She began to look around for another position, but found none that paid the salary she had been accustomed to receiving. While she was searching for a new position, she became a student of the Philosophy of American Achievement.

After hearing but one lecture on the Master Mind principle, she made a discovery that enabled her to create a business of her own from which she earns more than ten times as much as she had previously received as a private secretary.

Her idea was simple enough. Having developed a pleasing "telephone voice" while working as a secretary, she conceived the idea of turning her voice into a profit, by supplying certain classes of business firms with duly qualified prospective customers. At first she specialized on supplying prospective buyers of life insurance, automobiles, and real estate. Later she added to her list of clients, department stores and other business firms covering a wide range of different classes of business.

Working from the telephone directory, she communicated with every individual listed, procuring from each sufficient information to enable her to determine very accurately those who were prospective customers for her clients. Of course she had a sales approach for telephone use which enabled her to ascertain precisely for which of her clients an individual might be a prospective customer, and her sales talk was designed to qualify every person to whom she talked as being either a likely prospective customer or as not being interested.

One rainy day this clever young woman telephoned me in Washington, D.C., at my home. Speaking in her usual "million-dollar telephone tone of voice," she asked if I would be courteous enough to meet her assistant, Miss Smith, at counter number twelve, in the Men's Department of Woodward & Lothrop's Department Store, where I would be shown something I needed, something she was sure I wanted, and something for which I would be sure to thank her. I was agreeable, and consented to visit Miss Smith. The young woman's cleverly cultivated voice and expertly prepared sales talk made this visit something for the "must" list. Upon arriving at counter number twelve, I found myself at the end of a lineup of more than a dozen men, all of whom were waiting, along with me, to see what the mysterious Miss Smith had to show them. At the front end of the line Miss Smith was busy enough, fitting rain coats on the men in the waiting line—and selling them too!

> The only thing anyone controls completely is his own thoughts. How profoundly significant!

The day's business accounted for the sale of 156 coats, to say nothing of a handsome profit for the clever young woman with the "million dollar voice" who staged it. Every man in the lineup was in an agreeable frame of mind, but one of them bore the brunt of a joke that was unknown to the others. He was the man who trained this young woman in the art of selling by telephone. His name was Napoleon Hill; his coaching of his student on the Master Mind principle had been so complete that she had caught him with his own "bait."

This young woman extended her Master Mind alliance with merchants and business firms by training other young women to qualify by telephone prospective buyers of merchandise, until she now has organizations in several of the larger cities. She has no monopoly on the plan. Hence there is nothing to hinder others from adopting it, as some perhaps have done. I know of a General Agent for a life insurance company who adopted the plan and used it so effectively that he increased the sales of his fifty agents by more than forty percent the first year he put it into operation. He keeps one telephone operator steadily at work, telephoning housewives and arranging with them for his agents to call on their husbands.

To some it may seem quite a jump from the analysis of the business methods of a partner of Thomas A. Edison, to a description of the sales technique of a telephone operator; but the purpose of this chapter is to show how the Master Mind principle may be applied in all occupations, from the greatest to the most humble.

I will return, now, to an analysis of the Master Mind as it has been applied by America's most distinguished industrialist, Henry Ford, the man whose astounding achievements were so aptly foretold over thirty years ago by Andrew Carnegie. No attempt will be made to describe all the methods with which Mr. Ford has used the Master

Mind, but I will analyze two important applications he made of this principle, both of which are matters of public record.

First I will go back to the year 1914, when Mr. Ford shocked the entire industrial world by announcing that henceforth he would pay all of his day laborers a minimum wage of five dollars per day, regardless of their occupational duties. The prevailing wage, at that time, for similar work performed by a majority of the Ford workers, was about two dollars and a half per day. Other industrial leaders shouted their disapproval of Ford's minimum wage policy, and many prophesied that it would drive him into bankruptcy.

Let us take a look at the record and see what effect his policy actually had on his business. Most important of all, perhaps, it cut down his labor cost instead of increasing it, because it had the effect of causing his workers to deliver more service and better service than they had been in the habit of delivering.

It also improved the "mental attitude" in which they worked, thereby raising the morale of the entire works. Out of this new spirit of harmonious co-operation came an understanding between Ford and his men which practically insured him against labor troubles, since he had already given his men more wages and better working conditions than any labor leader would have had the courage to demand; and be it remembered that more than twenty years later, when labor agitators undertook to break up the spirit of co-operation between Ford and his men, they met with little encouragement.

The Master Mind alliance that Ford established between himself and his men, through his minimum wage policy, and in other ways coincidental with that policy, has been one of the strongest factors of his stupendous success, as it was this policy that enabled him to reduce the price of his automobiles down through the years when other manufacturers were increasing the prices of their products.

Long before Ford adopted the Master Mind principle as a means of insuring better co-operation from his workers, he put this principle to use in another direction which had far-reaching repercussions that affected his entire business, and made it possible for him to control his industry without going into the professional money market for operating capital.

The method by which he procured his operating capital was both practical and simple, as have been, in fact, all the Ford methods of doing business. It consisted of a Master Mind alliance between himself and the distributors of his automobiles, through which he arranged for the distributors to obligate themselves each year for a definite number of automobiles which they agreed to buy from him at the wholesale price, and for which they made an advance payment of a certain percentage of the purchase price of each automobile, the remainder payable on delivery of the cars. This advance payment was sufficient to give Ford the necessary working capital with which to produce the automobiles. Therefore it was unnecessary for him either to borrow money for operating purposes, or to sell stock in his business.

The merchandising value of this method of financing was stupendous, and it consists of a very subtle principle of selling psychology which but few people have ever taken the time to analyze, viz: Ford procured his working capital from the same source that purchased the entire product of his plant. Under this plan his distributors occupied the unique relationship equivalent to a partnership with Ford; a relationship which made his distributors both the purchasers and the salesmen of his entire product, as well as the providers of the necessary working capital with which to manufacture the cars. This strategy in financing relieved Ford of a costly selling job, as well as giving him the operating capital he needed, without subjecting him to the control of professional financiers.

As far as the author knows Ford is the only large-scale industrial operator who has had the vision to correlate the financing of a business with the distribution of its product in such a manner that both these important factors are handled through the same source. This is Master Mind application of great economic importance. The usual orthodox method of financing large industrial and business organizations entirely neglects the famous Ford plan of relating himself to his financiers and the purchasers of his product.

The circumstances of his plan insure him the fullest co-operation in the management of his business. The usual procedure in the management of industrial operations is to procure working capital from one group of people (generally by the sale of stock), and sell the products of the business to another entirely different group of people. In this case the owners of the business have little in common with the people who purchase the product of the business. Under the Ford plan everyone participating in any part of his business has a definite motive for co-operating with him.

It has been said that some of Ford's distributors have complained of his policy of forcing them to purchase a regular quota of automobiles, and pay for a portion of the purchase price in advance. The best reply to this complaint, from the Ford point of view, is the fact that every Ford Distributor's Franchise in the world is an asset that can be turned into money any day; therefore one concludes that the policy under which Ford is related to his distributors must be, on the whole, very profitable to them as well as to himself.

The Ford way of applying the Master Mind principle extends far beyond the alliance he has with his distributors and his immediate workers. It reaches out to nearly all parts of the inhabited portion of the world, and embraces a majority of the millions of men and women who own and drive his automobile.

Through this alliance with the public—and it is a voluntary alliance as far as the public is concerned—Henry Ford probably occupies more friendly space in the minds of the American people than any other living industrialist. This good-will asset is a form of riches which cannot be estimated in mere bank balances, automobiles and machinery. It is something which can be converted into cash, at will, and is greater and more enduring than any material thing. If Henry Ford were stripped of every dollar he possesses, and every automobile plant of his were burned to the ground, and if he were left stranded, deprived of every other material thing he possesses, he would still be richer than Croesus, because he could convert his good-will into all the capital he needed with which to make a comeback, just as quickly as he could send out a call to his millions of friends throughout the world. They would come forth with money, even to their last penny if necessary, and invest it in . . . in what? Why, they would invest it in their confidence in Henry Ford.

What a lesson this man Ford provides to all who will take the time to find out how and why he has succeeded so abundantly! Most of us look at Ford today, as he stands at the top of the heap of life's fortunes, and see nothing but a man who has been "lucky." If the real truth were known—and it is known to a few—no part of Ford's achievements was due to luck, nor to "favorable breaks," nor to anything else except an intelligent application of the Philosophy of American Achievement.

At Andrew Carnegie's insistent request, the author began, over thirty years ago, to study Henry Ford and his philosophy of life. This personal observation of the automobile king began long before Ford had been recognized as the world's greatest industrial leader. Therefore, I had an opportunity to observe the method, step by step, through which a man starts at scratch, with very little schooling, without any form of public recognition of his outstanding ability, with barely enough money to carry on—and yet lifts himself at long last to the position of number one industrialist in the greatest industrial country in the world.

Because of this extraordinary analysis of Henry Ford, extending as it has, over the major portion of his business life, I have given the students of this philosophy an accurate description of the vital portion of the Ford philosophy which never would have been known without this close scrutiny of the man and his business methods. Nowhere, in any published book concerning Henry Ford, has any writer disclosed what we know to be the real secrets of Henry Ford's astounding success, as they have been described by me.

Henry Ford is not without his deficiencies! Yet it is significant that he has succeeded despite all his mistakes. It is also worthwhile to take note of the fact that his mistakes, as far as the facts are known, seem always to have been on the side of caution and conservatism. It was perhaps a major mistake for him to have delayed changing models of his automobile from time to time, in keeping with the popular trend for streamlined beauty in automobiles, but his ability to recover from the results of his mistakes was so great that he absorbed the losses due to his mistakes, without seriously impairing his fortune or disturbing his harmonious relationship with the public and its confidence in him.

I turn, now, from the description of the Master Mind principle, as it has been and may be applied in sundry occupations, and introduce Dr. Elmer R. Gates and Dr. Alexander Graham Bell, the great American scientists to whom Andrew Carnegie sent me for collaborative aid in the organization of the Philosophy of American Achievement. The achievements of these two men are too well known to most of the people of America to make necessary a detailed description of their work. Dr. Bell was the inventor of the long distance telephone, and had to his credit other accomplishments of great value to mankind. Dr. Gates had to his credit patents on more inventions than any other American inventor, not excepting Thomas A. Edison and Dr. Bell. He specialized in the study of mental phenomena, and made valuable contributions to the altogether too meager stock of knowledge the world has acquired on this subject.

Over a period of more than three years these distinguished men collaborated with me in the organization of this philosophy, providing me with all they had learned of the mysteries of the human mind. Except for Andrew Carnegie's foresight in having sent me to study under these two men, the major portion of their priceless discoveries in connection with the operation of the mind would have been lost to the world, for neither of them left more than mere fragmentary portions of their discoveries in condition for use by others. Even these were in terms that made the information understandable only to men of science.

I now introduce Dr. Elmer R. Gates, who speaks for both himself and Dr. Bell, and give you his analysis of the Master Mind and other principles of mind operation, as nearly as possible in his own terminology, just as he described them to me.

HILL: Mr. Carnegie sent me to you, Dr. Gates, to request your co-operation in providing the people of America with a practical, workable philosophy of individual achievement based on the experiences of business and industrial leaders, and the discoveries of men of science, such as yourself. Will you, therefore, go ahead and give me the story of the high-lights of your research in the field of mental phenomena, bearing in mind that you are speaking for the benefit of men and women many of whom have not had an opportunity to acquire scientific knowledge of psychology; and some whose schooling, for the most part, has not extended beyond the high school?

DR. GATES: You have given me a sizable order, but I will fill it to the best of my ability. Where shall we begin?

HILL: First of all, I would like to compare notes with you on the subject of the Master Mind principle which Mr. Carnegie described as the major source of all his achievements. He defined this principle as "Coordination of two or more minds, working in perfect harmony for the attainment of a definite purpose." As Mr. Carnegie explained this principle, it appears to be the only known medium of contact through which one may use the great reservoir of spiritual power available to mankind, as well as the principle through which one individual may appropriate and use the knowledge, experience, education, and strategic, imaginative capacity of others.

DR. GATES: Yes, I know exactly what you want. Dr. Bell and I have spent many years experimenting with this principle. Of course I will be happy to give you the full benefit of all we have learned about it; but I must caution you, at the outset, not to jump at any conclusions in connection with your study of this subject until you have acquired a complete picture of all that has been learned about it. Neither Dr. Bell nor I can claim to have acquired more than surface knowledge of this subject, but we have gone far enough to convince ourselves that it opens the way of approach to a source of knowledge that cannot be drawn upon or used except through its application. Also, we have come to the conclusion that civilization will never reach its highest goal until knowledge of the Master Mind principle is the common property of all the people of the world.

Do not become alarmed at this warning, for I hope to give you what information I have acquired on the subject of the Master Mind, in terms that anyone may understand.

First, perhaps I should explain what I believe to be the two features of major interest in connection with the Master Mind principle, viz:

(a) When two or more minds are brought together and their forces are combined, for the attainment of a definite objective, the combination has the effect of stimulating each individual mind so it becomes more alert, more imaginative and more active in the use of faith, than an individual experiences when his mind functions independently. This fact (and we know, beyond room for the slightest doubt, that it is a fact) is of the utmost importance, because it suggests a practical approach by which an individual may supplement the powers of his own mind with a form of intelligence that recognizes no limitations. The extra stimulation of the mind which each individual experiences, through this sort of harmonious alliance with other minds, may be greatly increased by the simple procedure of discussion of the object of the alliance, and any form of action leading to the attainment of the purpose of the alliance. It appears that a meeting of the minds of individuals, accompanied by definite action for the purpose of achieving some definite objective, has the effect of developing in each individual the necessary faith to lead to success.

It was this sort of an alliance of minds which gave birth to the determined spirit that drove George Washington's armies to win against overwhelming odds. And it is this sort of alliance of minds that gives our American form of Government its stupendous power to maintain and defend itself against all foes. It is also the same sort of alliance that has established the great industrial system of America, our banking system, and the other institutions that distinguish ours from all other countries.

(b) The other feature of the Master Mind extends far beyond one's relationship with the material circumstances and things of life, and brings the individual within easy reach of the forces of Infinite Intelligence, from which and through which one may tap a source of knowledge which appears to embrace all of Nature's laws! It seems that this source of super-knowledge becomes available only to those individuals who are inspired and motivated by a desire to help mankind raise himself to a higher standard of intelligence, and it is never reached by those motivated only by the desire for personal aggrandizement in connection with material things. For evidence of the soundness of this theory (and mind you, I claim for it nothing more than a theory) take notice of the regularity with which the scientist, who deals entirely with laws governing material things, comes to the end of the trail, where he is stopped by a stone-wall beyond which physical laws cannot carry him. Only the philosopher, the metaphysician, and the individual who discards his physical laws for the higher law of faith seems to be able to scale that wall. At times I have assumed the role of both the scientist who follows the lead of physical laws, and the philosopher who goes beyond the dead-end wall, with faith as his guide; therefore I have the right to speak from personal observation when I say that there is a source of knowledge that is available to mankind through no approach other than faith.

And it may be well if we here define faith as a "state of mind in which an individual discards all limitations of his own reason, or will-power, and opens wide his mind for divine guidance of his efforts toward the achievement of a definite objective."

My experiments with the Master Mind principle have convinced me that an individual working through harmony with other minds, can more quickly reach that state of mind wherein he projects his mind power beyond the bounds of his reason and will, than he can when he moves independently. Even the animals of a lower order of intelligence, such as a dog, gain courage and initiative when driven by the spirit of the pack. A dog, for example, may never think of killing a sheep on its own initiative; but let that same dog join in a pack of dogs whose leader is bent on sheep killing and it will engage in the activity viciously and without hesitation. This same tendency may be found among boys, and of course it obtains as well among men. Mass effort, team work, collaboration between men who move together in a spirit of harmony, give an individual an incentive to action which comes from no other source.

There is still another feature of the Master Mind principle worthy of analysis. It is the fact that an individual whose mind has been "stepped up" through contact with other minds in a Master Mind meeting becomes conscious of a form of mind stimulation which amounts to intoxication, and this condition lasts often for many hours after the meeting ends. The mind, when acting under this form of intoxication, falls easily and naturally into that state of openness wherein the state of mind known as faith begins to manifest itself. For evidence of this, observe the state of mind of salesmen who have attended a sales "pep" meeting, where some dynamic leader worked the group up to a high pitch of enthusiasm, and you will notice that every salesman carries away with him a definite amount of courage far above that which he had when he entered the meeting. Here you have the cue by which successful sales managers get results. The man who knows best how to establish a spirit of rapport between the minds of his salesmen is always the ablest manager of salesmen, although he, himself, may be a very poor salesman. Here, too, is the cue to all men in all walks of life who wish to project their own influence in any calling, through alliance with other minds. Not always is the clergyman who can preach the most interesting sermon the best church leader. The real leader is the man who can best bring his followers together in a spirit of harmonious cooperation through which he induces them to think and act as one mind.

Take Andrew Carnegie, for example. Analyze his personality, study his educational background, and weigh him as you will. In the end you will be forced to the conclusion that in most respects he is only an average man. Observe his method of relating himself to the members of his Master Mind group and here you will find the secret of his power. He knows how to get men to form a composite mind and work together as one, subordinating entirely their own personal interests and ideas for the benefit of the group. Here is the entire secret of Carnegie's astounding success as a leader of industry. He would be just as effective a leader in any other field of endeavor as he is in the steel business, for he has discovered that the secret of all great personal power lies in the harmonious alliance of minds.

HILL: You say, Dr. Gates, that an individual who becomes mentally stimulated through association with other minds, in a Master Mind meeting, carries the effects of the stimulation with him for some time after the meeting. Do you mean that an individual's mind becomes and remains more alert for a time, so he may use his mind more effectively after subjecting it to the Master Mind influence, even though he acts independently?

DR. GATES: Yes, I mean just that. In some instances this stimulation lasts only a few hours. In other instances it may last several days, and in rare cases, several weeks.

HILL: Then it is necessary for the leader of a Master Mind group to keep in close contact with the members of his alliance, if he is to get the desired benefits from the alliance?

DR. GATES: Oh yes! by all means. Observe with what regularity Mr. Carnegie and other business leaders of his caliber meet with their staff members. Neglect in this respect will render the Master Mind alliance impotent. It must not be assumed that because a man is associated with others he will get the full benefit of their minds unless he keeps in almost continuous contact with those minds and keeps his alliance active through discussion, planning and action! Here, as everywhere else throughout Nature's world, the law of life is development and growth through use! Nature discourages vacuums and inaction. The best minds are those that are used the most.

HILL: Is it true, or not, Dr. Gates, that Andrew Carnegie, Thomas A. Edison, and others of their recognized standing in their respective fields of endeavor, were born with brain capacity superior to that of the average person? Is this not the reason why they have surpassed the majority of men?

> The whole world willingly follows the man who shows by his actions that he knows precisely where he is going

DR. GATES: Your question cannot be answered intelligently without safeguarding the answer with many modifications, ifs, buts and maybes! Let me answer it the only way it can be truthfully answered, first categorically, by saying that the complex and mysterious machinery of the human brain is such that no one has ever yet been smart enough to analyze any brain by any set standard of measurement of its capabilities. We know that a man like Thomas A. Edison came into this world with a brain that was seemingly so subnormal that his school teachers sent him home, after three months of apparently futile effort to teach him the simple fundamentals of a common school education, with the dictum that he "hadn't enough sense to take an education." In the light of this true story, we are forced, by the demonstrations of power he gave the world through that same brain later on, to admit that about all we really know of the brain is that we know nothing at all! By this I do not mean either to be facetious or to evade your question. I intend only to be honest. However, I would not be quite fair if I did not call attention to the equally significant fact that nature sometimes brings into the world individuals whose capacity to absorb knowledge (from the very tender years of childhood) forces the world to recognize them as prodigies. I would say that every brain in this class has possibilities of development and use far surpassing anything the average brain ever attains. Take the individuals under this classification who rise to unusual heights of achievement, analyze them carefully, and you will be impressed by the fact that they owe their achievements to the stimulus of some motive which caused them to take charge of their minds and use them intensely.

HILL: You are now coming pretty close to answering the question that interests me very keenly. This question doubtlessly will interest many others who are trying to make better use of their native abilities in the solution of life's far-flung and complex problems. That question is: Where and what is the starting point from which one may begin to take charge of his own mind so he can make better use of it in the business of earning a living?

DR. GATES: The beginning of all achievement is definiteness of purpose based on the right motive or incentive to influence one to put forth extraordinary effort!

HILL: That is a mighty brief answer for such an important question, Dr. Gates. Can you expand it so your answer will become a more definite guide for the man who is trying to find a place at which he can take a hold on his own mind?

DR. GATES: I could extend the answer into voluminous words and illustrations, but I doubt that I could improve it. The truth is this: A man can accomplish about whatever he makes up his mind to do.

The extent to which he makes up his mind is entirely a matter of motive. It is far more important for a man to become deeply inspired with a definite motive than it is for him to be brilliant, or that he be highly educated. Motive gives men vision, imagination, and initiative, self-reliance and definiteness of purpose. With these qualities of mind—plus the use of the Master Mind principle through which an individual may borrow the education, experience and ability of others—a man may lift himself above all limitations and attain just about any objective he sets out to attain.

One thing is certain. There is nothing to indicate that the majority of men of great financial and business achievement are anything but average men as far as their brain capacities and intelligence are concerned. Study these men, wherever you find them, and be convinced of this truth. The thing called genius usually is a myth. Upon close observation, so-called genius often turns out to be nothing but definiteness of purpose backed by strong motive.

HILL: Your statements are rather astounding, Dr. Gates. They are also quite reassuring to us who recognize that we are only average people, especially those of us who have acquired but little schooling. May I quote you on all you have said?

DR. GATES: By all means quote me! It might help if all men got over this false belief that success is for the few; that those few are blessed with some mysterious form of superior ability. I am no authorized agent to speak for the Creator, but I cannot help thinking that if He had not intended for the blessings of the world to be appropriated and used by the "average man" he would not have made so many average men!

And I am, by experience, impressed with the inescapable fact that the greatest achievements known to civilization have been the handiwork of average men! As paradoxical as it may seem, I must call attention to the fact that a truly great man is only an average man who has discovered his own mind and has taken charge of it.

I hope that my frankness will not disillusion you. If you came to me with the expectation of hearing me say that genius is born and not made through discovery and use of one's mind, that is the very thought I wish to discourage.

> Every adversity is a blessing in disguise, provided it teaches some lesson we would not have learned without it

HILL: You have agreeably surprised me, Dr. Gates; but you have not disillusioned me, for I came to you with the hope that I might learn, from your experiments in connection with the operation of the mind, exactly what you have told me. I shall be happy to give reassurance, to every person who becomes a student of the philosophy of achievement, that you are right when you say definiteness of purpose, backed by an intense motive, is more important than brilliancy of mind. Coming, as it has, from a man of your wide range of experiments in connection with the power of the mind, this statement may give hope and purpose to many who otherwise might despair of the hope of personal achievement.

This concluded my interview with Dr. Gates, and his observations are a fitting testimonial to the power of the Master Mind Principle, and a fitting conclusion to this chapter.

> NOTHING brings enduring happiness except that which helps others to find it.

CHAPTER THREE

GOING *the*

EXTRA MILE

It is a well-established fact that men who make themselves indispensable in any job, business or profession generally write their own price tag and the world willingly pays it.

This chapter covers a subject which, more than all others, describes the method by which one may make himself indispensable. Therefore, the chapter may be of priceless value to all readers who earn their living by rendering service to others.

Reduced to its simplest terms, Going the Extra Mile means the rendering of more service and better service than one is paid to render. When adopted and followed as a habit, this principle gives one the benefit of the law of increasing returns. Stated conversely, failure to apply this principle as a habit handicaps one through the operation of the law of diminishing returns.

A man who has been prominently engaged in the business of helping men and women to market their personal services to best advantages once said that a strict observance of the habit of doing more than one is paid to do is one unbeatable method by which an individual may promote himself to whatever position he is capable of filling.

Inasmuch as Andrew Carnegie founded the largest industrial organization in the United States, the great United States Steel Corporation, and during his business career became one of the largest employers of men, his views on the subject of this chapter should be of great help to the reader.

Not only was Mr. Carnegie one of the largest employers of men, but it is a well-known fact that he was one of America's keenest judges of men. It is believed that he helped his men relate themselves to one another and to the business so efficiently that he made more millionaires than any other American industrialist, therefore he became an authority on the ways and means by which men market their service to best advantage.

It is worthy of note, also, that all the more than 500 distinguished leaders in industry and business who collaborated in the organization of the Philosophy of American Achievement emphasized the value of rendering more service and better service than one is paid to render by scrupulously following this habit themselves.

I call attention to these facts at the beginning of this chapter because of the wide spread and growing tendency of people in America to reverse this principle by rendering as little service and as poor service as they can get away with.

Economic law makes it impossible for any man over a long period of time to take out of a job or commercial enterprise more than he puts into it. This law is not a man-made law entirely. It has its roots in the laws of nature, as there is evidence everywhere in the realm of nature that nature frowns upon the attempt to get something for nothing, or anything for less than its value.

Those who respond to this admonition are sure to discover that sooner or later they will be rewarded adequately for their wisdom, and the reward will consist of their receiving compensation far greater than the actual value of the services they render. The compensation will consist, not only of material gain, but it will be evidenced by greater strength of character, improved mental attitude and the development of self-reliance, initiative, enthusiasm and a reputation that will create an enduring market for their service.

There is a growing tendency on the part of a large number of people in America toward the habit of trying to get something for nothing. This dangerous trend began at the end of the First World War. It has been so definitely intensified during recent years that it now threatens to undermine the entire American way of life.

This trend has already begun to whittle away at the foundation of American industry, which is the chief source of employment.

No industry can operate successfully where men group themselves together in blocs and, by sheer strength of their numbers, or coercion, force the wage scales upward, and the quality and the quantity of service they perform, downward. There is a point beyond which this practice cannot be carried without bankrupting industry, and that point has just about been reached.

As this chapter is being written America faces the greatest crisis since that which gave this nation birth, 165 years ago. We are in the beginning of a great National Defense program which is dependent, entirely, upon American industry. The program cannot be successfully carried out by men who selfishly demand a full day's pay for a poor day's labor.

If there has ever been a time when every loyal American should do more than he is paid for, that time is now. The present emergency demands that the people of America forget their selfish interests and throw themselves wholeheartedly into the job of saving their right to liberty and freedom.

The time is at hand when every citizen is called upon to do more than he is paid for, not merely to promote his own private interests, but to contribute his part toward saving the American form of democracy which provides us all with our privilege of individual liberty and freedom.

The habit of Going the Extra Mile is, and always has been, the very hub of all personal promotion. No noteworthy success has ever been attained without following this habit. But the time has come, now, when we must go the extra mile to save the institution of Americanism.

If we wish to continue our enjoyment of a system of government that has given us the highest standard of living known to civilization, we must protect the foundation stones of that government and make them secure. This is a task which makes it not only desirable for us to Go the Extra Mile, but an absolute necessity.

Those of us who lack the ambition to do more than we are paid for as a means of self-promotion must adopt this habit as a means of self-protection. We may not wish personal luxury, but we surely have not sunk so low that we do not want personal liberty.

Liberty, like everything else that is worth having, has a price. We cannot buy liberty by doing as little as possible and demanding in return for this the fruits of liberty. No, the time is at hand when the American people will either take up and apply the spirit of the pioneers who risked their lives and their fortunes to give us liberty, or find themselves once more under the bondage of a foreign dictatorship which knows nothing of justice and liberty.

On this there can be no half-way point, no appeasement, no com-promise. We have our backs to the wall and there is only one way in which we can move, and that calls for our Going the Extra Mile, in a spirit of determination which knows no such reality as failure.

We cannot remain "the richest and freest country in the world" without paying for the privilege. There is no such thing as something for nothing. We either pay for what we want or take what is forced upon us!

Therefore, as you read this chapter, take it to heart and make up your mind to go the extra mile in support of something far more profound than the promotion of your own private interests.

Meanwhile, in so doing you will have learned a great lesson in self-promotion which will serve you the remainder of your life, just as it has served Andrew Carnegie and all others who have converted American opportunity into personal riches.

> Render more service and better service than you agree to render and very soon you will be willingly paid for more than you actually do.

Hidden behind the lines of this lesson is a secret of achievement which was uncovered by Andrew Carnegie and revealed to the man through whom he asked that the secret be given only to those who are known to have other qualities essential for success without which it might be dangerous.

This same secret was known to successful men who contributed to the organization of this philosophy. It is not likely that any reader will uncover the secret except by the habit of Going the Extra Mile, in which event it will reveal itself somewhere along the way, perhaps at some unexpected time and place.

Early one frosty morning, some twenty-odd years ago, the private railroad car of Charles M. Schwab was shifted to the side track at his steel plant, in Pennsylvania.

As he left the car he was met by a young man who explained that he was a stenographer in the office of the steel company and he had met the car with the hope that he might be of some service to Mr. Schwab.

"Who requested you to meet me here?" Schwab asked.

"It was my own idea, sir," the young man replied, "and I knew you were coming on the early morning train because I handled a telegram that stated you were coming. I brought my notebook with me, sir; and I'll be glad to take any letters or telegrams you may wish to send."

Mr. Schwab thanked the young man for his thoughtfulness, but said he needed no service at the moment, although he might send for the lad later in the day. And he did! When the private car returned to New York that night it carried that young man to the city, where he had been assigned, at Mr. Schwab's request, for duty in the steel magnate's private office.

The young man's name is Williams. Mr. Williams promoted himself from one job to another in the steel organization until he earned and saved enough money to enable him to go into business for himself, and he later founded a drug company of which he is the president and majority shareholder.

Nothing very dramatic or interesting about this brief story is there? Well, the answer depends altogether upon what one calls drama. To every man who is trying to find his place in the world, this story, if analyzed carefully, carries the deepest sort of drama, for it describes the practical application of one of the more important of the principles of individual achievement: the habit of Going the Extra Mile!

I said that this young man promoted himself from one job to another in the steel company. Let us find out how he managed this self-promotion in order that we may learn how others can profit by his technique. Let us learn, if we can, what young Williams had in the way of ability which other stenographers in the general plant operation office of the steel company did not have, that caused him to be singled out by Mr. Schwab and assigned to his personal service.

We have Mr. Schwab's own word that young Williams did not possess a single quality that entitled him to rate above the average as a stenographer, but he did have one quality; a quality that he developed on his own initiative and practiced as an inviolable habit, which but few people possess, and that was the habit of rendering more service and better service than he was paid for.

It was this habit that enabled him to promote himself! It was this habit that attracted the attention of Mr. Schwab. It was this habit that helped him to become the head of a corporation where he became his own boss.

And it was this habit which, many years previous to the incident here related, brought Mr. Schwab, himself, to the attention of Mr. Carnegie and gained for him his opportunity to promote himself into a position in which he became his own boss.

It was also this same habit that enabled the irrepressible Carnegie to rise from the position of day laborer to that of the owner of America's largest industry, where he accumulated a vast fortune in money and a still greater fortune in useful knowledge.

Mr. Carnegie's views on the subject of Going the Extra Mile provide the reader with a practical working technique with which he may use this principle effectively for his own self-promotion. His analysis of the subject is here presented in his own words, just as he explained it to the author at the beginning of the organization of the philosophy of individual achievement, viz:

HILL: Mr. Carnegie, I have heard some men express the belief that success often is the result of luck. Many people seem to believe that successful men achieve their success because they get the favorable "breaks" of life, and that others fail because they get the unfavorable "breaks."

Croesus, the wealthy Persian philosopher, made some such reference to chance when he said:

"There is a Wheel on which the affairs of men revolve, and its mechanism is such that it prevents any man from being always fortunate."

Have you, in the richness of your business experience, seen any evidence of such a wheel? Do you attribute any portion of your success to luck, or favorable "breaks?"

CARNEGIE: Your questions give me a suitable starting point for an appropriate description of the habit of Going the Extra Mile, by which I mean the habit of rendering more service and better service than one is paid for.

First, I will answer your question by saying yes, indeed, there is a wheel of life that controls human destinies, and I am happy to be able to tell you that this wheel can be definitely influenced to operate in one's favor. If this were not true there would be no object in organizing the rules of personal achievement.

HILL: Will you tell me, in the simplest words possible, just how one may control this wheel of fortune? I would like a description of this important success factor which the young man or young woman just beginning a business career may understand.

CARNEGIE: I will describe the particular rule of success which will, if properly applied, enable a person literally to write his own price tag, with more than an average chance of getting that which he desires. Moreover, this rule is so potent that it practically insures one against serious opposition from those who purchase his services. As I have already stated, this rule is known as the habit of Going the Extra Mile, which means the habit of doing more than one is paid to do. You will observe that I have injected an important word into the description of this rule: the word habit!

Before the application of the rule begins to bring back appreciable results it must become a habit, and it must be applied at all times, in all possible ways. It means that one must render the greatest amount of service of which he is capable, and he must render it in a friendly, harmonious manner. Moreover, he must do this regardless of the amount of the immediate compensation he receives and even if he receives no immediate compensation whatsoever.

HILL: But, Mr. Carnegie, most of the people I know, those who work for wages or a salary, claim that they are already doing more work than that for which they are paid. If this is true why aren't they doing a better job of influencing the wheel of fortune on their behalf than they appear to be doing? Why aren't they rich, as you are?

CARNEGIE: The answer to your question is simple enough, but it has many angles I shall have to explain before you'll understand it. In the first place, if you will accurately analyze those who work for wages you will learn that 98 out of every hundred have no Definite

Major Purpose greater than that of working for a daily wage. Therefore, no matter how much work they do, or how well they do it, the wheel of fortune will turn on past them without providing more than a bare living, because they neither expect nor demand more. Ponder over this truth for a moment and you will be better prepared to follow the logic I will present in the remainder of this discussion.

The major difference between those who accept a limitation of daily wages sufficient only for a bare living, and myself, is this: I demand riches in definite terms; I have a definite plan for acquiring riches; I am engaged in carrying out my plan, and I am giving an equivalent, in useful service, of the value of those riches I demand, while the others have no such plan or purpose.

Life is paying me off on my own terms. It is doing precisely the same thing for the man who asks no more than daily wages. You see, the wheel of fortune follows the mental blueprint that a man sets up in his own mind, and it brings back to him, in physical or financial measure, an exact equivalent of that blueprint.

Unless you grasp the full meaning of this statement of truth you will miss the important portion of this discussion. There is a law of Compensation through the operation of which a man may establish his own relationship with life, including the material possessions he accumulates. There is no escape from the acceptance of the reality of this law, for it is not a man-made law.

HILL: I can understand your viewpoint, Mr. Carnegie. Stating the matter in another way, may we not say that every man is where he is and what he is because of the use he makes of his own mind?

CARNEGIE: You have stated the idea correctly. The major

difficulty of most men who go through life poverty-stricken is that they neither recognize the power of their own minds nor make any attempt to take possession of their minds. That which a man can accomplish with his hands seldom brings more than a mere living. That which a man can accomplish through the use of his mind may give him whatever he asks of life.

Now let us get on with our analysis of the principle of *Going the Extra Mile*. I am going to explain some of the more practical advantages of this principle. I call them practical because they are benefits of which anyone may avail himself, without the consent of others.

Let us consider, first, the fact that the habit of doing more than one is paid for brings one to the *favorable attention* of those who have opportunities to offer. I have never yet known of any man *promoting himself* to a higher and more profitable position without adopting and following this habit.

The habit aids one in developing and maintaining the right "mental attitude" toward others, thereby serving as an effective means of gaining friendly co-operation.

It helps one to profit by the law of contrast, since obviously a majority of the people follow the exact opposite of this principle, by doing just as little work as they can get by with; and that is about all they are getting; *just getting by*!

It creates a continuous market for one's services. Moreover, it insures one a choice of jobs and working conditions, at the top of the scale of wages or other forms of compensation.

It attracts opportunities which are not available to those who render as little service as possible, and thereby serves as an effective medium for self-promotion from wage earning to business ownership.

Under some circumstances it enables one to become indispensable in his job, thereby paving the way for his naming his own compensation.

It aids one in the development of self-reliance.

Most important of all its benefits, it gives one the advantage of the law of increasing returns through which he will eventually receive compensation far beyond the actual market value of the service he renders. Therefore, the habit of doing more than one is paid for is a sound business principle, even if it is used purely as a measure of expediency, to promote one's personal interests advantageously.

The habit of doing more than one is paid for is one that an individual may practice without asking the permission of others; therefore it is under one's own control. Many other beneficial habits can be practiced only through the consent and the co-operation of other people.

HILL: Mr. Carnegie, do all the men who work for you have your permission to render more service and better service than that for which they are paid, and if so, how many are taking advantage of this privilege in a manner that is beneficial to themselves?

CARNEGIE: I'm glad you asked that question, because it gives me an opportunity to drive home an important viewpoint on this subject. First, let me say that every person working for me (and this applies with equal truth to all who have worked for me in the past) not only has the privilege of doing more than he is being paid for, but I encourage all who work for me to do this very thing, for their benefit as well as my own.

It may surprise you to hear that of the many thousands of men who work for me, but a very small number have taken the trouble to place me under obligations to them by rendering more service and better service than that for which they are paid. Among the few exceptions are members of our supervisory and managerial groups, and every one of them is receiving compensation far greater than that received by the majority of our workers, although every man in my employ has the privilege of rendering this sort of service without asking the consent of anyone.

Some of the members of my Master Mind group, such men as Charles Schwab, have made themselves so definitely indispensable to our business that they have earned as much as a million dollars in one year, over and above their fixed salaries. Not a few of the men who have thus promoted themselves into the higher brackets of income in our organization have attracted opportunities to go into business for themselves.

HILL: Couldn't you have driven a better bargain with those to whom you paid as much as a million dollars a year in extra compensation?

CARNEGIE: Oh, to be sure I could have had their services for much less money, but you must remember that this principle of doing more than one is paid for operates in favor of an employer just the same as it operates for the benefit of the employee. Therefore, it is just as much an act of wisdom for an employer to pay a man all he earns as it is for an employee to endeavor to earn more than he receives. By paying Charlie Schwab all he earned I thereby insured myself against the loss of his services.

HILL: You speak of paying your men who render more service than they are paid for, all they earn. If you do that, how can they render more service then they are paid for? It seems that there is an inconsistency in your statement.

CARNEGIE: That which you mistake for inconsistency is only

the mistake of many others on this subject, and is due to a lack of understanding of the habit of *Going the Extra Mile*. The apparent inconsistency is, therefore, an illusion, but I am glad you asked the question because I will set you right on this subject. It is a fact that I pay my men all they earn, even though I sometimes have to pay them huge sums, but there is one important point that you have overlooked. It is the fact that before I begin paying them all they earn they must establish their indispensability by doing more than they are paid for.

Now, here is the fine point that most people overlook. Until a man begins to render more service than that for which he is paid he is not entitled to more pay than he receives for that service, since obviously he is already receiving full pay for what he does.

I think I can make the point clear by calling attention to the simple illustration of the farmer. Before he collects pay for his services he carefully and intelligently prepares the soil, plows and harrows it, fertilizes it if need be, then plants it with seed.

Up to this point he has gained nothing whatsoever for his labor, but, understanding the law of growth, as he does, he rests after his labor while nature germinates the seed and yields him a crop.

Here the element of time enters into the farmer's labor. In due time nature gives him back the seed he planted in the ground, together with an abundant overplus to compensate him for his labor and his knowledge. If he sows a bushel of wheat in properly prepared soil he gets back the bushel of seed, together with perhaps as many as ten additional bushels as his compensation.

Here the law of increasing returns has stepped in and compensated the farmer for his labor and his intelligence. If there were no such law man could not exist on this earth, since obviously there would be no object in planting a bushel of wheat in the ground if nature yielded back only a bushel of grain. It is this overplus which nature yields, through the law of increasing returns, that makes it possible for man to produce from the ground the food needed for both man and beast.

But little imagination is needed to see that the man who renders more service and better service than that for which he is paid thereby places himself in a position to benefit by this same law.

If a man rendered only as much service as he is paid to render, then he would have no logical reason to expect or demand more than the fair value of that service.

One of the evils of today is the attempt, on the part of some, to reverse this rule and collect more pay than the value of the service they render. Some men endeavor to force down the hours of labor and boost up the rate of pay. This practice cannot be pursued indefinitely. When men continue to collect more for their labor than the value of their services, they ultimately exhaust the source of their own wages, and the sheriff makes the next move.

I want you to understand this point clearly, because lack of knowledge on this subject is destined to bring ruin to the American system of industry if the practice of endeavoring to receive more for labor than one puts into it is not corrected. The man to do the correcting is the man who depends upon his labor for a living, *for he is the only man who has the privilege of initiative in the correction of this unsound practice.*

Please do not misunderstand me to be speaking disparagingly of the man who earns his living from daily labor, for the truth is that I am endeavoring to aid the laboring man by giving him a sounder philosophy of relationship in connection with the marketing of his services.

HILL: If I understand you correctly, Mr. Carnegie, you believe it would be just as unwise for an employer to withhold from an employee any portion of the wages he had justly earned, as it would be for an employee to set up a handicap for himself by doing less than he is paid to do. And I reach the conclusion, from what you have said, that your reasoning on this entire subject is based on your understanding of sound economics and the principle of increasing returns.

CARNEGIE: You have grasped the idea perfectly, and allow me to congratulate you, because most people never seem to understand the great potential benefits available to those who follow the habit of rendering more service than that for which they are paid.

Often I have heard working men say, "I'm not paid to do that;" or, "This is not my responsibility;" and "I'll be blankety-blankety blank if I'll do anything I'm not paid for." You've heard statements like that. Everyone has.

Well, when you hear a man talking like this you may mark him down as one who never will get more than a bare living from his work. Moreover, that sort of "mental attitude" makes one disliked by his associates, and it therefore discourages favorable opportunities for self-promotion.

When I go in search of a man to fill a responsible position, the very first quality I look for is that of a positive, agreeable mental attitude. You may wonder why I do not look first for ability to do the work I want done. I'll tell you why! The man with a negative mental attitude will disturb the harmony of relationship of all with whom he works; therefore, he is a disintegrating influence which no efficient manager wants to deal with. I look first for the right mental attitude also because where this is found one generally finds along with it a willingness to learn. Then the ability necessary to do a certain job can be developed.

When Charlie Schwab first went to work for me he had no ability as far as surface appearances went, other than that possessed by any other day laborer. But Charlie had an unbeatable mental attitude and a disarming personality that enabled him to win friends among all classes of men.

He also had a natural willingness to do more than he was paid for. This quality was so pronounced in him that he actually went out of his way to get into the way of work. He not only went the extra mile, but he added two or three extra miles, and went with a smile upon his face and the right attitude in his heart.

He also went in a hurry and came back for more when he had finished any task assigned to him. He took hold on a hard job as eagerly as a hungry man takes on food when it is set before him.

Now, what can one do with a man like that, except to give him plenty of rein and let him go as fast as he pleases? That sort of mental attitude inspires confidence. It also attracts opportunities that would run away from the man who carries a frown on his face and a grouch in his heart.

I tell you frankly that there is no way to hold back a man with that sort of mental attitude. He writes his own price tag and *gets it willingly*. If one employer is shortsighted enough to withhold recognition of such a man, through adequate compensation, some wiser employer will soon discover him and give him a better job. The law of supply and demand, therefore, steps in and forces the proper reward for such a man. The employer has very little to do about such circumstances. The initiative is entirely in the hands of the employee.

Nor is this example of the wisdom of rendering more service than one is paid for applicable only to the relationship of employer and employee. The same rules apply with equal definiteness to professional men; in fact to all who make their living by serving others. The grocer who tilts the scales in favor of the customer when he is weighing a pound of sugar is wiser, by far, than the grocer who waters his sugar to make it weigh more.

The merchant who "rounds down" and gives the customer the odd half cent, in making change, instead of taking it himself, is wiser by far than the merchant who refuses to do this. I have known merchants to lose the business of customers worth hundreds of dollars a year by this pinch-penny habit that some merchants have, of taking the odd half cent in making change.

I once knew a little merchant who went up and down the Monongahela Valley, near Pittsburgh, peddling his merchandise from a pack that he carried on his back. I have heard it said that the pack weighed more than the man who carried it.

When the merchant made a sale he usually threw in some extra article that had not been paid for, as an expression of his gratitude for the patronage given him. Oh, the gift did not amount to much as far as its monetary value was concerned, but he made it with such a pleasant mental attitude that the customer always spoke of the courtesy to all the neighbors, thereby giving the merchant free publicity he could not have purchased with money alone.

In a little while this merchant disappeared from his established route. His customers began to make enquiries as to what had happened to him. The enquiries were prompted by a genuine affection for "the little man with the big pack," as they called him.

Within a few months the little man showed up again. This time he came without his big pack. He came to tell all his customers that he had opened a store of his own in Pittsburgh.

> If you do not render more services than that for which you are paid, you are already getting all you're worth, and you've no right to ask for more.

That store is now one of the largest and most prosperous in the city. It is known as the Horn Department Store, founded and owned by "the little man with the big pack" and, one might add, "the little man with the big heart and the wise brain."

We look at men who have "arrived" and say "how fortunate" or "how lucky." All too often we fail to enquire into the source of their "luck," for if we did we might learn that their luck consisted of their habit of rendering more service and better service than they were paid for, as in the case of "the little man with the big pack."

Word has reached my ears, many times, that Charlie Schwab got a favorable "break" because old man Carnegie took a fancy to him and pushed him up front, ahead of all the others. The truth is that Charlie pushed himself up front. All I had to do in the matter was to keep out of his way and let him go. Any favorable "break" that he received he created for himself, through his own initiative.

When you describe this principle in the philosophy of individual achievement be sure to emphasize what I have told you about it, because it is the one safe and sure rule through which anyone may Influence the wheel of life so it will yield benefits that will more than offset any misfortunes it may bring.

When you take the philosophy to the world be sure to tell the people how to use this principle of doing more than they are paid for, as a definite means of making themselves indispensable to those whom they serve. Be sure, also, to explain that this is the success rule through which the Law of Compensation can be deliberately put into operation in one's behalf.

I have always thought it was a great tragedy that Emerson did not explain more clearly, in his essay on Compensation, that the habit of rendering more service and better service than one is paid for has the effect of placing the Law of Compensation back of one's efforts.

HILL: Do you know of successful men who do not follow the habit of doing more than they are paid for?

CARNEGIE: I know of no successful man, in any calling or business, who does not follow this habit either consciously or unconsciously. Study any successful man, regardless of his vocation, and you will learn quickly enough that *he does not work by the clock*.

If you study carefully those who let their picks hang in the air the moment the whistle blows for quitting time, you will learn that they are making nothing but a bare living.

Find me one person who is an exception to this rule and I'll give you a check for a thousand dollars, on the spot, provided that this man will permit me to have a photograph of himself.

If any such man exists he is a rare specimen and I want to preserve his picture for the museum, so all may see the man who "successfully" defied nature's laws. Successful men are not looking for short hours and easy jobs, for if they are truly successful they know that no such circumstance exists. Successful men are always looking for ways to lengthen instead of shorten the working days.

HILL: Have you always followed the habit of doing more than you were paid for, Mr. Carnegie?

CARNEGIE: If I had not done so you would not be here, seeking to learn the rules of successful achievement, for I would still be working as a day laborer, right where I began. If you asked me which of the principles of achievement has aided me most I think I would be compelled to say it was *Going the Extra Mile*. However, you must not reach the conclusion that this principle, alone can be depended upon for success. There are other success principles, some combination of which must be used by all who achieve outstanding and enduring success.

Now is an appropriate time to call your attention to the importance of combining Definiteness of Purpose with the habit of Going the Extra Mile. In going that extra mile one should have a definite, final destination in view, and I see no reason why one should not render more service than he is paid for as a deliberate means of influencing the wheel of life in the attainment of a definite goal.

What if one does follow this habit as a matter of expediency? It is every man's privilege to promote himself in every legitimate way possible, and especially it is his privilege to advance himself through methods which *satisfy and benefit others.*

The habit of rendering more than one is paid for is one habit against which no opposition can be legitimately offered. It is a habit which anyone may exercise on his own initiative, without the necessity of asking permission to do so. *No purchaser* of services will object if the seller delivers more than he promises. And surely no purchaser of services will object if the seller delivers the services with a friendly, pleasing mental attitude. These are privileges within the rights of the seller.

HILL: What about the man whose lack of education forces him to accept only such opportunities as are available to common laborers who work with their hands? Would you say that this man has an equal opportunity with those who have educated themselves?

CARNEGIE: I'm very glad you asked that question, because I want to set you right on a common mistake that people make in connection with this question of education.

First, let me explain that the word "educate" means something entirely different from that which many believe it to mean. The word has its roots in the Latin word educare, which means "to educe, to draw out, to develop from within." An educated man is one who has taken possession of his own mind and has so developed it, through organized thought, that it aids him efficiently in the solution of his daily problems in the business of living.

Some people believe that education consists of the acquisition of knowledge, but in a truer sense it means that one has learned how to use knowledge. I know many men who are walking encyclopedias of knowledge, but make such poor use of it that they cannot earn a living.

Another mistake that many people make is that of believing that schooling and education are synonymous terms. Schooling may enable a man to acquire much knowledge and assemble many useful facts, but schooling alone does not make a man educated. Education is self-acquired, and it comes through development and use of the mind, and in no other way.

Take Thomas A. Edison, for example. His entire schooling was a little more than three months, and it was not the most efficient of schooling at that. His real "schooling" came from the great School of

Experience, from which he learned how to take possession of his own mind and to use it. Through this use he became one of the best educated men of our times. Such technical knowledge as he needed in the business of inventing he acquired from other men, through application of the Master Mind principle. In his work he requires knowledge of chemistry, physics, mathematics, and a great variety of other scientific subjects, none of which he personally understands. But since he is *educated*, he knows how and where to procure knowledge on these and all other subjects which are essential in his work.

So, disabuse your mind of the belief that knowledge, of itself, is education! The man who knows where and how to procure the knowledge he needs, when he needs it, is much more of a man of education than *the man who has the knowledge but does not know what to do with it.*

Now, there is another angle in connection with this old, time-worn alibi through which men explain away their failure by claiming they have had no opportunity to acquire education. It is the fact that schooling is free in this country, and it is so abundantly provided that any man can go to school at night if he really wishes to do so. We also have correspondence schools through which men may acquire knowledge on almost any subject, and for a very small price.

I have but little patience with those who claim that they have not succeeded because they lacked schooling, because I know that any man who really wants schooling can acquire it. The fallacy of this "no schooling" alibi, in most instances, is that it is used as an apology for plain *laziness or lack of ambition.*

I had but little schooling, and I began my career on exactly the same basis that any other working man begins. I had no "pull," no extra favors, no "rich uncle" to help me along, and no one to inspire me to promote myself into a more favorable economic status in life. The idea of doing so was entirely my own. Moreover, I found the task to be comparatively easy. It consisted, mainly, of my taking possession of my own mind and using it with *Definiteness of Purpose*. I did not like poverty, therefore I refused to remain under it. My own mental attitude on this subject was the determining factor that helped me to force poverty to give place to riches. I can truthfully tell you that of all the thousands of working men who have been employed by me, I do not know of one person who could not have equaled if not excelled me if he had wanted to do so.

HILL: Your analysis of the subject of education is both interesting and revealing, Mr. Carnegie, and you may rest assured I will include it in my writings on the philosophy of achievement, because I feel sure there are many others who have the wrong conception of the relationship between "schooling" and "education." If I understand you correctly, you believe the better part of one's education comes from doing and not merely from the acquisition of knowledge. Is that correct?

CARNEGIE: That is exactly correct! I have men working for me who have college degrees, but many of them find their college training only incidental to their success. Those who combine college training with practical experience soon become educated in a practical sense, provided they do not lean too heavily upon their academic degrees as a means of minimizing the importance of practical experience.

Right here is an appropriate place to tell you that the college graduates whom I have employed who develop the habit of rendering more service than they are paid for usually advance themselves to more responsible and better-paying positions very quickly, while those who neglect or refuse to adopt this principle make no more progress than the average man without college training.

HILL: Do you mean that college training is worth relatively less than the habit of doing more than one is paid for?

CARNEGIE: Yes, you might put it that way; but I have observed that men with college training who follow the habit of doing more than they are paid for, combining their college training with the advantages they gain from this habit, get ahead much more rapidly than men who do more than they are paid for but have no college training. From this I have reached the conclusion that there is a certain amount of thought discipline that a man gets from college training which men without this training do not generally possess.

HILL: Are the majority of the members of your Master Mind group men with college training, Mr. Carnegie?

CARNEGIE: No; about two-thirds of them are without college training, and I might add that the one who has been of greatest service to me, weighing everything they have all done, did not finish his common school training. It may be interesting, also, to know that his voluntary habit of rendering more service than he was paid for was the quality which made him of greatest value to me.

I say this because his example seemed to set the pace for other members of my Master Mind group. Moreover, his attitude on this subject spread to the rank and file of our workers, many of whom caught his spirit, practiced it, and thereby promoted themselves into better-paying and more responsible positions with the company.

HILL: Have you any definite method by which you endeavor to inform all your men of the advantages they may gain by rendering more service than they are paid for?

CARNEGIE: We have no direct method of doing this, although the news has been passed along, by the "grapevine" route, that the men who promote themselves to better positions follow the habit of doing more than they are paid for. I have often thought we should have gone much further by some form of more direct approach by which our men would have been taught the benefits of rendering this sort of service, and we would have done so had we not feared our efforts would have been misconstrued as an attempt on our part to get more work from our men without paying for it.

You see, most working men are skeptical and suspicious of all efforts on the part of an employer to influence them to improve themselves. Perhaps some smarter man than I will find a way through which employers may gain the confidence of their employees and convince them of the benefits, to employer and employee alike, of the habit of rendering more service than the wage scale calls for.

Of course the rule must work both ways, and it will where an employee understands this principle and applies it deliberately. The matter is in the hands of the employee entirely. This is something he can do on his own initiative, without consulting the employer. *The wiser employees discover and apply this principle voluntarily!*

There is not a man in my Master Mind group who did not voluntarily promote himself to that position through the habit of doing more than was expected of him. I tell you frankly that the man who follows this habit voluntarily soon makes himself indispensable and thereby sets his own wages and chooses his own job. There is nothing an employer can do but cooperate with a man who has the sound judgment to do more than he is paid for.

HILL: But, Mr. Carnegie, aren't there some employers who selfishly refuse to recognize and reward an employee for the habit of doing more than he is paid for?

CARNEGIE: Undoubtedly there are some employers who are shortsighted enough to withhold reward from a man of this type, but you must remember that the man who habitually does more than he is paid for is so rare, that there is keen competition among employers for his services.

If a man has the sound judgment to understand the advantages of doing more than he is paid for, he generally has sense enough, also, to know that all employers are seeking this sort of help; and even those who do not know this will, sooner or later, come to the attention of an employer who is looking for that sort of service, even though they do not deliberately endeavor to promote themselves.

Every man gravitates to where he belongs in life, just as surely as water seeks and finds its level!

Charlie Schwab, for example, did not seek me out (as far as I know) and say, "See here, I am doing more than I am paid for." I made the discovery in my own way because I was searching for that sort of mental attitude.

No employer can successfully conduct an industry of the size of ours without the aid of a large number of men who put heart, soul, and all the ability they have into their jobs. Therefore, I keep a close lookout at all times for this type of man, and when I find one I single him out for close observation, *to make sure that he follows the habit consistently.* The truth is that all successful employers do the same thing. That is one reason why they are successful.

Whether a man occupies the position of employer or employee, the space he occupies in the world is measured precisely by the quality and the quantity of the service he renders, plus the mental attitude in which he relates himself to other people. Emerson said, "Do the thing and you shall have the power." He never expressed a more truthful thought than this. Moreover, it applies to every calling, and to every human relationship. Men who gain and hold power do so by making themselves useful to others. All this talk about men holding fat jobs through "pull" is nonsense. A man may procure a good job through pull, but take my word for it when I tell you that if he remains in the job he will do so through "push," and the more of it he puts into the job the higher will he rise.

I have known of a few young men who were placed in positions beyond their earned merits and ability, through the influence of relatives or others, but seldom have I known of one of them making the fullest use of this unearned advantage; and such exceptions as I have known were due to their having acquired the habit of putting into their jobs more than they tried to take out.

HILL: What about the man who does not work for wages? The small merchant, or the doctor or lawyer? How can they promote themselves by rendering more service than they are paid for?

CARNEGIE: The rule applies to them the same as to the man who works for wages. As a matter of fact, those who fail to render such service remain small, and often they fail completely. There is a factor in a successful man's life known as "good will," without which no man can achieve noteworthy success in any calling.

The finest of all methods of building good will is that of rendering more service and better service than that which is expected. The man who does this, in the right sort of mental attitude, is sure to make friends who will continue to patronize him out of choice.

Moreover, his patrons will tell their friends about him, thereby putting the law of increasing returns into operation in his behalf.

The merchant may not be always in a position to put more merchandise in a package than the customer pays for, but he can wrap courteous service in the package and thereby build friendships that insure him continuous patronage.

You see, good will and confidence are essentials of success in all walks of life. Without these one is forever confined to mediocrity. There is no better way of building these relationships than that of rendering more service and better service than that which is customary. This is one method of self-advancement which one may exercise on his own initiative, and generally speaking it is a form of service that can be rendered *during odd time which would be otherwise wasted.*

I have in mind a case that illustrates my point perfectly. Several years ago a policeman noticed a light burning at a late hour at night, in a small machine shop on his beat in which he knew no night work was done. Becoming suspicious, he telephoned the owner of the shop who came down immediately, unlocked the door and cautiously crept inside, with the policeman, gun in hand, at his side. When they reached the small room where the light appeared the owner of the shop looked in and, to his amazement, found one of his employees busily at work at a machine.

> When you run out of something to do, try your hand at writing down a list of all the reasons why the world needs you. The experiment may surprise you.

The young man looked up, saw the employer and the policeman with a pistol pointed at him, then hurriedly explained that he had been in the habit of coming back to the shop at night so he could learn how to operate the machine and thereby make himself more useful to the employer.

I saw a small newspaper article concerning the circumstance, which claimed but three inches of space, one column, and described the event as something of a joke on the young man. But, to me, it was a joke on his employer. I sent for the young man to come to see me, talked with him a few minutes, and employed him at double the wages he was getting. Today he is the head of one of our most important plant operation departments, at a salary approximately four times as much as he was receiving when I found him.

But this is not the end of the story. This young man is on the way to still higher positions, and if he keeps on working with his present mental attitude he may fill the best job in the plant, or get into business for himself.

I tell you there is no way to hold down these fellows who spend their spare time preparing to render greater and better service. They go right on to the top of their profession or calling, as naturally as cork rises to the top in water.

I belong to a club, whose membership is made up of some two hundred men, a majority of whom have achieved success in their respective callings. A few weeks ago one of the members gave a banquet at which I was the guest speaker. It occurred to me to speak on the subject of the principles of individual achievement, so I had a list of these principles placed on each man's plate. In my talk I requested each man to place each of these principles in what he believed its relative position of importance to be, and to number each accordingly.

It was no surprise to me when I learned that more than two-thirds of those present placed the habit of doing more than is paid for at the head of the list.

Analyze any man who is an acknowledged success in his occupation and you will be likely to find that he follows the habit of doing more than is demanded of him, although in many instances he may be doing so unconsciously.

HILL: Mr. Carnegie, suppose that an employee renders more service and better service than he is paid for, but finds that his employer takes no cognizance of this sort of service? Should he go on rendering that sort of service without saying anything about increased pay, or would it be proper for him to bring the matter to the attention of his employer, with a direct request for the proper reward?

CARNEGIE: Every successful man is also an able salesman. Remember that! It is an individual's privilege to render more service than he is paid for, and it certainly is his duty to himself to market his services to best advantage. If he is doing more than he is paid for he has a sound reason for asking for increased compensation. As a matter of fact, he has no adequate reason for asking for more pay unless and until he can show that he is earning more than he is receiving.

I have seen many men ask for promotions, or increased pay, who did not have a single argument to support their requests. I remember a man coming into my office one day and asking for an increase of pay on the grounds that he had been working in the job he then held much longer than another man who was doing similar work, but receiving greater pay.

I replied to his demands by sending for the records of the two men from which it was obvious that the new man was turning out more work and better work than the one who had asked for increased pay. I wound up the interview by asking this man what he would do if he were in my place, and he replied that he would do just what he knew I was going to do—nothing.

However, not all men are as reasonable as this man was, under similar circumstances. There are many men who believe that priority in the matter of the period of their employment should entitle them to higher pay regardless of the quality and the quantity of service they render.

Obviously, the purchase and sale of personal services in trade and commerce is not unlike the purchase and sale of any commodity. The buyer cannot pay more than the value of that which he purchases and remain in business.

The law of supply and demand also enters into the bargain, and becomes a determining factor in the price of personal services, just the same as it does in connection with the purchase and sale of merchandise. The seller of personal services is in competition with others who have similar services for sale. When the saturation point in the market has been reached, the selling price naturally declines.

HILL: What can a man do when he finds himself in competition with others who are willing to work for less money than he desires or needs? How may an individual meet such competition?

CARNEGIE: He can meet it by delivering a better product than his competitor, and in no other way. All the king's horses and all the king's men cannot change this.

He can go still another long step forward in meeting competition by rendering service in the right sort of mental attitude. Beyond this there is only one thing a man can do to market personal services to better advantage and that is to specialize in some particular field in which competition is not so keen.

This may involve a change in his vocation, but it is a step I have known many ambitious men to take. If a man's work does not yield him enough to satisfy his needs, then the only thing he can do is to change into some other field, where the pay for services is higher.

In this connection I wish to warn you of a common mistake made by men who work for wages. It is the all-too-common habit of confusing one's financial needs with one's demands for wages. I have known men whose habits were so extravagant, and whose home economics were so poorly managed, that they endeavored to solve their problem of need for more money than they were making by demanding that it come in the form of higher wages, although they were already receiving the full value of their services.

On the whole I think that both the employers and the employees in American industry are fair and reasonable. No sensible employer wants to purchase personal services for less than their value, and no fair-minded employee expects or demands pay out of proportion to the value of the services he renders; but there are some men on both sides who seem not to have a clear idea of how to arrive at a fair price for personal services.

HILL: In speaking of the relationship between employers and employees I take it for granted, Mr. Carnegie, that you have reference to this relationship in its broadest meaning; that you refer to all circumstances under which personal services are purchased and sold such, for example, as the relationship between professional men and their clients, where the "wages" consist of a fixed fee; and the merchant and his patrons, where the "wages" consist of a profit on the merchandise sold.

CARNEGIE: Yes, you are correct; but you might have extended the scope of employer-employee relationship to include all relationships where one person renders service to another. The habit of doing more than one is expected to do can be applied very effectively in purely friendly relationships, where one person serves another without any thought of pecuniary gain. Here the object in rendering such service might be that of a desire to develop a more enduring friendship.

The principle may be applied effectively in family relationships, where the service rendered by one member of a family to other members comes under the classification of family duty. Here, as in all other relationships, it is beneficial to render more service and better service than is customary, and above all it pays to render the service in the right sort of mental attitude. Half the domestic disagreements in families could be overcome through a faithful application of the habit of doing more than is expected, and doing it in a pleasing spirit.

HILL: From what you have said, I have reached the conclusion that the habit of doing more than one is paid for has such broad possibilities of application that it may affect all human relationships.

CARNEGIE: Yes; it may serve beneficially in those relationships of mere acquaintanceship, where the question of service is not involved, and no obligation to render service exists. There are situations where the entire relationship consists of the mere exchange of pleasantries between strangers.

Right here I wish to emphasize the fact that the service one renders without pay, and without any expectation of direct compensation of a monetary nature, generally proves to be the most profitable service one can render, because such service builds friendships and places others under obligation in ways and to a degree that would be impossible if the service were paid for! Through the operation of the principles of retaliation and reciprocation all people express in some form their appreciation of the favors extended them, and as definitely show resentment of injuries done to them.

The favors may consist of nothing more tangible than mere words of courtesy, and the injuries may be no greater than the failure of a neglectful person to speak to an acquaintance whom he passes on the street, but the repercussions in both cases may be widespread and serious.

And I might carry the illustration a step further by saying that not only do mere words, or the lack of them, serve to alter relationships between people, but the tone of voice in which words are spoken may make either friends or enemies.

I know a very successful business man who never speaks to one of his employees without carefully modifying his voice so as to make it carry a feeling of kindliness. For that matter he never speaks to anyone without controlling his voice so it will convey the feeling he desires it to convey.

This man not only injects pleasing tones into his voice when he speaks to his employees, but I have observed that when he gives an order he always does so by asking an employee *if he will do thus and so*, instead of demanding that he do it. The results of this, approach are astounding.

I have often wondered why people in all walks of life who wish to gain the friendly cooperation of others do not resort to this habit of asking for co-operation in a pleasant tone of voice instead of bluntly demanding it, as a majority of the people do.

Wouldn't it be better for all concerned if members of a family requested favors of one another, in a kindly tone of voice, instead of bluntly demanding attention? I have one neighbor who never gives an order to any of his children. If he desires one of them to do something he modifies the tone of his voice so that it carries a feeling of deep affection, and expresses his desires in the form of a question, *Will you please do this or that?* Or, *Would you mind refraining from doing this or that?*

The results are immediate and effective. His children respond in the same affectionate tone of voice, thereby signifying that it is a pleasure to comply with the request.

Here, then, is another illustration of how the principle of reciprocation works in practice. Whether in business, social, or family relationships, the habit of *Going the Extra Mile* pays handsomely. And it is surprising when one observes closely and discovers the great variety of human relationships in which one may go the extra mile with direct benefits.

HILL: Mr. Carnegie, you have given a very lucid description of the benefits available through the application of the habit of Going the Extra Mile. Will you now give a brief summary of the most practical methods of developing this habit?

CARNEGIE: With this, as with all the other principles of the philosophy of achievement, perfection is attained only through practice. The word habit connotes repetition of a thought, word or deed. There is no other way to develop any habit.

To answer your question more specifically I would suggest that the best way to develop the habit of *Going the Extra Mile is to adopt the policy of actually going the extra mile in all human relationships.*

One might well begin at home, with the members of one's family. Most families need to practice this habit more.

Next, one might very profitably begin to go the extra mile on behalf of one's daily associates in business or vocational activity.

It might be very helpful, as a means of developing this habit, if not directly profitable otherwise, if one adopted the policy of Going the Extra Mile with chance acquaintances, through words and acts of courtesy. I have known of great opportunities for self-promotion to come from this sort of courtesy.

> If you want something done, and done well, go to a busy man who so organizes his time that he has some to spare for emergencies.

Lastly, if one would adopt and deliberately follow the habit of Going the Extra Mile in all relationships with others, then there would be little chance of misunderstandings and practically no risk of loss of the opportunity for self-promotion.

One cannot overemphasize the importance of doing more than one is paid for as a matter of habit. It is not enough merely to do this for the sake of temporary expediency, when it is obvious that the act will bring benefits, for this leads to many an oversight of opportunities for self-promotion which can be uncovered only by those who are known to Go the Extra Mile as a matter of habit. This habit will attract and reveal opportunities that the average person would pass by unnoticed. Moreover, the habit has a strong tendency to create opportunities where none existed before.

All habits have the peculiarity of inspiring related habits. The habit of doing more than one is paid for will automatically aid in the development of the habits of initiative, perseverance, enthusiasm, imagination, self-control, definiteness of purpose, self-reliance, attractive personality, and many other qualities essential for success, among them a genuine affection for people.

You see, therefore, there are more benefits connected with the habit of doing more than one is paid for than those that are discernible by quick, surface analysis. I emphasize this fact because one may make the mistake of misjudging the importance of this habit because of the simplicity of its title. All of us should remember that the big things of life are nothing but an assembly of smaller things.

The difference between the acts that lead to success and those which lead to definite failure is often so slight that it is unnoticed by all except those who have a keenly discriminating sense of observation and analysis of the circumstances of human relationship.

Above all, we should remember that all success depends upon the manner with which one relates himself to others. Human relationship, therefore, is the most important subject of life. Here is where one becomes "the master of his fate, the captain of his soul," or goes down into the darkness of oblivion, through failure.

The tragedy of those who fail lies in the fact that human relationship is subject to manipulation, direction, influence and control, through established rules of success. If it were not so, there would be no purpose in presenting this philosophy of achievement.

In addition to all the other benefits available to those who habitually render more service and better service than they are paid for, this habit brings one a certain inner feeling of happiness which, of itself, would be adequate compensation for following the habit.

I have never known a person who followed this habit who did not reflect a disposition of *optimism and cheerfulness!* It would be well-nigh impossible for one to make it a part of his daily habits to render useful service to as many people as possible and at the same time express a grouchy, pessimistic mental attitude.

Another very effective method for the development of the habit of *Going the Extra Mile* is that of carefully analyzing and studying those who follow the habit and those who do not, and comparing the achievements of these two classes. One month of daily observation of people will be sufficient to convince one of the stupendous possibilities available to all who go the extra mile and go willingly and pleasantly.

HILL: I reach the conclusion that the term "Doing more than is paid for" is somewhat a misnomer in that it is impossible, in the broader meaning of this term, for one to do more than he is paid for. Is that your understanding, Mr. Carnegie?

CARNEGIE: I was waiting to see if you would grasp this point without my calling it to your attention! You are correct. All forms of constructive labor are rewarded, in one way or another, and in the broader sense there really is no such possibility as that of "Doing more than one is paid for."

Now let us see what specific benefits are available to man (through his exalted powers of thought and speech) which compensate him for Going the Extra Mile. The more useful of these compensating advantages are these:

Some Advantages of Doing More Than One Is Paid For:

1. The habit of Going the Extra Mile gives one the benefit of the Law of Increasing Returns, in a variety of ways too numerous to be described here.

2. This habit places one in a position to benefit by the Law of Compensation, through which no act or deed will or can be expressed without an equivalent response (after its own nature).

3. It gives one the benefit of growth through resistance and use, thereby leading to mental development and increased skill in the use of the body. (It is a well-known fact that both body and mind attain efficiency and skill through systematic discipline and use which call for the rendering of service that temporarily is not paid for.)

4. The habit develops the important factor of initiative, without which no individual ever rises above mediocrity in any calling.

5. It develops self-reliance, which is likewise an essential in all forms of personal achievement.

6. It enables an individual to profit by the law of contrast, since obviously a majority of the people do not follow the habit of doing more than they are paid for. On the contrary, they endeavor to "get by" with a minimum amount of service.

7. It helps one to defeat the habit of drifting aimlessly, thereby checking the habit which stands at the head of the major causes of failure.

8. It definitely aids in development of the habit of Definiteness of Purpose, which is the first principle of individual achievement.

9. It tends strongly to aid in the development of Attractiveness of Personality, thereby leading to the means by which one

may relate himself to others so as to gain their friendly cooperation.

10. It often gives an individual a preferred position of relationship with others through which he may become indispensable, thereby fixing his own price on his services.

11. It insures continuous employment, thereby serving as insurance against want in connection with the necessities of life.

12. It is the greatest of all the known methods by which the man who works for wages may promote himself to higher positions and better wages, and serves as a practical means by which a man may attain the position of ownership of a business or industry.

13. It develops alertness of the imagination, the faculty through which one may create practical plans for the attainment of one's aims and purposes in any calling.

14. It develops a positive "mental attitude", which is one of the more important qualities that are essential in all human relationships.

15. It serves to build the confidence of others in one's integrity and general ability, which is an indispensable essential for noteworthy achievement in every calling.

16. Finally, it is a habit which one may adopt and follow on his own initiative, without being under the necessity of asking the permission of anyone to do so.

Compare these sixteen definite advantages that are available to man, in return for doing more than he is paid for, with the one sole benefit of acquiring food necessary for existence that is available to the other creatures of the earth through the same habit, and you will be forced to the conclusion that overwhelmingly the greater number of benefits enjoyed by man serve as adequate compensation for his development and use of this habit. This comparison substantiates your statement that it is an impossibility for one to do more than one is paid for, and for the very obvious reason that in the mere act of doing that which is constructive one acquires power that can be converted into whatever one desires.

This analysis gives greater meaning to Emerson's statement, "Do the thing and you shall have the power."

No one who follows this analysis carefully can help discovering the truth that it is impossible for one to do more than one is paid for. The pay consists in the self-discipline and self-development one attains through the rendering of service, as well as in the material effects of the service, in the form of economic compensation.

HILL: Your analysis of the habit of doing more than one is paid for suggests that this habit is one of the "musts" of the philosophy of individual achievement. Will you describe some of the definite circumstances in your own business experience through which you have profited by the habit, Mr. Carnegie?

CARNEGIE: You have given me a big order. First, let me give you a blanket answer by saying that all the material riches I possess, and every business advantage I enjoy, might be attributable to my having followed this habit. But I will give you one specific example of an experience which gave me one of the greatest opportunities to promote myself that I ever enjoyed. I mention this particular experience because it was one of the most dramatic of my life, and I might add that it carried with it one of the greatest risks that I ever assumed in order to Go the Extra Mile. The risk was of that type which one should never assume unless he knows he is making the right move, and even then it is the sort of risk which might be fatal to one's opportunities for self-promotion under most circumstances.

> It is more profitable to be for something than it is to be against something

When I was a very young lad I studied telegraphy at night and learned to operate a telegraph key efficiently. (I was not paid to do this, nor did anyone tell me to do it.) I was rewarded for my labor, however, by attracting the attention of Thomas Scott, division superintendent of the Pennsylvania Railroad, in Pittsburgh, who gave me the position as his private operator and clerk.

One morning I arrived at the office ahead of everyone else, and discovered that a bad train wreck had tied up the line and the whole division was in a jam.

The dispatcher was frantically calling Mr. Scott's office when I walked in, so I took the key and found out quickly what had happened. I tried to reach Mr. Scott by telephone, but his wife reported that he had left home. So, there I was, sitting on top of a veritable volcano that was sure to explode and ruin my chances with the Pennsylvania Railroad forever if I made the wrong move, and it might do the same *thing if I made no move at all.*

I knew precisely what my chief would have done had he been there, and also knew well enough what he might do to me if I assumed the risk of acting for him in such an important emergency.

But time was important, so I took the plunge and sent out to the train orders in his name that re-routed traffic and untied the traffic snarl.

When my chief arrived at the office he found a written report of what I had done, with my resignation attached to it, on his desk. I had violated one of the strictest rules of the railroad, so I made it easy for my chief to save face with his superiors by placing my own head on the block.

About two hours later I received the verdict. My resignation came back to me with the words "Resignation refused" boldly written across it in the chief's handwriting. He made no further reference to the circumstance until several days later, and even then he brought the subject up, discussed it in his own way, and dismissed it without either reprimanding me or giving me a clean bill of health for my violation of the rules. He simply said: "There are two types of men who never get far in life. One is the type that cannot do what he is told, and the other is the type that can do nothing else." Here the subject was dismissed with an air of finality which enabled me to determine that he did not place me in either group.

It should be the aim of every young man to go beyond the sphere of his immediate instructions and render service that is not required of him, but one should be extremely cautious in assuming such risks beyond the letter of his instructions as I did on this occasion. Above all, he must know that he is making the right move, but even then he may at times run into difficulty.

A young man who worked as confidential secretary to a New York broker lost his job by mixing bad judgment with his well-meant exercise of the habit of going beyond the letter of his instructions. His chief went away for a vacation and left him in charge of certain funds which he was to invest in the stock market, at a definite time and in a definite manner. Instead of following his instructions, he invested the funds in an entirely different manner. The transaction yielded a much greater profit than would have been received had the employer's instructions been carried out, but the employer took the view that the young man's violation of specific instructions clearly marked him as one who lacked sound judgment, and reasoned that he might violate his instructions again some time, under circumstances that would be disastrous. The result was a discharge.

So, I repeat, with emphasis, be sure you are right before breaking rules in order to do more than you are paid for, and be sure of your relationship with the man who may swing the axe above your neck for doing so. There is no quality that can take the place of sound, well-balanced judgment. Be active, be persistent, be definite, but also be cautious in your judgment.

HILL: Mr. Carnegie, would you mind explaining what benefits you received from having taken so great a risk as you did by breaking a strict rule of the railroad in order to do more than you were authorized to do? Would you say that the benefits you received justified the risk you assumed?

CARNEGIE: I can best answer your questions by saying that the move I made brought me to the attention of men outside of the railroad officials under whom I worked, who afterward supplied the money I needed to get started in the steel business. The very daring step I took gave me an opportunity to attract attention where it was of greatest help to me, although of course I did not have this in mind when I exceeded my authority and cleared the traffic jam.

The circumstance not only attracted attention to me, but it gave me a chance to prove that I had the courage to break rules when they

THE PATH TO PERSONAL POWER

should have been broken. It also established my ability to use sound judgment. If my judgment had been unsound the move I made would have had the effect of ruining my immediate chance to attract the favorable attention of men who were in a position to be of great help to me, and of course it would have meant my discharge by the railroad company.

Many years after this incident, when I invited a group of men to join me in supplying the capital for my first steel plant, Thomas Scott was the man who convinced the others that their money would be wisely invested in my enterprise. He referred to the circumstance of the railroad wreck as evidence that I had ability to deal with business emergencies in a dependable manner.

If I had to deal with the same emergency again I would handle it exactly as I did. The man who cannot deal with emergencies with sound judgment never can become indispensable in any business, as business cannot be operated successfully on unbreakable rules. The rub comes in knowing when to break them.

HILL: Mr. Carnegie, is it your policy always to encourage your employees to use their own judgment when they go beyond the letter of their instructions in applying the principle of doing more than they are paid for?

CARNEGIE: Every person associated with me, in any capacity, knows that he has the privilege of using his own initiative wherever he is willing to back it with his own judgment, and I encourage all my associates to do this, but I also go out of my way to emphasize, by example, the importance of using sound judgment where one exceeds his specific instructions. Up to the point where a man moves entirely on his specific instructions I back him, whether he succeeds or fails, but beyond that point, where a man moves on his own judgment he must assume the responsibility of his mistakes. Any other policy would be ruinous, both to an employer and an employee, because it would invite carelessness.

HILL: Are there any circumstances which you can recall, Mr. Carnegie, under which the habit of doing more than one is paid for would be inadvisable or harmful to anyone?

CARNEGIE: Let me answer your question by asking one: How could any habit which benefits both the purchaser and the seller of personal services harm anyone? In this transaction there are only two parties. Therefore, no circumstance in connection with the habit of doing more than one is paid for that I can think of would be objectionable, to either the buyer or the seller, or to any outside person.

HILL: Let me put the question in another way, then, by asking which of the parties, the buyer or the seller of personal services rendered under the habit of delivering more than is paid for, is apt to get the better part of the bargain?

CARNEGIE: Generally speaking, I would say that there is no "better part" of any bargain which satisfies all parties to the transaction. However, in this particular instance I think you see that the seller gets the better part of the bargain. I have given you a description of sixteen definite benefits that accrue to the advantage of the seller of services under this policy, while it is obvious that the advantages to the purchaser from the same transaction are fewer by far.

When you consider the fact that the habit of doing more than is paid for is the most dependable of all methods of self-promotion through which an ordinary workman may raise himself to a position of economic security, I think you will need no further evidence that this habit should be of greater concern to an employee than it is to an employer.

HILL: Would you say that you could have achieved the success you have attained if you had refused to deliver more service than you were paid for? Is there any other policy that you could have substituted for that of doing more than you were paid for which would have served the same end?

CARNEGIE: There is no substitute for the habit of Going the Extra Mile, although some very smart men have tried, without satisfactory results, to achieve success without observing this rule. It would have been utterly impossible for me to have promoted my own interests, as I have done, if I had not formed the habit, early in life, of doing more than was expected of me.

HILL: I take it then, from your statement, that you consider the habit of doing more than one is paid for to have been more beneficial to you than the Master Mind principle to which you have paid a high tribute as a contributory influence in your business?

CARNEGIE: Yes, that is true, and I might add that if I had not followed the habit of doing more than I was paid for, I probably would never have reached the point at which a Master Mind alliance would have been of any benefit to me.

If you recall what I have said about my relationship with the members of my Master Mind group, you will see that the benefits I received from my associates were due, in a large measure, to my having arranged for each of them to earn more than he probably could have earned without my help.

You must remember that the habit of Going the Extra Mile is a privilege that is as available and as profitable to an employer, in some respects, as it is to an employee. From an employer's viewpoint the habit of paying for more services than he actually receives, if he does it under the right sort of an understanding, often has the effect of enabling him not only to get, eventually, all that he pays for, but he may receive an overplus of great value in the form of loyalty and dependability.

HILL: That is exactly the point I wished to bring out. From your analysis one is left no alternative but to conclude that both the employer and the employee may profit by dealing with one another on the basis of delivering more than is paid for. Endeavoring to determine which receives the better part of the bargain, under such a policy, the employer or the employee, is something like trying to decide which comes first, the hen or the egg.

CARNEGIE: Your analysis is quite correct. Analyze this policy from any angle you wish and you will come, finally, to recognize that it is beneficial to all whom it affects, whether it be the employer or the employee. And you might well go a step further and say that the policy also benefits in a majority of the cases the public which is served by both employer and employee. The one element you cannot find, in connection with this policy, is any circumstance whereby anyone is injured.

On the other hand, I can easily name a long list of circumstances under which both the employer and the employee, as well as the public they serve, are irreparably injured by failure to observe this policy. I will not mention these circumstances because they are so obvious and well known that to describe them would be a waste of time. It might also trample on the toes of those who like to attribute their failure to get ahead in life to greedy employers who refuse to pay them what they think they are worth.

You know of course that most men who do not get ahead make the mistake of looking everywhere except in a mirror for the cause of their misfortune. This is one trait of human nature for which I refuse to suggest any remedy, and for the very good reason that the remedy would not be accepted if it were offered to such men.

I have always claimed that no man of sound mind and body, who is a citizen of our country, has any legitimate right to charge others with his failure to get ahead. Under our form of democracy every man has the privilege of promoting himself into whatever position in life he is capable of filling, and you may be sure that most of the complaints about lack of opportunity are nothing but thin alibis with which people try to explain away indifference, lack of ambition, or outright laziness.

I speak from both personal experience and observation when I say that American opportunities are so abundant and American resources are so great that the humblest person, with a sound body and a sound mind, can attain economic security. And I could name many men who have attained independence without a sound body.

HILL: What about the man who belongs to a trade union and is forced, by the rules of his union, to limit the quantity of work he performs? What chance has he to profit by the habit of doing more than he is paid for?

CARNEGIE: I knew you would be getting around to that question sooner or later. Now that you have asked it, let me deal with the question fairly and frankly, because I may as well tell you now my view on this subject.

In the first place, I wish to preface my remarks with the statement that I believe working men have the same right to organize for co-operative bargaining that any other group has. On this point there can be no room for argument. But the mere fact that men pool their power, whether it is for collective bargaining in connection with the sale of their personal services or the marketing of commodities, does not provide them with the right or the power to ignore the principles of economics or the public welfare.

No one can take out of any transaction more than has been put into it in equivalent values. That is an acknowledged rule of economics.

Very well, let me answer your question by saying that the man who allies himself with others under rules which force him to limit the quantity of service he renders in proportion to his remuneration thereby places himself in a position where he is forced to accept limited compensation. He may be able to command the top of the wage scale fixed by his union, but there he must stop. No union alliance can take him one step further, and no union leader can assure him anything more.

The question then becomes one of determining whether or not an individual is willing to limit his style of living to fit the limited pay his union rules force upon him. That is something every man must decide for himself.

HILL: Judging by your business achievements, I assume that you chose to take your chances without the protection of a trade union, because you desired greater compensation than you could command through such an alliance. Is that correct?

CARNEGIE: That states my case exactly. I was approached many times by fellow workmen who invited me to join trade unions, but I declined, and for the very sound reason that I preferred to market my services in the open market where I could take advantage of a greater portion of the American opportunity to accumulate wealth than would have been available to me through the limited protection of a trade union. I had the right to make this choice. The American form of government was founded with that right as one of its major foundation stones, and I think it is this very privilege which, more than all others, makes this the greatest country in the world.

Where, except in this country, can a man start at scratch, without working capital, without great influence, and exchange his personal services for whatever amount of wealth he is capable of earning?

HILL: What would happen, Mr. Carnegie, if all men were forced, by law, to buy and sell personal services under trade union rules which limit the quantity of service any man can perform? Would that be a help or a hindrance to the majority of the people?

CARNEGIE: If that happened we would no longer have the right of free enterprise. It would have its repercussions in many other forms of curtailment of personal liberty, and very soon American freedom and liberty would be nothing but an empty phrase. I do not believe the American people would welcome anything that would curtail their privilege of self-determination because they have established a standard of living they could not maintain under such a curtailment.

HILL: But, Mr. Carnegie, wouldn't it help the poor and the weak if wage scales and working hours were established by law? Wouldn't such a law have the effect of distributing the wealth of America more evenly?

CARNEGIE: I will answer your questions in the light of what I have learned about laws and people from personal observation and practical business experience. In the first place, let us be perfectly frank in answering this question concerning the poor and the weak. If you will observe nature's plan carefully you will see that nature does not protect the weak. She kills off the weak and encourages the strong in every species of living things, from the smallest insect to man himself. The law of survival of the fittest is so well recognized that it needs no further proof of its existence.

The greatest help that anyone can extend to the weak and the poor is that which enables them to help themselves. I had this very fact in mind when I told you I intended to distribute the better portion of my riches to the people, through the philosophy of individual achievement, because I knew that material wealth gravitates to the man who has the knowledge with which wealth is accumulated, just as definitely as water seeks its level.

This fact was well demonstrated during the War Between the States when the government gave a group of prisoners the privilege of gaining their freedom on the condition that they join the Union Army and go West and help put down Indian skirmishes. Many of them accepted, the condition being that inasmuch as they would be away for a long while they were to receive several months' pay in advance. The army started on its way, and I was informed by one of the soldiers in charge that by the end of the first week out every dollar of that advance pay was in the hands of fewer than half a dozen men who were clever with cards.

The same thing would occur if every dollar in America were placed in a pool and the entire amount were divided equally between the people. In a very short time the money would be back into the hands of those who are money-conscious—those who have the knowledge with which money is accumulated.

Now this is human nature of which I am speaking. All this talk about helping the weak and the poor by giving them something for nothing comes from men who have no practical understanding of how this can be done. I believe in helping the weak and the poor. I wouldn't be quite human if I didn't. Yet I know that the only way to permanently help anyone is to help him solve his problems through his own efforts.

Moreover, I have learned from experience that this is all the help a real man desires. Only the professional beggar and the indolent who are too lazy to work for a living would ask others to give them something for nothing. This class we will have with us always, but there is no charity in giving to those who will not try to help themselves.

HILL: You believe, then, that the best way to distribute the wealth of America is by providing all who will use it with the knowledge through which wealth is earned?

CARNEGIE: That is the only safe way. And there is another fact in connection with the term "wealth" to which I wish to call attention. It is the fact that the "American wealth" of which you speak consists of a combination of intelligently applied knowledge and the material resources of the nation. The material resources were here while the Indians owned the country, but it was worth nothing until men of practical education took it over and gave it bankable values by mixing knowledge with it.

Now this is my idea of helping the weak and the poor!

And here is something else I wish to mention in connection with this sort of help: It is a form of riches which cannot be lost, stolen or dissipated through unwise use. The wealth represented by knowledge and experience is perpetual. No bank failure can diminish it. No panic can destroy it. No wastrel can inherit it and destroy himself through its unwise use, as inherited money is often the means of self-destruction.

The giving of money often does more harm than good. The giving of knowledge never does harm, but it may insure one against many forms of injury. If you doubt this, study carefully what happens to many who are born to a legacy of money which they did not earn.

There is still another point about the earning of money I wish to emphasize. It is the fact that it can become, and that it generally does become, a fascinating game through which one develops the pride of achievement. It also develops creative ability and adds to the national wealth in the form of able leadership which may be of great benefit in times of national emergencies.

HILL: Then you believe in the spirit of pioneering through which men take chances on their own initiative?

CARNEGIE: I have a sound reason for believing in it. If there had been no such spirit in America we would have none of the great industrial enterprises through which our natural resources have been developed.

It was the spirit of the pioneer which inspired James J. Hill to marry the East to the West, through the Great Northern Railroad.

It was the spirit of the pioneer which urged Thomas A. Edison on through ten thousand failures, until he triumphed, at last, in perfecting the incandescent electric lamp and a hundred other useful inventions which have added hundreds of millions of dollars of wealth to the country, to say nothing of providing employment for thousands of men and women.

It was the spirit of the pioneer which gave America the great Wanamaker store, and the Marshall Field store.

It was the spirit of the pioneer which gave America her birth of liberty and freedom. All these leaders were urged on by the spirit of the pioneer which asks for no subsidies and recognizes no such thing as something for nothing.

Every great business and every industry in America owes its birth to the pioneering spirit of some man or group of men who asked nothing except the privilege of exercising their American rights of liberty and freedom through which they moved on their own initiative. These men made no demands in the name of the weak and the poor, although most of them were exceedingly poor at the outset.

I know a great deal about the weak and the poor. I was poor when I came to this country, but I was not weak. My strength consisted in my will to win by rendering useful service in return for the material riches I desired.

I am thankful that no misguided person coddled me because I was "a poor immigrant boy." If anyone had done so I might have been misled into believing, as some others are, that this country owed me a living.

Because I was not weak I recognized that this country owed me nothing except that which is the privilege of every citizen, and that is the right to render useful service and collect an equivalent return in the form of riches.

HILL: If I follow your analysis clearly, Mr. Carnegie, it is your belief that any gift which places in one's hands something of value which has not been earned may do that person an injury by destroying his incentive to render service. Is that your belief?

CARNEGIE: Yes, that is my belief, and I acquired it from a lifetime of practical experience in dealing with many thousands of men. A man's greatest asset is his desire to create, on his own initiative. There is no thrill like that which a man experiences when he begins to acquire economic freedom through his own efforts. Riches acquired in this manner not only give their owner more pleasure than those which come without effort, but they are more easily retained, for it generally follows that the man who learns how to acquire wealth learns at the same time how to use it and how to keep it.

Parents who are wealthy often condemn their children to eternal penury and failure by removing from them the necessity of rendering useful service. We have a case of that sort right here in Pittsburgh, at the present time. A young man named Harry Thaw inherited an income of $85,000 a year, right after leaving college. Instead of going to work and making himself useful he went to New York City and began to dazzle Broadway with his unearned riches. Very soon his debauchery led to his murdering a prominent architect, and now he is in prison for life, having barely escaped a worse fate.

I regret to say I do not place the blame for his sad plight on the young man. The real offender was the one who condemned the young man to a life of idleness and dissipation, by depriving him of the privilege of working, through a gift of money he did not earn.

HILL: Do you mean that the principle of Going the Extra Mile should not be applied between parents and their children?

CARNEGIE: Oh, no! I don't mean that. Parents owe their children a gift, but it should be a gift of education and preparation for life, and not a gift of money. Money is never a greater curse than when it is lavished on children by their parents, for purposes other than those of preparing them to become self-determining.

HILL: From your own experience can you say that great wealth brings happiness?

CARNEGIE: Nothing brings enduring happiness except some form of useful service. Understand this truth and you will have the soundest of all reasons for rendering more service and better service than you are paid for directly. The man who goes the extra mile brings back with him a feeling of satisfaction he can get in no other way. This is one form of compensation which, alone, is sufficient justification for doing more than one is paid for. It is a compensation which cannot be withheld; a form of riches of which one cannot be deprived.

HILL: Why do so few people make use of the principle of Going the Extra Mile?

CARNEGIE: Because so few have been taught the benefits this habit will yield. The place to begin teaching this principle is in the home. Every child should be taught that it is profitable to render useful service for which it receives no immediate pay other than the satisfaction that comes from the service. But the teaching should go beyond this point and clearly show the child that this habit can become a great asset throughout life. Similar training should be a part of every public school curriculum, so that by the time boys and girls reach high school they will observe and apply this principle as definitely as they perform any other duty connected with their studies.

Here, as in most other instances where training of children is neglected, we adults are to blame for their lack of knowledge. Children are the victims of older people who are responsible for their guidance. Neglect in such important matters as that of failing to teach them the benefits of Going the Extra Mile is very little short of a criminal act.

ANALYSIS OF CHAPTER THREE: GOING THE EXTRA MILE

by Napoleon Hill

Nature has so arranged the universe that there is no such reality as something for nothing. Everything has its price, or its equivalent in something else. Sometimes men unwisely spend their time trying to invent machines of perpetual motion which they hope will enable them to circumvent the laws of motion. All of them have ended in severe disappointment.

Other men just as unwisely try to collect a full day's pay for a poor day's labor. By force of numbers they may ally themselves in groups and succeed, for a time; but sooner than is convenient for them they pay for their folly by the loss of the market for their services. Nature cannot be successfully defied, although some men never seem to learn this truth.

In this chapter Mr. Carnegie has presented an understandable description of several principles of human conduct, as they apply in the ordinary daily relationships of men. His description has been frank and definite. Coming, as it has, from one of America's recognized leaders in industry, his analysis is unavoidably impressive.

The most important test of these principles will be that which an individual gives them by applying them in his own personal relationships with others. The test will be more beneficial if one makes it deliberately with a definite purpose in mind.

Fortunately, the author had the rare privileges of observation of those who have risen to great heights of achievement as well as those who have gone down in defeat. Some twenty years ago the editor of *The Golden Rule Magazine* was invited to deliver a speech at the Palmer School in Davenport, Iowa. He accepted the invitation on his regular fee basis, which was $100 and traveling expenses.

While the editor was at the college he picked up enough editorial material for several stories for his magazine. After he had delivered the speech and was ready to return to Chicago, he was asked by Dr. B. J. Palmer to turn in his expense account and receive his pay. He declined to accept any money for either his address or his expenses, explaining that he had already been paid adequately by the material he had procured for his magazine. He took the train and went back to Chicago, feeling well repaid for his trip.

The following week he began to receive from Davenport many

subscriptions to his magazine. By the end of the week he had received over $6,000 in cash subscriptions. Then followed a letter from Dr. Palmer, explaining that the subscriptions had come from his students, who had been told of the editor's refusal to accept money he had been promised and had earned.

During the following two years the students and graduates of the Palmer School sent in more than $50,000 in subscriptions to *The Golden Rule Magazine*. The story was so impressive that it was written up in a magazine that had a circulation throughout the English-speaking world, and then subscriptions came from many different countries.

Thus, by rendering $100 worth of service without collecting for it, the editor had started the law of Increasing Returns to work in his behalf, and it yielded him a return of over 500% on his investment. Going the Extra Mile is no pipe-dream. It pays off, and pays off handsomely!

Moreover, it never forgets! Like other types of investment, the habit of Going the Extra Mile often yields dividends throughout one's lifetime.

Let's look at what may happen when one neglects an opportunity to Go the Extra Mile. Late one rainy afternoon an automobile salesman sat at his desk, in the showroom of the New York branch office. The door opened and in walked a man jauntily swinging a cane.

The salesman looked up from the reading of the afternoon paper, took a swift glance at the newcomer, and immediately spotted him as another of those Broadway "window shoppers" who do nothing but waste one's valuable time. He went ahead with his newspaper, not taking the trouble to get up from his seat.

The man with the cane walked through the showroom, looking

at first one car and then another. Finally, he walked over to where the salesman was sitting, teetered himself on his cane, and nonchalantly asked the price of three different automobiles he had seen. Without looking up from his newspaper, the salesman gave the prices and went on with his reading.

The man with the cane walked back over to the three automobiles at which he had been looking, kicked the tires of each one, then walked back to the busy man at the desk and said, "Well, I hardly know whether I shall take this one, or that one over there; or whether I shall just buy all three."

The busy man at the desk responded with a sort of smirky, wiseacre smile, as much as to say, "Just as I thought!"

Then the man with the cane said, "Oh, I guess I will only buy one of them. Send that one with the yellow wheels up to my house tomorrow. And, by the way, how much did you say it was?"

He took out his check book and wrote out a check, handed it to the salesman, and walked out. When the salesman saw the name on the check, he turned pink and nearly fainted. The man who signed the check was Charles Payne Whitney, and the salesman knew then, as well as he knew his own name, that if he had only taken the time to get up from his seat he might have sold all three automobiles without any great effort.

When the management heard of the incident, the salesman was fired on the spot! The punishment was mild. He probably should have been forced to pay for the loss of profits on the two cars he did not sell. Withholding anything short of the best service of which one is capable is costly business, a fact which many have learned after it was too late. The right of personal initiative is not worth much to the fellow who is too indifferent or too lazy to exercise it. Many people are in this class without recognizing the reason why they never accumulate riches.

Over forty years ago a young salesman in a hardware store observed that the store had a lot of odds and ends which were out of date and were not selling. Having time on his hands, he rigged up a special table in the middle of the store. He loaded it with some of the unsalable merchandise, marking it at the bargain price of a dime an article. To his surprise and that of the owner of the store, the gadgets sold readily.

Out of that experience grew the great F. W. Woolworth Five and Ten Cent chain store system. The young man who stumbled upon the idea by Going the Extra Mile was Frank W. Woolworth.

Before he died, the idea yielded him a fortune estimated at more than $50,000,000. Moreover, the same idea made several other persons rich, and applications of the idea are at the heart of many more profitable merchandising systems of America.

No one told young Woolworth to exercise his right to personal initiative. No one paid him for doing so; yet his action led to ever-increasing returns for his efforts. Once he put the idea into practice, increasing returns nearly ran him down.

There is something about this habit of doing more than one is paid for which works in one's behalf even while one sleeps. Once it begins to work, it piles up riches so fast that it seems like some queer sort of magic which, like Aladdin's Lamp, draws to one's aid an army of genii which come laden with bags of gold.

The habit of Going the Extra Mile is one that does not confine its rewards to wage earners. It works as well for an employer as it does for an employee, as one merchant whom I knew quite well has gratefully testified.

His name was Arthur Nash, and his business was that of a merchant tailor. Some twenty-odd years ago Mr. Nash found his business just one step ahead of the sheriff. The First World War and other conditions over which he seemed to have no control had brought him to the brink of financial ruin. One of his most serious handicaps was that his employees caught his spirit of defeatism and expressed it in their work by slowing down and becoming disgruntled. His situation was desperate. Something had to be done, and it had to be done quickly if he was to continue in business.

Out of sheer desperation he called his employees together and told them of the condition he was in. While he was speaking, an idea occurred to him. He said he had been reading a story in *The Golden Rule Magazine* which told how its editor had Gone the Extra Mile by rendering service for which he refused to accept any pay, only to be voluntarily rewarded with more than $6,000 worth of subscriptions to his magazine. He wound up by suggesting that if he and all his employees caught the spirit and began to Go the Extra Mile they might save the business. He promised his employees that if they would join with him in an experiment he would endeavor to carry on the business, with the understanding that everyone would forget wages, forget working hours, pitch in and do his best, and take chances on receiving pay for his work. If the business could be made to pay, every employee would receive his back wages, with a bonus thrown in for good measure.

The employees liked the idea and agreed to give it a trial. The next day they began to come in with their meager savings which they voluntarily loaned to Mr. Nash. Everyone went to work with a new spirit, and the business began to show signs of new life. Very soon it was back on a paying basis. Then it began to prosper as it had never prospered before. Ten years later the business had made Mr. Nash richer than he needed to be. The employees were more prosperous than they had ever been, and everyone was happy.

Arthur Nash has passed on, but today the business continues as one of the more successful merchant tailoring businesses of America. The employees took over the business when Mr. Nash laid it down. Ask any one of them what he thinks of this business of Going the Extra Mile, and you will get the answer in a hurry! Moreover, talk with one of the Nash salesmen, wherever you meet one, and observe his spirit of enthusiasm and self-reliance. When this "extra-mile" stimulant gets into a man's mind, he becomes a different sort of person. The outlook on the world appears different to him, and he appears different because he is different!

Here is the right place to remind you of an important thing about the habit of Going the Extra Mile by doing more than one is paid for. It is the strange influence it has on the man who does it. The greatest benefit from this habit does not come from those to whom the service is rendered. It comes from the one who renders the service in the form of a changed "mental attitude" which gives him more influence with other people, more self-reliance, greater initiative, enthusiasm, vision and definiteness of purpose; all of these are qualities of successful achievement.

"Do the thing and you shall have the power," said Emerson. Ah yes, the power! What can a man do in our world without power? But it must be the sort of power that attracts other people instead of repelling them. It must be a form of power which gains momentum from natural law, through the operation of which one's acts and deeds come back to him greatly multiplied.

To benefit by the habit of doing more than one is paid for, one should understand the meaning back of the Biblical quotation, "Whatsoever a man soweth that shall he also reap." The sort of seed a man sows is important! It is important because every seed of service one sows brings back a crop after its own kind.

You who work for wages should learn more about this sowing and reaping business. Then you would understand why no man can go on forever sowing the seed of inadequate service and reaping a harvest of full-grown pay. You would know that there must come a halt to the habit of demanding a full day's pay for a poor day's work.

By force men may, for a time, squeeze more blood out of a turnip than nature placed in it, but nature is too resourceful to tolerate such a violation of her plans for long. Sooner or later she strikes back with a terrible vengeance at those who either ignorantly or willfully run counter to her plans.

And you who do not work for wages but wish to get more of the better things of life. Let me have a word with you, too. Why don't you turn smart and start getting what you want the easy and sure way? Yes, there is an easy and sure way to promote one's self into whatever he wants from life, and its secret becomes known to every person who makes it his business to Go the Extra Mile. The secret can be uncovered in no other manner, for it is wrapped up in that extra mile.

The pot of gold at the "end of the rainbow" is no mere fairy tale! The end of that extra mile is the spot where the rainbow ends, and there is where the pot of gold is hidden.

Few people ever catch up with the end of the rainbow. When one gets to where he thought the rainbow ended, he finds it is still far in the distance. The trouble with most of us is that we do not know how to follow rainbows. Those who know the secret know that the rainbow really can be reached only by Going the Extra Mile.

Late one afternoon, some twenty-five years ago, William C. Durant, the founder of General Motors, walked into his bank after banking hours, and asked for some favor which, in the ordinary course of business, should have been requested during banking hours.

The man who granted the favor was Carrol Downes, an under-official of the bank. He not only served Mr. Durant with efficiency, but he went the Extra Mile and added courtesy to the service. He made Mr. Durant feel that it was a real pleasure to serve him. The incident seemed trivial, and of itself it was of very little importance. Unknown to Mr. Downes, this courtesy was destined to have repercussions of a far-reaching nature.

The next day Mr. Durant asked Mr. Downes to come to see him at his office. That visit led to the offer of a position which Downes accepted. He was given a desk in a general office where nearly a hundred other people worked, and notified that the office hours were from 8:30 A. M. to 5:30 P. M. His salary to begin with was modest.

At the end of the first day, when the gong rang, announcing the close of the day's work, Downes noticed that everyone grabbed his hat and coat and made a rush for the door. He sat still, waiting for the others to get out. After they had gone he remained at his desk, pondering in his own mind the cause of the great haste everyone had shown to get away on the very second of quitting time. Fifteen minutes later Mr. Durant opened the door of his private office, saw Downes still at his desk, and asked if he hadn't understood that he was privileged to quit work at 5:30.

"Oh yes," Downes replied, "but I didn't wish to be run over in the rush." Then he asked if he could be of any service to Mr. Durant. He was told that he might find a pencil for the motor magnate. He got the pencil, ran it through the pencil sharpener, then took it in. Mr. Durant thanked him and said good night.

The next day at quitting time Downes remained at his desk again, after the "rush" was over. This time he waited with purpose aforethought. In a little while Mr. Durant came out of his private office and asked, again, if Downes didn't understand that 5:30 was quitting time.

"Yes," Downes smiled, "I understand it is quitting time for the others, but I have heard no one say that I have to leave the office when the day is officially closed, so I chose to remain here with the hope that I might be of some slight service to you."

"What an unusual hope!" Durant exclaimed. "Where did you get the idea?"

"I got it from the scene I witness here at closing time every day," Downes replied. Mr. Durant grunted some reply which Downes didn't hear clearly, and went back into his office.

From then on Downes perched himself at his desk at quitting time, and remained there until he saw Mr. Durant put on his hat and coat and leave for the day. He was not paid to remain over time. No one told him to do it. No one promised him anything for remaining, and as far as the casual observer might know, he was wasting his time.

Several months later Downes was called into Mr. Durant's office and informed that he had been chosen to go out to a new plant that had been recently purchased, to supervise the installation of the plant machinery. Imagine that! A former bank official becoming a machinery expert in a few months.

Without quibbling, Downes accepted the assignment and went on his way. He didn't say, "Why, Mr. Durant, I know nothing about the installation of machinery." He didn't say, "That's not my job," or

"I'm not paid to install machinery." No, he went to work and did what was requested of him. Moreover, he went at the job with a pleasant "mental attitude."

Three months later the job was completed. It was done so well that Mr. Durant called Downes into his office and asked him where he learned about machinery. "Oh," Downes explained, "I never learned, Mr. Durant. I merely looked around, found men who knew how to get the job done, put them to work, and they did it."

"Splendid!" Durant shouted. "There are two types of men who are valuable. One is the fellow who can do something and do it well, without complaining that he is being overworked. The other is the fellow who can get other people to do things well, without complaining. You are both types wrapped into one package."

Downes thanked him for the compliment and turned to go.

"Wait a moment," Durant requested. "I forgot to tell you that you are the new manager of the plant you have installed, and your salary to start with is $50,000 a year!"

The following ten years of association with Durant were worth between ten and twelve million dollars to Carroll Downes. He became an intimate advisor of the motor king and made himself rich for his pains.

The main trouble with so many of us is that we see men who have arrived and weigh them in the hour of their triumph without taking the pains to find out how or why they "arrived."

There is nothing very dramatic about the story of Carroll Downes. The incidents mentioned occurred in the day's business, without even passing notice by the average person who worked along with Downes. And I doubt not that many of these fellow workers envied him because they believed he had been favored by

Durant, through some sort of pull or luck or whatever it is that men who do not succeed use as an excuse to explain their failure.

Well, to be candid, Downes did have an inside "pull" with Durant!

He created that "pull" on his own initiative. He created it by Going the Extra Mile in as trivial a matter as that of placing a neat point on a pencil when nothing was requested except a plain pencil. He created it by remaining at his desk "with the hope" that he might be of service to Durant after the "rush" was over at 5:30 each evening. He created it by using his right of personal initiative by finding men who understood how to install machinery instead of asking Durant where or how to find such men.

Trace down this incident, step by step, and you will find that Downes' success was due solely to his own initiative. Moreover, it consists of a series of little tasks well performed, in the right "mental attitude."

Perhaps there were a hundred other men working for Durant who could have done as well as Downes, but the trouble with them was that they were searching for the end of the rainbow by running away from it in the 5:30 rush each afternoon.

Long years after this incident, this writer asked Carroll Downes how he got his opportunity with Mr. Durant. "Oh," he modestly replied, "I just made it my business to get in his way, so he could see me. When he looked around, wanting some little service, he called on me because I was the only one in sight. In time he got into the habit of calling on me."

There you have it! Mr. Durant "got into the habit" of calling on Downes. Moreover, he found that Downes could and would assume responsibilities by Going the Extra Mile. What a pity that all of the American people do not catch something of this spirit of assuming greater responsibilities. What a pity that more of us do not begin speaking more of our "privileges" of service under the American way of life, and less of the lack of opportunities in America.

Is there a man living in America today who would seriously claim that Carroll Downes would have been better off if he had been forced, by law or by group rule, to join the mad rush and quit his work at 5:30 in the afternoon? If he had done so, he would have received the standard wages for the sort of work he performed, but nothing more. Why should he receive more?

His destiny was in his own hands. It was wrapped up in this one lone privilege which should be the privilege of every American citizen: the right of personal initiative through the exercise of which he made it a habit always to Go the Extra Mile. That tells the whole story. There is no other secret to Downes' success. He admits it and everyone familiar with the circumstances of his promotion from poverty to riches knows it.

There is one thing no one seems to know: Why are there so few men who, like Carroll Downes, discover the power back of this business of doing more than one is paid for? It has in it the seed of all great achievement. It is the secret of all noteworthy success, and yet it is so little understood that most people look upon it as some clever trick with which employers try to get more work out of men.

This spirit of indifference toward the habit of Going the Extra Mile was dramatically expressed by a "wiseacre" who once applied to Henry Ford for a job. Mr. Ford questioned the man about his experience, his habits, and other routine matters, and was satisfied. Then he asked, "How much money do you want for your services?" The man was evasive on this point, so Mr. Ford finally said, "Well suppose you start in and show us what you can do, and we will pay you all you are worth after we have tried you out." He declined and explained, "I'm getting more than that where I am now employed." And I doubt not that he told the truth.

That explains precisely why so many people do not get ahead in life. They are "getting more than they are worth" where they are, and they seem never to learn how to get ahead by becoming worth more!

Just after the end of the Spanish-American War, Elbert Hubbard wrote a story entitled "A Message to Garcia." He told briefly how President William McKinley commissioned a young soldier by the name of Rowan to carry a message from the United States Government to Garcia, the Cuban rebel chieftain, whose exact whereabouts were not known. This young soldier took the message, made his way through the vastness of the Cuban jungle, finally found Garcia, and delivered the note to him. That was all there was to the story—just a private soldier carrying out his orders under difficulties and getting the job done without coming back with an excuse.

The story fired imaginations all over the world. The simple act of a man doing what he was told and doing it well became news of the first magnitude. "A Message to Garcia" was printed in booklet form and sales reached an all-time high for such publications, amounting to more than ten million copies. This one story made Elbert Hubbard famous, to say nothing of helping to make him rich.

The story was translated into several foreign languages. The Japanese Government had it printed and distributed to every Japanese soldier. The Pennsylvania Railroad Company presented a copy of it to each of its thousands of employees. The big life insurance companies of America presented it to their salesmen. Long after Elbert Hubbard went down on the ill-fated *Lusitania* in 1915, "A Message to Garcia" continued as a bestseller throughout America.

The story was popular because it had in it something of the magic power that belongs to the man who does something and does it well.

The whole world is clamoring for such men. They are needed and wanted in every walk of life. American industry has always had princely berths for men who can and will assume responsibilities and get the thing done in the right "mental attitude" by Going the Extra Mile.

Andrew Carnegie lifted no fewer than forty such men from the lowly station of day laborers to that of millionaires. He understood the value of men who were willing to Go the Extra Mile.

Wherever he found such a man, he brought "his find" into the inner circle of his business and gave him an opportunity to earn "all he was worth."

Charles M. Schwab was one of those who gained the favor of the steel master by the simple expedient of Going the Extra Mile. He began work with Carnegie in the humble capacity of a stake driver at day wages. Step by step he climbed to the top and became Carnegie's right-hand man. Some years his income amounted to more than a million dollars in extra pay, in the form of a bonus.

The bonus was his compensation for Going the Extra Mile! His other pay was for the actual work he performed. Let us not forget that the "big money" is always the result, directly or indirectly, of that extra mile!

America is now passing through a great national crisis which seriously threatens the personal liberty which has made it possible for persons in all walks of life to Go the Extra Mile by exercising their own initiative.

The chief cause of this crisis has been the widespread endeavor of the people to get something for nothing, in direct opposition to the principle of Going the Extra Mile.

Human greed has taken the place of the desire to extend human kindness through useful service. The principle is exactly opposite to a demand for more pay and less work. Thousands have injured themselves by depending on public relief and substituting it for private initiative. The outlook of the future of the United States is indeed discouraging. Despite this handicap, I believe there are still enough people left in this country who are blessed with the common sense to stand up and speak out until the American people become aware of the abyss of self-destruction over which they are hanging.

People do things or refrain from doing them because of a motive. The soundest of motives for the habit of Going the Extra Mile is the fact that it yields enduring dividends in ways too numerous for mention, to all who follow the habit.

Americans want greater individual shares of the vast resources of this country. That is a healthy desire. The wealth is here in abundance, but let us stop this foolish attempt to get it the wrong way. Let us get our wealth by giving something of value in return for it. That is how Andrew Carnegie, Thomas A. Edison, Henry Ford, and many others of their type got theirs.

We know what are the rules by which success is attained. Let us appropriate these rules and use them intelligently, thereby acquiring the personal riches we demand, and adding to the wealth of the nation as well.

Some will say, "I am already doing more than I am paid for, but my employer is so selfish and greedy he will not recognize the sort of service I am rendering." We all know there are greedy men who want something for nothing; at least they want more than they earn. Selfish employers are like pieces of clay in the hands of a potter. Through their greed they can be induced to reward the man who renders them more service than is paid for. Greedy employers do not wish to lose the services of one who makes a habit of Going the Extra Mile. They know the value of such employees. Here, then, is the crow-bar and the fulcrum with which employers can be pried loose from their greed. Any clever man will know how to use this crow-bar, not by withholding the quality or the quantity of the service he renders, but by increasing it.

I have seen this technique applied at least a hundred times, as a means of manipulating greedy employers through the recognition and use of their own weakness. On some occasions the employer failed to move as quickly as expected but that proved to be his hard luck, because his employee attracted the attention of a competitive employer who made a bid for his services and got them.

There is no way to cheat the man who follows the habit of Going the Extra Mile. If he does not get the proper recognition from one source, it comes voluntarily from some other source, generally when he least expects it. It always does come if one does more than he is paid for.

The man who Goes the Extra Mile and does it in the right sort of "mental attitude" never spends much time looking for a job. He doesn't have to, for the job is always looking for him. Depressions may come and go; business may be good or poor, the country may be at war or peace: but the man who renders more service and better service than he is paid for becomes indispensable to someone and thereby insures himself against unemployment. The fallacy in much of our social security program is in the fact that it too frequently ignores the principle of the extra mile. It is based upon selfish protection by law.

High wages and indispensability are twin sisters. They always have been and they always will be!

The man who is smart enough to make himself indispensable to someone is smart enough to keep himself continuously employed, and at wages which are far greater than those coerced by group demands.

Henry Ford understands the value of indispensability. He also knows the value of Going the Extra Mile.

That is why some years ago he voluntarily raised the wages of his workers to an all-time high minimum daily wage of five dollars per day. By that act he did for his employees something that no labor leader could have forced him to do, and it was a smart move because it insured him the sympathy and co-operation of his workers for more than a quarter of a century.

Andrew Carnegie understood the value of Going the Extra Mile. By putting that rule to work, he piled up a fortune of more than half a billion dollars. By some he was accused of being greedy, but he was never accused of being weak in the management of men. If he were greedy, he made wise use of his deficiency by paying some of his men (those who had the good sense to make themselves indispensable to him, by Going the Extra Mile) as much as a million dollars a year in extra bonuses. His policy was that of encouraging men to become indispensable to him by doing more than they were paid for (a privilege that was always available to his humblest worker), and then insuring himself against their setting themselves up as rivals in business by paying them all they were actually worth.

By their recognition of the principle of Going the Extra Mile these great men added many billions of dollars of additional wealth to the nation, provided profitable employment to many millions of men (employment that continued all through the depression), and piled up huge fortunes for their own use.

There has never been a time during the entire history of the

United States when one could have benefited by the habit of doing more than paid for as he can today. The very fact that so many people are endeavoring to get something for nothing provides an unprecedented opportunity for those who refuse to yield to this common weakness. These few may profit by the law of contrast, by adopting and applying the habit of Going the Extra Mile.

Readers should grasp the full meaning of the principle of Going the Extra Mile, and make the most of it now, in this hour of national emergency when one's loyalty to his country can best be demonstrated by useful service. The present emergency threatens to destroy the very institution which makes it possible for men to promote themselves by rendering superior service. Therefore, it is not only a profitable privilege to go the extra mile, but it is absolutely essential that we do so. The principle of the extra mile is typical of and vital to democracy.

Our country still is a "land of opportunity" for every man who is willing to render useful service in return for the better things of life. Our country can remain "the cradle of human liberty and freedom" only as long as we deserve this privilege, by rendering useful service in a spirit of unselfishness.

There comes a time in the history of every nation when its people must put aside greed and selfishness and work for the common good of one another or perish. Throughout the world people today are forced to meet the challenge of brute force and human greed for power! Whenever such emergencies have arisen in this country, the people have met them successfully by putting aside selfishness and voluntarily Going the Extra Mile.

There is a definite reason why our country is known as the "richest and the freest" country. That reason has its roots in the efficiency of the men who have pioneered in the organization of our industrial and economic development.

Industry, which is the major foundation stone of Americanism, has thrived because of the great army of farsighted men who have made it their business to do more than they were paid for. These leaders have accumulated riches in abundance; but their riches have been used in a manner that has provided employment for a vast majority of those who work for wages. Therefore, their individual wealth has become a part of the national wealth of this country.

Take Henry Ford, for example. He has accumulated a great fortune, but who would deny that this country would be better off today if it could boast of a thousand such men, each of whom provided employment to millions of men, as Mr. Ford has done? It is estimated that directly and indirectly Henry Ford provides employment for no fewer than 6,000,000 men. His influence on the American way of life is beyond estimate, but we do know that he has been largely responsible for the network of improved highways which make every portion of the country easily accessible by dependable, rapid transportation. The taxes collected annually by both state and federal governments because of Mr. Ford's industry are beyond estimate.

Henry Ford's success has not been accidental. It is the result of definite rules of procedure. We know the nature of these rules, one of the most prominent of which is that of Going the Extra Mile.

The author has been guided by a strict adherence to the discoveries of science and the laws of nature. Nowhere in the entire field of science do we find any justification for regulatory laws that discourage men from using their personal initiative to the fullest extent possible, but we do find definite justification of the habit of Going the Extra Mile. That justification consists in the fact that nowhere at any time have we found a successful industry, or a successful individual, who did not practice this principle. On the other hand, we have examined thousands of instances in connection with which individuals met with defeat and went down in many forms of personal and business failure by neglecting or refusing to Go the Extra Mile.

It is a well-known fact that men of science and men of education reach conclusions and create plans by the safe method of learning from the experiences of men of established authority in their respective fields of individual endeavor. The purpose of the great libraries of the country is mainly that of providing all the people with a record of the knowledge that civilization has sifted from the experiences of people. Men who think, men who are successful, make it their business to learn, through systematic research into these records of past experiences, all that has been recorded in connection with their own interests in life. The man who neglects or refuses to find out what others in his chosen field of endeavor have learned which may be of use to him, overlooks a great privilege.

> The Depression taught us that there is something worse than being forced to work. It is being forced not to work.

Before this philosophy in this chapter was completed more than twenty years of painstaking research was devoted to the study of the records of men who have been recognized as the ablest thinkers and philosophers the world has known. A staff of intelligent research specialists were kept busy, and they combed the libraries for authentic records of the experiences of men who have been recognized as the leaders in almost every field of human endeavor. The substance of their findings was written into this philosophy. In addition to this form of research into the history of the experiences of men, more than 500 of the most successful men known to the American people collaborated over a long period of years by providing the essence of the knowledge they had gathered from the trial-and-error system in the field of industry and business. Moreover, a careful personal analysis was made of thousands of men and women in all walks of life, representing a cross section of the American people and the American way of life, from which the author uncovered the causes of failure as well as the causes of success. From the findings of this extensive research, this philosophy was organized.

So, when I present the readers with a clearly marked road map that leads to individual achievement, they may be assured that the map was drawn from the footprints of men who have traveled that road before them.

Application of the principles of Going the Extra Mile, Definiteness of Purpose, and the Mastermind Group are the sure way to find the Path to Personal Power.

INDEX

ABOUT THE AUTHOR

Napoleon Hill was born in 1883 in Wise County, Virginia. He worked as a secretary, a "mountain reporter" for a local newspaper, the manager of a coal mine and a lumber yard, and attended law school, before he began working as a journalist for *Bob Taylor's Magazine*—a job that led to his meeting steel magnate Andrew Carnegie, which changed the course of his life. Carnegie believed success could be distilled into principles that any person could follow, and urged Hill to interview the greatest industrialists and inventors of the era in order to discover these principles. Hill took on the challenge, which lasted twenty years and formed the building block for *Think and Grow Rich*, the wealth-building classic and all-time bestseller of its kind, which has sold more than 100 million copies worldwide. Hill devoted the remainder of his life to discovering and refining the principles of success. After a long and rich career as an author, magazine publisher, lecturer, and consultant to business leaders, the motivational pioneer died in 1970 in South Carolina.

Don't miss these

KEEPSAKE DELUXE EDITIONS

of

NAPOLEON HILL